Calcium in
Reproductive Physiology

Calcium in Reproductive Physiology

A COMPARATIVE STUDY OF VERTEBRATES

K. SIMKISS

Department of Physiology and Biochemistry,
University of Reading, Berkshire

MODERN BIOLOGICAL STUDIES

LONDON: CHAPMAN AND HALL LTD
NEW YORK: REINHOLD PUBLISHING CORPORATION

First published 1967
© 1967 Kenneth Simkiss
Printed in Great Britain by
Richard Clay (The Chaucer Press) Ltd,
Bungay, Suffolk

QP 535
.C255
1967

Editors' Foreword

The purpose of the Modern Biological Studies series is to place outstanding monographs before the world of biological scholarship; this policy is continued most strongly with Dr. Simkiss's book.

Because the great majority of vertebrates have calcified skeletons the metabolism of calcium is of central importance in the economy of inorganic cations in their bodies. Though other vertebrates are not usually viviparous, nevertheless a study of their calcium balance can throw light on the mechanisms lying behind the formation of the calcified skeleton in the mammalian foetus. Dr. Simkiss has re-evaluated the results of other workers, and added his own original experiments and thoughts, to produce this stimulating book. It demonstrates clearly the value of comparative studies of vertebrates not only for themselves but also for their importance to human physiology and thus to medicine.

It is a pleasure to see published a further volume in this series which so well supports our intentions to bring new approaches to the study of their subject before biologists.

J. D. CARTHY
Scientific Director
The Field Studies Council, London

PETER GRAY
Professor of Biological Sciences
University of Pittsburgh

Author's Preface

It is often stated that the unfortunate result of an education in contemporary science is that it produces specialists who restrict themselves to studying and commenting on only a small aspect of a subject. This book may appear to be the work of such a product. In writing it, however, I must admit that I have found it difficult both to act as a specialist and to behave like a scientist. The first difficulty is easily explained by the comparative approach adopted in this book. Thus, although only a small aspect of reproductive physiology is discussed I have attempted to draw attention to a general phenomenon by considering the problem in different groups of animals. The hazards of such an approach lie in the mass of isolated information available and in the difficulty of presenting a coherent account. The rewards are generally found in the ingenuity and variety of the adaptations shown by different species, and this has largely been the inspiration for this work. The problem of acting as a scientist while writing a book is to achieve a balance between the presentation of ideas and concepts and the need to provide the experimental data upon which they are based. I have attempted partially to solve this problem by the use of a large number of tables and graphs which have been inserted so as to provide a factual source for many of the generalized statements in the text.

The book would never have appeared without the help of a number of people. Miss Nora Howe undertook the difficult task of converting the manuscript into typescript and at the same time provided a valuable service by questioning some of the statements in the text. Miss Susan Watts helped with the redrawing of many of the figures, and finally my wife has borne the many insults to family life, which writing this book has entailed, with only encouragement as a response.

K. S.

Acknowledgements

Permission to reproduce the undermentioned figures is gratefully acknowledged by the author:

FIG. 2.2 Redrawn from Leblond, C. P., Wilkinson, G. W., Belanger, L. F., and Robichon, J. (1950), *Amer. J. Anat.*, **86**, 289. Courtesy of Wistar Institute of Anatomy and Biology.

FIG. 2.4 Based upon Jowsey, J. (1960), *Clin. Orthopaedics*, **7**, 210. Courtesy of J. B. Lippincott Co.; and Villarwera, A. R., Sedlin, E. D., and Frost, H. M. (1963), *Anat. Rec.*, **146**, 209. Courtesy of Wistar Institute of Anatomy and Biology.

FIG. 3.1 From Fleisch, H. and Neuman, W. H. (1960), *J. Amer. chem. Soc.*, **82**, 996. Courtesy of American Chemical Society.

FIG. 3.2 Redrawn from Fleisch, H. and Neuman, W. H. (1961), *Amer. J. Physiol.*, **200**, 1296. Courtesy of American Physiological Society.

FIG. 3.3 Redrawn from Bauer, G. C. H., Carlsson, A., and Lindquist, B. (1955), *Acta Physiol. Scand.*, **35**, 56. Courtesy of Karolinska Institutet.

FIG. 3.4 Redrawn from Bauer, G. C. H., Carlsson, A., and Lindquist, B. (1961), *Mineral Metabolism*, **1B**, 609. Courtesy of Academic Press.

FIG. 4.1 Redrawn from Greenberg, D. M. and Miller, W. D. (1941), *J. Nutr.*, **22**, 1. Courtesy of Wistar Institute of Anatomy and Biology.

FIG. 4.2 Redrawn from Stoerk, H. C. and Carnes, W. H. (1945), *J. Nutr.*, **29**, 43. Courtesy of Wistar Institute of Anatomy and Biology.

FIG. 5.1 Redrawn from Stoerk, H. C. and Carnes, W. H. (1945), *J. Nutr.*, **29**, 43. Courtesy of Wistar Institute of Anatomy and Biology.

FIG. 5.2 Redrawn from Talmage, R. V. and Toft, R. J. (1961), *The Parathyroids*. Courtesy of Charles C. Thomas, Publisher, Illinois.

FIG. 5.3 Redrawn from Copp, D. H., Cameron, E. C., Cheney, B. A. Davidson, A. G. F., and Henzie, K. G. (1962), *Endocrinology*, **70**, 638. Courtesy of J. B. Lippincott Co.

FIG. 5.4 Redrawn from Albright, F. and Reifenstein, E. C. (1948), *Parathyroid glands and metabolic bone disease*. Courtesy of Williams and Wilkins Co.

FIG. 5.5 Redrawn from Rasmussen, H. (1961), *Amer. J. Med.*, **30**, 112. Courtesy of the publishers.

FIG. 5.6 Redrawn from Bartter, F. C. (1961), *The Parathyroids*. Courtesy of Charles C. Thomas, Publisher, Illinois.

FIG. 5.7 Redrawn from Cramer, C. F., Suiker, A. P., and Copp, D. H. (1961), *The Parathyroids*. Courtesy of Charles C. Thomas, Publisher, Illinois.

FIG. 6.1 Redrawn from Dowdle, E. B., Schachter, D., and Schenker, H.

(1960), *Amer. J. Physiol.*, **198,** 269. Courtesy of American Physiological Society.

FIG. 6.2   Redrawn from Cramer, C. F. (1963), *The Transfer of Calcium and Strontium across Biological Membranes.* Courtesy of Academic Press.

FIG. 6.3   Redrawn from Dupuis, Y. and Fournier, P. (1963), *The Transfer of Calcium and Strontium across Biological Membranes.* Courtesy of Academic Press.

FIG. 7.1   Redrawn from Warren, D. C. and Conrad, R. M. (1939), *J. agric. Res.,* **58,** 875.

FIG. 7.2   Redrawn from Schjeide, O. A. and Urist, M. R. (1960), *Nature, Lond.,* **188,** 291. Courtesy of MacMillan (Journals) Ltd.

FIG. 7.3   Redrawn from Mok, C., Martin, W. G., and Common, R. H. (1961), *Can. J. Biochem. Physiol.,* **39,** 109. Reproduced by permission of the National Research Council of Canada.

FIG. 8.2   Redrawn from Paterson, N. F. (1949), *Proc. zool. Soc. Lond.,* **119,** 269. Courtesy of Zoological Society of London.

FIG. 9.1   Redrawn from Hummel, F. C., Sternberger, H. R., Hunscher, H. A., and Macy, I. G. (1936), *J. Nutr.,* **11,** 235. Courtesy of Wistar Institute of Anatomy and Biology.

FIG. 9.2   Redrawn from Hammond, J. (1947), *Biol. Rev.,* **22,** 195. Courtesy of Cambridge University Press.

FIG. 9.3   Redrawn from Hamilton, B., Dasel, L., Highman, W. J., and Schwartz, C. (1936), *J. clin. Invest.,* **15,** 323. Courtesy of American Society for Clinical Investigation.

FIG. 9.4   Redrawn from Mull, J. W. and Bill, A. H. (1934), *Amer. J. Obstet. Gynec.,* **27,** 510. Courtesy of C. V. Mosby Co., Missouri.

FIG. 9.5   Redrawn from Benzie, D., Bayne, A. W., Dalgarno, A. C., Duckworth, J., Hill, R., and Walker, D. M. (1955), *J. agric. Sci.,* **46,** 425. Courtesy of Cambridge University Press.

FIG. 10.1   Redrawn from Cox, W. M. and Imboden, M. (1936), *J. Nutr.,* **11,** 147. Courtesy of Wistar Institute of Anatomy and Biology.

FIG. 10.2   Redrawn from Blosser, T. H. and Albright, J. L. (1956), *Ann. N.Y. Acad. Sci.,* **64,** 386. Courtesy of New York Academy of Sciences.

FIG. 11.1   Redrawn from Appleton, A. B. (1929), *C. R. Ass. Anat.,* **24,** 3. Courtesy of Association des Anatomistes.

FIG. 11.2   Redrawn from Bruck, E. and Weintraub, D. H. (1955), *Amer. J. Dis. Child.,* **90,** 653. Courtesy of American Medical Association.

FIG. 11.3   Redrawn from Stearns, G. (1939), *Physiol. Rev.,* **19,** 415. Courtesy of American Physiological Society.

FIG. 12.1   Redrawn from Riddle, O. and Reinhart, W. H. (1926), *Amer. J. Physiol.,* **76,** 660. Courtesy of American Physiological Society.

FIG. 12.2   Modified after McDonald, M. R. and Riddle, O. (1945), *J. biol. Chem.,* **159,** 455. Courtesy of American Society of Biological Chemists.

FIG. 12.3   Redrawn from McDonald, M. R. and Riddle, O. (1945), *J. biol. Chem.,* **159,** 455. Courtesy of American Society of Biological Chemists.

FIG. 12.4   Redrawn from Common, R. H. (1941), *J. agric. Sci.,* **31,** 281. Courtesy of Cambridge University Press.

FIG. 12.5   Data from Common, R. H. (1933), *J. agric. Sci.,* **23,** 555. Courtesy of Cambridge University Press.

FIG. 12.6   Redrawn from Common, R. H., Rutledge, N. A., and Hale, R. W. (1948), *J. agric. Sci.*, **38**, 64. Courtesy of Cambridge University Press.

FIG. 12.7   Redrawn from Tyler, C. (1940), *Biochem. J.*, **34**, 202. Courtesy of the publishers.

FIG. 12.8   Redrawn from Bloom, W., Bloom, M. A., and McLean, F. C. (1941), *Anat. Rec.*, **81**, 443. Courtesy of Wistar Institute of Anatomy and Biology.

FIG. 12.10   Redrawn from Mueller, W. J., Schraer, R., and Schraer, H. (1964), *J. Nutr.*, **84**, 20. Courtesy of Wistar Institute of Anatomy and Biology.

FIG. 12.11   Redrawn from Polin, P., Sturkie, P. D., and Hunsaker, W. (1957), *Endocrinology*, **60**, 1. Courtesy of J. B. Lippincott Co.

FIG. 12.13   Redrawn from Taylor, T. G., Williams, A., and Kirkley, J. (1965), *Can. J. Physiol.*, **43**, 451. Courtesy of National Research Council of Canada.

FIG. 13.1   Redrawn from Johnston, P. M. and Comar, C. L. (1955), *Amer. J. Physiol.*, **183**, 365. Courtesy of American Physiological Society.

FIG. 13.2   Redrawn from McIndoe, W. M. (1960), *J. Embryol. exp. Morph.*, **8**, 47. Courtesy of Company of Biologists.

FIG. 13.3   Redrawn from Johnston, P. M. and Comar, C. L. (1955), *Amer. J. Physiol.*, **183**, 365. Courtesy of American Physiological Society.

FIG. 14.1   Redrawn from Dessauer, H. C. and Fox, W. (1959), *Amer. J. Physiol.*, **197**, 360. Courtesy of American Physiological Society.

FIG. 14.2   Redrawn from Dessauer, H. C. and Fox, W. (1959), *Amer. J. Physiol.*, **197**, 360. Courtesy of American Physiological Society.

FIG. 14.3   Redrawn from Edgren, R. A. (1960), *Comp. Biochem. Physiol.*, **1**, 213. Courtesy of Pergamon Press Ltd.

FIG. 15.1   Redrawn from Carus, C. G. (1841), *Arch. Anatomie Physiologie*, 216.

FIG. 16.1   Redrawn from Zwarenstein, H. and Shapiro, H. A. (1933), *J. exp. Biol.*, **10**, 372. Courtesy of Company of Biologists.

FIG. 16.2   Based upon Etkin, W. (1955), *Analysis of Development*. Courtesy of W. B. Saunders Co. Philadelphia; and Etkin, W. (1964), *Physiology of Amphibia*. Courtesy of Academic Press.

FIG. 16.3   Data from Pilkington, J. B. and Simkiss, K. (1966), *J. exp. Biol.* **45**, 329.

PLATE 2   From Urist, M. R., Deutsch, N. M., Pomerantz, G., and McLean, F. C. (1960), *Amer. J. Physiol.*, **199**, 851. Courtesy of American Physiological Society.

PLATE 3   Electron micrograph from Simons, P. C. M. and Wiertz, G. (1963), *Z. Zellforsch.*, **59**, 555. Courtesy of Springer, Berlin.

PLATE 6   From Simkiss, K. (1962), *Comp. Biochem. Physiol.*, **7**, 23. Courtesy of Pergamon Press Ltd.

PLATE 7   From Simkiss, K. (1962), *Comp. Biochem. Physiol.*, **7**, 23. Courtesy of Pergamon Press Ltd.

PLATE 8   Photographs from Guardabassi, A. (1953), *Arch. Anat. microsc. Morph. exp.*, **42**, 143. Courtesy of Masson et Cie.

PLATE 9   Autoradiographs from Guardabassi, A. (1960), *Z. Zellforsch.*, **51**, 278. Courtesy of Springer, Berlin.

Contents

PLATES

(between pages 226 and 227)

CHAPTER I

Introduction

The theme of this book is that reproduction frequently produces a strain upon the calcium metabolism of tetrapods. In developing this theme it has become apparent that it involves two assumptions, and it is important to state these at the beginning.

First, it is assumed that all vertebrates start their terrestrial life with a well-formed skeleton. A study of the offspring of mammals, birds, and reptiles supports this idea which may be extended to include amphibians at the end of metamorphosis. Unfortunately, however, there is relatively little information on this topic for most wild animals and since there is as yet no well-substantiated explanation as to why the skeleton should be mineralized so early in life it cannot necessarily be taken to occur in all tetrapods. The obvious suggestion as to the need for this early ossification is that if there was only a cartilaginous skeleton it would not be able to withstand the compressive, tensile, and shearing forces applied to it by the muscular system, but there are not enough data to substantiate this and the measurements which are available leave the proposition open to doubt. An alternative suggestion is that the initiation of ossification may lead to a heterogenous structure in which islands of bone mineral concentrate the stresses on the limb into certain areas of the cartilage (fig. 1.1). Thus, for a while, the cartilage may actually be weakened by the onset of mineralization and in order to avoid this 'stress concentrator' effect [1] it might be supposed that the limb, or at least its most vulnerable parts, are ossified before it is put under any stress. Again, there is no evidence to support this theory and much depends upon the nature of the organic–inorganic interrelationships in the structure as to whether this effect would occur. Finally, it may be suggested that the early formation of the bones is essential in order that the concentration of certain ions in the blood can be maintained and the skeleton is therefore formed along with many other regulatory systems early in life [3]. Whatever the explanation, however, the first basic assumption of this book is that the newly formed offspring has a well-developed skeleton, even though the reason for this is not clear.

Reproduction is normally a process with strict temporal limitations variously based upon the time to form the egg or upon the time for the embryo to develop sufficiently for it to survive after parturition. Thus, the time available for physiological contact between the mother and her offspring is limited. From this it follows that if the offspring are formed with a mineralized skeleton, then one not only has to consider the source of calcium for ossification but also the rate at which it can be mobilized, supplied, and utilized. Thus the second assumption is that if the calcium reserves of

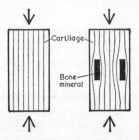

FIG. 1.1. The possible effect of bone mineral in concentrating stresses into certain regions of calcifying bone. In the left-hand illustration a homogeneous block of cartilage is shown with lines of stress running uniformly through it. The initiation of mineralization (*right*) may concentrate stress into particular parts of the cartilage so making it more vulnerable to failure.

the body can only be mobilized at a certain limited rate, then this might be a limiting factor in some forms of reproduction, or at least a feature which may have led to various physiological adaptations.

The fact that this book is concerned with the supply of calcium to the embryo obviously suggests that it will involve a study of various methods of reproduction. The tetrapods are an interesting group in this respect, for the mammals have perfected viviparity and the birds oviparity. The reptiles show a remarkable series of reproductive adaptations and the amphibia have retained a larval form. In all these animals, however, it is necessary to consider the following four requirements:

1. A source of calcium for the reproducing adult.
2. A physiology capable of utilizing this at the rate required for reproduction.
3. A source of calcium for the embryo.
4. An embryo capable of utilizing this at the rate required in order to mineralize the embryonic skeleton.

The four phenomena obviously interact in various ways, depending upon the type of reproduction used by the animal. In viviparity there is, to some extent, a physiological continuity between the mother and foetus

via the placenta, and much depends upon the ability of this organ to transfer calcium from one circulation to the other. In oviparity the two individuals are completely separated in both time and space, so that there has
to be a storage system in the reproductive process into which the mother
can deposit calcium and from which the embryo can withdraw it as required.
In those animals where there is a larval form there may have to be two
storage systems, one between parent and larva and a second between larva
and the newly metamorphosed adult, for it is only at this latter stage that
much of the skeleton is formed.

In order to be as concise as possible in discussing these storage systems,
the sources of calcium available to an animal and the limitations in its rate
of utilization, this book has been divided into two sections. The first part
deals with the information on these organ systems in as comparative a way
as possible. The second part of the book is concerned with the physiology
of these organs in relation to the problems and adaptations involved in the
different methods of reproduction.

None of the book is specifically devoted to an explanation of the experimental methods used in studying calcium metabolism, although these have
been mentioned in the text wherever possible. The one method which
deserves some comment, however, is the balance experiment, for although
this is the classical method of investigating calcium metabolism it may contain some surprising experimental errors. In a balance experiment, the intake of calcium is estimated and compared with the output of an animal
during a particular length of time. If the animal is absorbing more calcium
than it is losing, it is in positive balance by that amount. If the opposite
occurs, the animal is in negative balance. In a protracted balance experiment the 'input' and 'loss' values tend to become large and may involve
accumulative errors. The important information, however, is the difference between these large values, and this may be very small, especially if
the animal fluctuates between positive and negative balance. It is easy,
therefore, to over- or under-estimate these values by relatively small errors
in obtaining the input or loss data and this will lead to erratic results. Even
worse, however, is when there is a consistent error in assessing either the
intake or excretion of calcium during a long-term experiment when very
aberrant results may be obtained. This has been clearly demonstrated in a
52-week experiment on the domestic fowl, when the following data were
obtained for the calcium metabolism:

bird	intake	droppings	eggs	balance
C 12	1637·6 g	1189·1 g	380·9 g	+67·6 g

An analysis of the carcass of this bird at the end of the experiment
showed that it contained only 32·0 g Ca, and this was only about 10 g more

B

than in control birds killed at the start of the experiment. Obviously, the result of the balance experiment is physiologically impossible as the bird appears to have retained twice as much calcium as it actually contains, but this has become apparent only because the experiment was extended for such a long period and many short-term balance experiments may have similar cumulative errors concealed within them [2]. There are, therefore, reasons for questioning some balance data, although many of these experiments appear to provide reliable information which could not be obtained otherwise.

In comparing physiological measurements from different animals two expressions have been used throughout this book. The term mg% refers to the quantity of a substance in mg per 100 ml of fluid or 100 g of solid. Thus, a serum-calcium level of 10 mg % indicates 10 mg of calcium per 100 ml of fluid. The term mg/kg body wt/hr is a means of comparing the rate of metabolism of a particular substance in different animals. Thus, if calcium can be resorbed from the skeleton of a 50-kg human at a rate of 480 mg/day this would be a rate of calcium metabolism of 480/(50 × 24) or 0·4 mg/kg body wt/hr. Not enough is known about the rate of calcium metabolism in animals of different sizes to discover how it is influenced by body weight and the expression has simply been used in this book to provide a common basis for comparisons.

REFERENCES

[1] CURREY, J. D. (1962), 'Stress concentrations in bone', *Quart. J. micr. Sci.*, **103**, 111–33.
[2] JENKINS, N. K. and TYLER, C. (1960), 'A critical study of the failure of a long-term calcium and phosphorus balance experiment with laying hens', *J. agric. Sci.*, **54**, 131–139.
[3] URIST, M. R. (1964), 'Further Observations bearing on the Bone-body Fluid Continuum', in *Bone Biodynamics*, ed. Frost, H. M., Little Brown.

PART I

The Organ Systems

CHAPTER 2

The Structure of Bone

Bone is the main skeletal material of vertebrates and, like cartilage, it is a specialized type of connective tissue. Connective tissues are mainly composed of two types of organic material, the protein collagen and polysaccharides such as chondroitin sulphate. The inorganic bone mineral is a chemically complex material composed of a mass of small crystals with the general formula $Ca_{10} (PO_4)_6 (OH)_2$ and corresponding approximately to an hydroxyapatite. Under conditions which are not completely understood, these crystals form upon the surfaces or within the material of collagen fibres and so lead to the ossification of the tissue. The process normally occurs only in the presence of certain types of cells.

The bone-forming cells are called osteoblasts. They occur in large numbers on the surfaces of developing bones and may form sheets, attaching to each other by means of thin cytoplasmic processes. The cells are generally cuboid in shape, 15–20μ long and with a large nucleus. They have a well-developed Golgi apparatus and the cytoplasm possesses a number of interesting features. It contains granules 0.3–0.6μ across, which are stained by the periodic acid–Schiffs (P.A.S.) reaction for carbohydrates. The cytoplasm also contains alkaline phosphatase and is strongly basophilic due to the presence of ribonucleic acid (R.N.A.) (table 2.1).

The osteoblasts induce the formation of bone and thus, by their own activity, become surrounded by mineral. They are then called osteocytes. They retain some of their cytoplasmic connexions with other bone cells so that typically osteocytes occur within lacunae, 20–$50\ \mu$ long and about $10\ \mu$ wide and deep, which interconnect through canalicules in the bone substance. Osteocytes retain a few P.A.S.-reactive granules in their cytoplasm, but the basophilia has largely disappeared and the cytoplasm may contain glycogen and fat droplets. It has always been assumed, without much evidence, that the osteocytes continued the slow accretion of mineral into the skeleton and maintained the organization of the bones. This, however, appears to be the function of only the smaller osteocytes, and a second type of cell, the large osteocyte, appears to be involved in osteolysis. This is a process whereby bone mineral is removed, via changes in the organic matrix, from the deeper regions of bone tissue. Small and large osteocytes with these two different functions have been described in chickens, rats, and dogs, and it has been shown that the osteolysis, induced by the large osteocytes, occurs whenever calcium is removed from the skeleton as, for example, when parathyroid hormone is injected into the animal [1].

The surfaces of bone are resorbed by a third type of cell, the osteoclast. These are giant cells which typically contain a large number of up to twenty nuclei. They are often found lying in grooves called Howship's lacunae, which are thought to be produced by the cell's own resorptive activity. The

Table 2.1 *Substances which have been demonstrated histochemically in bone cells. Concentrations assessed visually and scored on an arbitrary scale of* 0 *to* + + + + *(after* [1a])

	Osteoblast	Osteocyte	Osteoclast
Glycogen	± or + + + +	0 or +	0
R.N.A.	+ + + +	+	+ + + +
Mucoprotein (P.A.S.)	+	±	+ + +
Alkaline phosphatase	+ + + +	0	0
Acid phosphatase	0 or ±	0	+ + + +
Phosphorylase	+ + +	0	0
β-glucuronidase	+ + +	0	+ + + +
Succinic dehydrogenase	+	0	+ + + +
Cytochrome oxidase	+	0	+ + + +

cytoplasm contains granules of carbohydrate material and the enzyme acid phosphatase. Electron micrographs of these cells show that they have a finely folded plasma membrane in contact with the bone. Small pieces of inorganic debris can be seen between the folds of the cell surface apparently in the process of being broken away from the main mass of bone material [10].

Bone may form in one of two ways. In intramembranous ossification the intercellular connective tissue increases in amount and density. Some of the connective tissue cells appear to take on the characteristics of osteoblasts and shortly afterwards bone mineral becomes deposited. The second situation in which bone is normally formed is more complex, for it occurs in localities where the rudiment of the skeletal element already exists as a cartilaginous structure. The formation of bone in these circumstances involves the erosion of this cartilage and its replacement by ossified material. It is therefore termed intracartilaginous ossification, but the actual process of mineralization appears to be very similar to that seen in the intramembranous system. The process of bone formation and resorption will be described here only in sufficient detail to enable the dynamic aspects of calcium metabolism to be understood.

Intramembranous bone formation is restricted in the tetrapods to the formation of some of the bones in the skull, jaws, pectoral girdle, and of any dermal bones which may be present. The other bones of the skeleton originate in the embryo as cartilaginous models often appearing as miniature replicas of the adult structure. The ossification of these structures starts with the degeneration of the cartilage at the sites of future ossification. These sites occur in the centre of the limb bones, and extend towards

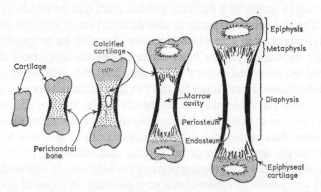

FIG. 2.1. The ossification and growth of a mammalian long bone. Cartilage is shown by shading, calcified cartilage by stipple and bone mineral in black.

the distal ends where the cartilage cells begin to multiply and arrange themselves in longitudinal rows at these locations. The cartilage between these columns of cells mineralizes, but is then resorbed when blood vessels penetrate into this central region of the structure and destroy the cartilage, replacing it with bone marrow. Osteoblasts arise at about this time and lay down true bone minerals in the surface layers of the cartilage, generally in the form of a central collar which gradually extends towards either end of the skeletal element (fig. 2.1). The replacement of cartilage by bone proceeds continuously, but the cartilage itself continues to grow, so that the ends of the bone are not ossified until this growth ceases. There is therefore always a layer of cartilage on the articular surfaces of the limb bones of growing vertebrates, except in mammals and a few reptiles, where secondary centres of ossification occur to form caps or epiphyses over the articulating ends of the bones. In this case, growth occurs by means of a layer of epiphyseal cartilage situated between the epiphysis and the diaphysis (or shaft) of the limb bone.

The bone between the epiphysis and the diaphysis forms the metaphysis, and consists of interconnecting bars of various thicknesses and shapes. It is therefore called spongy bone to distinguish it from the hard mass of macroscopically solid or compact bone, and by its formation the limb bones increase in length. The bone grows in width by a different process. The original layer of connective tissue cells surrounding the cartilage rudiment is called the perichondrium, and this is renamed the periosteum as soon as bone formation occurs. The periosteum consists of two ill-defined layers, the inner of which is responsible, in the growing animal, for the formation of concentric layers of bone on the outer periphery of the shaft. Thus the bone grows in length by a different process from that by which it grows in width. The two processes occur at very different rates, with the result that the bone increases in size without greatly changing its proportions. The continual deposition of new bone derived from the epiphyseal cartilages and from the periosteal surface would soon lead to a very heavy and relatively solid skeleton were it not for the fact that the bones are also continually resorbed. The resorption occurs mainly on the inner or endosteal surfaces of the bone at a rate which is roughly the same as the rate of formation on the outer part of the bone. These processes can be observed by feeding animals on the dye alizarin or on certain radio-isotopes, which become concentrated in actively growing parts of the skeleton. In one such experiment, it was possible to show that a 50-g growing rat renewed the spongy bone beneath the epiphysis three times during an 8-day period, while only one-tenth of the bone in the mid-shaft region had been replaced, i.e. the bone was growing about thirty times faster in length than in width [8] (fig. 2.2). This dynamic process of continual formation and resorption persists as long as the animal is able to grow. It is not the only remodelling of the bone which occurs, however, for there is another process which continues throughout the life of many animals.

It will be recalled that during growth both spongy bone and concentric lamellae of compact bone are formed. Some of the spongy bone is resorbed, but other parts are converted into compact bone by the deposition of bone as concentric layers over the spicules. This process continues until only a series of small canals remain, which are sometimes called the protohaversian systems. A somewhat similar process occurs in other parts of the bone, including the compact bone, but here the process begins with the destruction of the existing bone, so that long winding tunnels are eroded in the direction of the long axis of the limb bones. These tunnels are formed by osteoclastic activity and they penetrate all parts of the cortical bone. Eventually the resorption of bone ceases in any particular cavity and the tunnel is re-ossified by osteoblastic activity which produces concentric layers of bone on the walls of the resorption spaces. These are the true Haversian systems, or osteons, and they continue to be formed throughout life, so that a single region of bone may be resorbed and reformed may times, even in an adult animal (fig. 2.3). Not all vertebrates possess Haversian systems for they are absent, for example, from the bones of modern amphibia, small birds, and

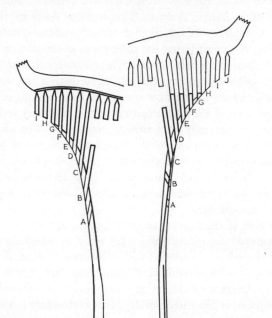

FIG. 2.2. The head of a rat tibia two hours after the injection of P³² (*left*) and after a further eight days (*right*). The distribution of radio-isotope is shown in thick black lines. Note the rapid growth of the epiphyseal plate and the rapid formation and destruction of the trabeculae. In contrast, the diaphysis has laid down relatively little new bone on the periosteal surface during the eight days of the experiment. Note the formation of endosteal bone in the region of the metaphysis (after [8]).

rodents [2], and even in those animals which show this secondary remodelling of the bones the rate at which osteons are formed varies in different bones and throughout the life of the animal. This can be demonstrated by feeding tetracycline to animals and then examining thin sections of their bones in ultra-violet light. The tetracycline is attached to regions of active bone formation and is fluorescent, so that it provides a marker for osteon formation. By using suitably timed doses of this antibiotic, it is possible to show that in the human rib an Haversian canal forms in about 42 days in a $7\frac{1}{2}$-year-old infant and in about 79 days in a 43-year-old adult. Long bones require about 25 % longer for the canals to form. It is also possible to estimate how long a particular mass of bone will last before it is resorbed and reformed. In the 5-year-old child, it takes 2·2 years; at the age of 26 it would take 28·4 years; and at 48, 37 years. The same method allows one to estimate that about 104 mg calcium/day are deposited and resorbed in various parts of the human skeleton. This estimate is several times smaller than estimates of the rate of turnover of calcium as demonstrated by radio-isotope studies, but considering the differences in techniques and the assumptions involved in the calculations, it is reasonably similar [4].

It is also possible to estimate the rate of formation and destruction of osteons by microradiographic examination of thin sections of bone. This shows that the rates of formation and resorption may vary independently, although they are normally of a similar magnitude. The amount of re-modelling in the bone appears to decrease up to the age of 35, and then increase again with an excessive amount of resorption in old age (fig. 2.4) [5]. If the parathyroid glands are removed from an animal, the degree of calcification in the Haversian canals decreases, although the number of osteons is not affected [6].

The formation of the Haversian canal system is probably only one of several methods of bone reconstruction [2], but it has attracted considerable attention from workers interested in the process of bone formation [3]. Microradiographs of thin sections of bone show that various osteons are mineralized to different extents at any one time. It is apparent that about 70 % of the mineral is deposited rapidly as the osteon forms, although complete calcification is a protracted process. The immature, incompletely mineralized osteon is very sensitive to changes in the ionic composition of the blood, and has been called metabolic bone to distinguish it from the less reactive fully mineralized or structural bone [12]. Histological examination of the Haversian system has shown that there is another inner layer of preosseous material which does not even show on microradiographs. This preosseous layer stains histochemically as if it contained carbohydrate material, but differs from the ossified layers in not being metachromatic with toluidine blue (fig. 2.3). This metachromasia is normally due to substances similar to chondroitin sulphates, and radio-isotope work with S^{35} suggests that such compounds are formed in the preosseous layer shortly before it mineralizes [7].

A bone is therefore, structurally, a very complex organ. A long bone grows in length and width by two different processes which occur at different

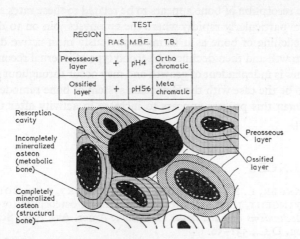

REGION	TEST		
	P.A.S.	M.B.E.	T.B.
Preosseous layer	+	pH4	Ortho chromatic
Ossified layer	+	pH5·6	Meta chromatic

Resorption cavity

Incompletely mineralized osteon (metabolic bone)

Completely mineralized osteon (structural bone)

Preosseous layer

Ossified layer

FIG. 2.3. Microradiographic appearance of a small region of bone in transverse section showing a resorption cavity and several generations of osteons. The inner layer of a mineralizing Haversian canal is not calcified but is histologically distinguished on account of its different staining properties. PAS = periodic acid Schiff's test; MBE = methylene blue extinction; TB = toluidine blue staining. (Histological data from [7].)

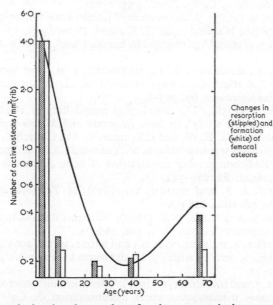

Changes in resorption (stippled) and formation (white) of femoral osteons

FIG. 2.4. A graph showing the number of active osteons in human ribs of various ages compared with an arbitrary assessment of the activity of osteons in the femur (data from [5 and 11]).

rates. The resorption of bone appears to be related to these rates and therefore occurs particularly rapidly where the epiphyses join on to the shafts. This remodelling of bone as it forms is obviously most active during the years of growth and then declines. A second type of internal reconstruction of the bones is independent of growth and may occur throughout life. Such appears to be the case with the Haversian system of bone remodelling, and in the human this process appears to increase in activity after the age of 35 (fig. 2.4).

REFERENCES

[1] BELANGER, L. F., ROBICHON, J., MIGICOVSKY, B. B., COPP, D. H., and VINCENT, J. (1963), 'Resorption without osteoclasts (osteolysis)', in *Mechanisms of hard tissue resorption*, Amer. Ass. Adv. Sci., Washington, D.C., 531–56.

[1a] CABRINI, R. L. (1961), 'Histochemistry of ossification', *Int. Rev. Cytol.* 11, 283–306.

[2] ENLOW, D. H. and BROWN, S. O. (1956–8), 'A comparative histological study of fossil and recent bone tissues', Part 1, *Texas J. Sci.*, 8, 405–43; Part 2, *Texas J. Sci.*, 9, 186–214; Part 3, *Texas J. Sci.*, 10, 187–230.

[3] FOOTE, J. S. (1916), 'A contribution to the comparative histology of the femur', *Smithson, Contr. Knowl.*, 35, 1–242.

[4] FROST, H. M. (1963), 'Measurement of human bone formation by means of tetracycline labelling', *Can. J. Biochem. Physiol.*, 41, 31–42.

[5] JOWSEY, J. (1960), 'Age changes in human bone', *Clin. Orthopaedics*, 7, 210–18.

[6] JOWSEY, J., ROWLAND, R. E., MARSHALL, J. H., and MCLEAN, F. C. (1958), 'The effect of parathyroidectomy on Haversian remodelling of bone', *Endocrinology*, 63, 903–8.

[7] LACROIX, P. (1956), 'The histological remodelling of adult bone. An autoradiographic study', in *Bone Structure and Metabolism (Ciba)*, ed. Wolstenholme, G. E. W. and O'Connor, C. M., Churchill, 36–44.

[8] LEBLOND, C. P., WILKINSSON, G. W., BELANGER, L. F. and ROBICHON, J. (1950), 'Radioautographic visualization of bone formation in the rat', *Amer. J. Anat.* 86, 289–342.

[9] MAXIMOW, A. A. and BLOOM, W. (1957), *A Textbook of Histology*, Saunders, 7th edn., 628 pp.

[10] SCOTT, B. L. and PEASE, D. C. (1956), 'Electron microscopy of the epiphyseal apparatus', *Anat. Rec.*, 126, 465–95.

[11] VILLANVERA, A. R., SEDLIN, E. D., and FROST, H. M. (1963), 'Variations in osteoblastic activity with age by the osteoid seam index', *Anat. Rec.*, 146, 209–13.

[12] VINCENT, J. and HAUMONT, S. (1960), 'Identification autoradiographique des osteones metaboliques apres administration de Ca^{45}', *Revue fr. Etud. clin. biol.*, 5, 348–53.

CHAPTER 3

The Kinetics of the Metabolism of Bone Mineral

The role of the skeleton in calcium metabolism can only be understood when the kinetics of the movement of ions between the body fluids and the bone mineral are fully appreciated. The basis of these relationships is a two-way movement of ions in and out of the bone, but it is convenient to consider first the formation of bone from the body fluids.

If crystals of bone mineral are shaken with physiological salines it is possible to determine a dissociation product for the hydroxyapatite. The results obtained vary a great deal depending upon the experimental conditions, but typically the solution equilibrates with a [Ca] . [inorganic P] product of about 10 (mg %)^2. If, instead of determining the dissociation product, one attempts to obtain a solubility product by artificially raising the concentration of calcium and phosphate ions in a saline until mineral precipitates, one obtains a [Ca] . [inorganic P] value of between 35 and 50.

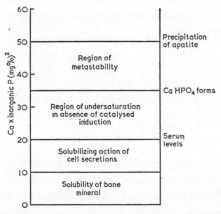

FIG. 3.1. The calcium and phosphate products necessary to precipitate apatite in relation to their level in serum and the solubility product of bone mineral (after [7]).

15

Human serum has a value of about 20 (mg %)[2] and is therefore under-saturated for the precipitation of bone salts and supersaturated as regards the dissociation of existing minerals (fig. 3.1). This paradox has been discussed by Neuman and Neuman [13] who resolve the difficulty by invoking two concepts. The first is that it is secondary calcium phosphate ($CaHPO_4$) which actually precipitates from the salines and this then hydrolyses to form hydroxyapatite. Thus, chemically, the difficulty is due to the fact that the system involves two different minerals. Biologically, however, the difficulty remains, for even if the formation of bone mineral does involve secondary calcium phosphate as an intermediate step, it still requires a solubility product about twice that which is normally found in the serum. This difficulty is avoided by the second concept. It is postulated that bone mineral does not form by precipitation, but rather by crystallization. Energetically, these two processes are very different, for precipitation involves the collision of a large number of ions to form a stable product, whereas the crystallization of apatite depends upon the growth of crystal lattices by the gradual addition of extra ions in their correct positions and thus might be expected to occur at much lower concentrations. It is suggested that bone mineral may form by a crystallization process even in regions which have not yet ossified, because collagen is thought to have a similar crystal lattice to apatite (table 3.1). Thus bone mineral forms

Table 3.1 *A comparison of the X-ray reflections of collagen and apatite suggesting that there may be some similarities in crystalline structure* [13]

Index of axial repeat (collagen)	Spacings in fibre direction		Spacings transverse to fibre	
	Collagen (Å)	Apatite (Å)	Collagen (Å)	Apatite (Å)
0	20	—	10·4–11·6	9·88
2	9·55	—	5·7	—
4	5·0	6·88	4·6	—
5	3·97	—	—	—
7	2·86–3·26	3·44	—	—

in the organic collagen fibres by a process of crystal overgrowth or epitaxy similar to that known to occur between isomorphic crystals.

The first of these two concepts, namely that bone mineralization occurs through the reaction

$$Ca^{++} + HPO_4^{--} \rightarrow Ca\,HPO_4 \rightarrow hydroxyapatite$$

has been questioned on a number of occasions [9] and a discussion of this problem is not necessary for the purposes of this chapter. The role of collagen in mineralization is more important, and although several variations to the theory have been proposed recently they agree in their essentials. These are, first, that collagen induces the formation of bone minerals at concentrations which are much less than would be necessary if the protein was absent, and secondly, that these [Ca] . [P] products are, in fact, within the normal physiological range for blood (fig. 3.2). The only alternative to the epitaxy theory is one which involves a local increase in the concentration

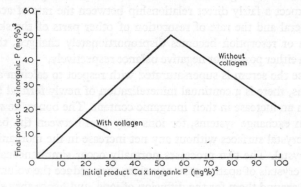

FIG. 3.2. The calcium and phosphate ion products necessary to form bone mineral in the presence or absence of collagen. Note that these protein fibres induce the formation of apatite at products similar to those found in serum (after [8]).

of either calcium or phoshate ions at sites of mineralization. There is some evidence in favour of such a mechanism [16] and, in fact, the two theories are not mutually exclusive.

It will be apparent from this introduction that blood is normally supersaturated with respect to apatite and therefore calcium and phosphate ions are constantly being lost from the blood either by the formation of new crystals upon collagen fibres or by the continual crystal growth of existing bone salts. In both cases, the movement of ions is out of the blood to form inorganic crystals and, if there was no reversal of the process, the blood would rapidly fall from its supersaturated condition to one in which the bone mineral and the blood were in equilibrium. Under normal conditions this never occurs, because there are areas of the skeleton where physiological processes, using the energy of cellular metabolism, reverse these reactions and pass ions from the mineral into the already supersaturated blood. These processes are apparent as the resorption of bone by the osteoclasts and they are partly under the control of the parathyroid glands. This necessity for cellular activity, resorbing bone and returning the ions to the blood, explains the continual remodelling of bone, even in the adult, and seems to be the principle underlying the activity of the Haversian canal system. If the blood was not kept supersaturated with bone minerals, there would be a fall in the calcium level of the blood with the disturbance of a number of physiological processes and increasing difficulty in the repair of any skeletal damage. Thus supersaturation seems to be a necessary attribute of the blood, and it can only be maintained in this dynamic state either by a large intake of calcium and phosphate ions from the intestine or by the continual remodelling of the bone. If this latter process predominates, one would expect a fairly direct relationship between the rate of accretion of new mineral and the rate of resorption of other parts of the skeleton. If accretion or resorption becomes disproportionately changed, the animal will be in either positive or negative balance respectively.

Because the serum is supersaturated with respect to calcium and phosphate ions, there is a continual mineralization of newly formed bones, resulting in an increase in their inorganic content. The bones, however, also act as ion exchange systems, for ions may pass between the body fluids and the crystal surfaces without any net increase in the inorganic content of the crystal. The two processes normally occur simultaneously, but as adjacent crystals of apatite grow together, they reduce the volume of fluid available around them for the diffusion of ions, and hence they slow down both their own rate of mineralization and also their ion exchange properties. This probably explains the rapid initial ossification of a Haversian canal system and the slow rate of final mineralization. Some crystals may undergo internal rearrangements or recrystallization, in which case the deeper lying ions may be brought to the surface of the crystal but, eventually, the crystal becomes so surrounded by other mineral that the possibility of it exchanging ions with the body fluids is almost nil. This is the basis for considering some parts of the skeleton to be readily exchangeable and available to the body fluids while other parts are non-exchangeable and relatively inert.

Investigations into the movements of ions in and out of the skeleton have depended almost entirely upon the use of radio-isotopes. These substances first became available for biological work on bone in the 1930s and a new era in skeletal physiology began in 1935 when Chievitz and Hevesy [6] added P^{32} to the diets of rats and found that after 1 month about 25 % of the original dose was concentrated in the skeleton (table 3.2). They further found that about 30 % of the phosphorus deposited in the skeleton was removed in about 20 days. They realized that there were probably two processes involved in the uptake of P^{32} by the skeleton, but were unable to distinguish between ion exchange and bone formation because of the varying level of P^{32} in the blood. In a later experiment, the technique was modified so that the P^{32} level of the blood remained constant throughout the experiment, and it was then possible to show the importance of bone growth in the fixation of radio-isotopes [10]. By this means the amount of the skeleton formed in a given length of time could be determined, and it be-

Table 3.2 *Distribution of P^{32} in rats 1 month after feeding (% original dose)* [6]

	%		%
Urine	26·3	Liver	1·7
Faeces	31·8	Blood	0·4
Brain	0·5	Skeleton	24·8
Spleen and kidneys	0·2	Muscle and fat	17·4

came apparent that different bones, and even different regions of the same bone, varied in this respect (table 3.3). Unfortunately, this technique was not capable of determining whether some ions were renewed several times.

When Ca^{45} became readily available, it was used to extend these studies on the dynamics of the exchange of skeletal minerals. It was found that after the injection of a single dose of Ca^{45} into rats, the radioactivity present in the blood fell rapidly, while that in the skeleton increased. This could

Table 3.3 *The extent of replacement of phosphorus in the bones as assessed by maintaining a constant level of P^{32} in the blood of a rabbit* [10].

	% P replaced
Femur epiphysis	29·7
Femur diaphysis	6·7
Tibia epiphysis	28·6
Tibia diaphysis	7·6
Scapula	43·8

be explained as simply reflecting an intimate association between these two systems, but when the experiment was continued for 10 days, it was found that the specific activity (i.e. $Ca^{45}/Ca^{45} + Ca^{40}$) of the blood was several times smaller than that of the bones. It was concluded that the concept of a simple equilibrium between the blood and the bones was no longer capable of explaining these results, but that there must be additional complications due to certain physical and/or metabolic factors [14]. It was apparent that if these so-called 'complicating factors' could be investigated quantitatively it would provide an far-reaching insight into the physiology of bones.

c

A number of attempts have been made to investigate the partitioning of elements within the skeleton, but the most successful and interesting analysis to date is that devised by Bauer, Carlsson, and Lindquist [1] and recently reviewed by them [4]. They argued that if, for the moment, one ignored the possibility of any newly formed bone being resorbed during the time of the experiment, then the amount of radio-isotope found in any particular bone (Ca_{obs}^{45}) was the sum of the amount of isotope included by exchange phenomena (Ca_E^{45}) plus the amount included by the accretion of any new bone (Ca_A^{45}),

$$\text{i.e.} \quad Ca_{obs}^{45} = Ca_E^{45} + Ca_A^{45} \tag{1}$$

The argument was therefore a natural extension of previous work. The great advance came, however, because it was realized that if a single injection of radio-isotope was given, then the changes with time in this system enabled one to distinguish between Ca_E^{45} and Ca_A^{45} and thus to estimate the amount of exchangeable calcium in the skeleton and the amount of new

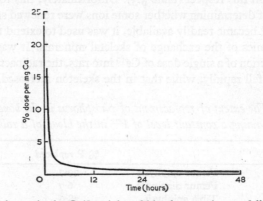

FIG. 3.3. The change in the Ca^{45} activity of blood serum in rats following a single injection of the radio-isotope (after [2]).

bone which is formed during a particular length of time. The basic assumption in this analysis is that the specific activity of the plasma calcium is the same as the specific activity of the exchangeable calcium in the skeleton. This follows because the exchangeable calcium in the skeleton is in equilibrium with the plasma calcium. Thus a measurement of the specific activity of one is an assessment of the other at any particular time. The specific activity of the blood falls continuously after the injection of a single dose of Ca^{45}, and can be assessed by simply sampling the blood (fig. 3.3). As the blood and exchangeable bone are in equilibrium, it follows that the quantity Ca_E^{45} at any moment (t) is the product of the specific activity of the blood at that time (i.e. $S_t^\star$) and the total amount of calcium in the exchangeable bone (E),

$$\text{i.e.} \quad Ca_E{}^{45} = S_t^\star \cdot E \tag{II}$$

The amount of radio-isotope deposited as new bone is given by a different expression because it must be assumed that the Ca^{45} and the Ca^{40} in the bone are laid down in the same proportions as they exist in the blood and this changes with time (fig. 3.3). Thus during the time (t) of the experiment, the Ca^{45} laid down as new bone $(Ca_A{}^{45})$ is equal to the product of the rate of new bone formation (A), the time of the experiment (t) and the *average* specific activity of the blood $(S_m^\star)$ during this time t,

$$\text{i.e.} \quad Ca_A{}^{45} = A \cdot t \cdot S_m^\star \tag{III}$$

Note that expression (II) relates to the events as they occur at time t, the end of the experiment, whereas expression (III) includes the average events during the whole experiment. This is a basic distinction, and for this reason, expression (III) is better written as

$$Ca_A{}^{45} = A. \int_0^t S^\star(t) \cdot dt \tag{IV}$$

where $\int_0^t S^\star(t) \, dt$ is the area under the specific activity curve of Ca^{45} in the serum between the start of the experiment (time 0) and time t.

Rewriting equation (I) we now get

$$Ca_{obs}{}^{45} = S_t^\star E + A \int_0^t S^\star(t) \cdot dt \tag{V}$$

This equation now contains two variables which can be measured, i.e. the total Ca^{45} in the skeleton $(Ca_{obs}{}^{45})$ and the specific activity of the serum $(S_t^\star)$. It also has two constants E and A which can therefore be determined from the results obtained at different time intervals by the use of two simultaneous equations.

This analysis contains a number of assumptions, some of which have been over-simplified in the explanation just given [5]. In particular, it should be pointed out that there is actually a slight time lag between the equilibration of serum Ca^{45} with the exchangeable fraction of the bone. Because of this, one should really substitute a constant k, for the term E. In practice, however, the direct use of the term E does not introduce an error of more than 20%, and this approximation has therefore been used. A similar error exists in formulating A in equation (V) since the first bone which is laid down probably exists as exchangeable calcium and is only later overlaid and rendered non-exchangeable. The constant k_2 is therefore sometimes substituted for A to account for this error, although this is again generally small. Perhaps the greatest difficulty in this analysis is, however, the meaning of the fractions called 'exchangeable' and 'accretion'. As long as 'exchangeable' simply means a fraction of the skeleton which exchanges rapidly with the serum, there is no confusion. Similarly, if one calls the remainder of the skeleton 'non-exchangeable' so that calcium can only be added to it by 'accretion', then the term is perfectly well defined. It is not possible, however, to relate these kinetic terms to single physiological processes, for although it is easy to see how the different fractions arise, it is impossible to tell how completely the kinetic and the physiological fractions coincide, and the exchangeable fraction in particular probably contains many sub-fractions all of which react slightly differently [3].

When the Bauer, Carlsson, and Lindquist analysis is put into practice, remarkably good results are obtained. In fig. 3.4 can be seen the results obtained after injecting 3-month-old rats with a single dose of Ca^{45} and measuring the amount of radio-isotopes in the diaphyses of the tibia (shown as circles in fig. 3.4 (a)). The specific activity of the blood was also measured at various times up to 120 hours after the injection, and from this it is possible to calculate both E and A. The sum of E and A should then match the observed value for the percentage of the dose in the tibia diaphysis and the close correspondence is clearly shown in fig. 3.4 (a) where all these values are plotted together.

When these experiments were repeated, using the ends of the tibiae as the sources of labelled bone, an entirely different set of results was obtained, and it was found to be impossible to obtain constant values for the expressions E and A by the use of equation (V) unless very short time intervals were used. A set of curves were therefore constructed, using the data from 4 and 16 hours after the injection of the radio-isotope. The results are shown in fig. 3.4 (b) and it is at once apparent that there is no longer a close correspondence between the calculated values of E and A and the experimental data observed for the radio-activity of the bone (B). This anomaly is readily explained, however, for it will be remembered that in describing the analysis of the kinetics of bones, it was decided that the effects of resorption (Ca_R^{45}) would be ignored. If we no longer make this assumption, equation (1) becomes modified to

$$Ca_{obs}^{45} = Ca_E^{45} + Ca_A^{45} - Ca_R^{45} \qquad \text{(VI)}$$

i.e. if we are dealing with a bone in which the rate of resorption is large in relation to the duration of the experiment, then this effect can no longer be ignored, for some Ca^{45} is then being returned to the blood from the non-exchangeable bone. It will be recalled that tracer experiments had previously shown that the ends of a rat tibia are renewed about three times in an 8-day period (p. 10) and this would explain the need to consider resorption in this region of bone, whereas it could be ignored in the relatively slowly metabolized bone of the tibia diaphysis. If this is the explanation of the results obtained with the tibia ends, then the difference between Ca_{obs}^{45} and the calculated values of Ca_E^{45} and Ca_A^{45} must be due to the resorbed calcium (Ca_R^{45}). This is shown in fig. 3.4 (b) where curve R is the difference between curves $E + A$ and B.

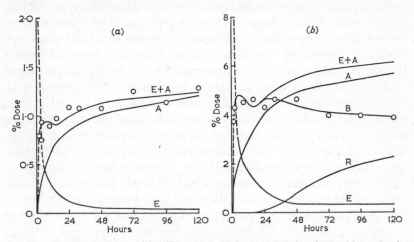

FIG. 3.4. (a) The exchangeable (E) and newly formed (A) fractions of bone in the diaphyses of rat tibias as calculated from radio-isotope studies. The open circles show the actual distribution of Ca^{45} determined experimentally in comparison with the expected values ($E + A$).

(b) In the epiphyseal ends of the tibias the experimentally determined values of Ca^{45} (open circles) do not correspond to the values of $E + A$ as calculated. The difference between these experimental values (B) and the curve $E + A$ is shown as the curve R which is interpreted as being the quantity of Ca^{45} removed from the bone by resorption (after [4]).

This, then, is the principle of the analysis of the kinetics of bone mineral. By measuring the Ca^{45} in a piece of bone at time t after the injection of a single dose of the radio-isotope, it is possible to relate the amount of labelled calcium in the skeleton to the specific activity of the serum and thus to obtain a measure of the quantity of exchangeable bone and the rate of bone accretion. If the experiment extends over such a length of time that it exceeds the lifespan of the tissue, then it is also possible to estimate the rate of resorption of the labelled bone. Using this system of analysis it is possible to obtain values of A and E, but although these are reasonably constant over a significant portion of the kinetic study they do tend to vary with time. This makes the physiological interpretation of these fractions rather difficult. It has therefore been postulated by Marshall [12] that the retention of Ca^{45} in the body should be regarded as a modified power function of time, i.e. (t^{-b}), until equilibrium is obtained. This term 'retention' is obviously time dependent and by including it in the Bauer, Carlsson, and Lindquist expressions for A and E it is possible to make a formal provision for the observed time variation which is found in the measurement of these values. In using these power function expressions Marshall accepts the fact that his values of, for example, A are no longer identical with bone mineralization. Other systems for the analysis of the movement of ions in and out of skeletal minerals are even more abstract. They are referred to as compartmental analyses and they are concerned with the development of purely mathematical models which reproduce the kinetics of the distribution of isotopes in biological systems. The term compartment is used in two senses, either to describe a physiologically demarcated region or to refer to the presence of a particular chemical fraction which possesses some identifying characteristic [15]. Compartmental analysis can be a very useful tool, but its abstractions often makes it difficult to correlate anatomical, physiological, and kinetic investigations, whereas the Bauer, Carlsson, and Lindquist analysis is at least partially successful in this approach. This can be seen in the following examples based upon an analysis of the skeletal kinetics of 3-month-old rats (table 3.4). These animals were still growing,

Table 3.4 *Calcium metabolism in the tibias of a 3-month-old rat as estimated by kinetic studies* [1]

	Whole tibia	Ends	Shafts
Calcium content mg	66	36	30
Net increase mg Ca/hr	0·04	0·02	0·02
Accretion (A) mg Ca/hr	0·17	0·14	0·03
Resorption (R) mg Ca/hr	0·13	0·12	0·01
Exchangeable (E) fraction mg Ca	2·0	1·7	0·3

and the accretion rate is greater than the resorption, so that there is a net increase of about 0·04 mg Ca/hr in the tibiae of these animals. The results also demonstrate very clearly that the ends of the long bones have a much greater activity both in accretion and resorption of mineral than do the shafts. About 3% of the calcium in the whole tibia is in the exchangeable form with corresponding figures for the shaft and the ends being 1% and 5% respectively. This suggests that there might be some correlation between the accretion rate in a particular region of the bone and the amount of exchangeable calcium in that structure. This appears, in fact, to be the case, for the ratio E/A is approximately 12 for both the shafts and the ends. This confirms previous suggestions that the exchangeable bone is a product of the formation of new bone, although one would perhaps have thought that the surface area of mature bone and the effects of resorption would have also influenced the availability of bone mineral for exchange with the blood.

As animals age the rate of accretion of new bone often appears to decrease. In old rats the accretion rate of femur shafts was 0·01 mg Ca/hr or 0·7% of the total Ca content/day. This is only a third of the accretion rate of tibia shafts in young rats (table 3.4). In the adult human the accretion rate in the whole skeleton amounts to about 0·5 g Ca/day which is a renewal rate of about 0·05% of the skeleton/day. The exchangeable calcium is also fairly constant with a value of about 3 to 6 g which is 0·3–0·4% of the adult skeleton. The accretion and resorption rates of whole skeletons are shown in table 3.5 for various rats and humans [4, 5]. The rates are calculated as

Table 3.5 *The accretion and resorption rates of calcium in whole skeletons.* (*partly after* [5])

Species	Age (years)	Sex	Formation rate mg/day	mg/kg body/hr*	Resorption rate mg/day	mg/kg body/hr*
Human	16	Female	720	0·50	—	0·50
	41	Female	520	0·34	—	0·34
	22	Male	820	0·50	—	0·50
Rat	0·25	Female	62	10·0	—	10·0
	1·0	Female	10	2·0	—	2·0
	'averaged' values		54	9·0	46	8·0

* Estimated.

mg Ca/kg body wt/hr for later comparison with the rates of calcium metabolism during pregnancy and lactation.

These analyses of the dynamics of bone metabolism are also of interest when applied to animals in various physiological conditions. When rats were fed on diets either rich or poor in calcium, it was possible to show that in both conditions the rate of bone accretion was the same. The low calcium diet stimulated bone resorption, however, and this presumably is the way in which the skeleton performs a homeostatic function and regulates the metabolism of this ion in the body (table 3.6). It is important to note, therefore, that the resorption rate can be varied independently of the accretion rate, and thus is capable of releasing extra minerals from the skeleton. These modifications to skeletal functions are regulated by a number of mechanisms of which the parathyroid is probably the most sensitive. Certainly,

Table 3.6   *Effect of various treatments on skeletal kinetics of rat femur* [1]

	Rachitic rats receiving vitamin D	Control rachitic rats	Rats on Ca-rich diet	Rats on Ca-deficient diet
Net increase mg Ca/hr	0·02	0	0·04	0·02
Accretion (A) mg Ca/hr	0·11	0·05	0·14	0·14
Resorption (R) mg Ca/hr	0·09	0·05	0·10	0·12
Exchangeable (E) fraction mg Ca	1·0	0·55	—	—

hyperparathyroidism in humans results in an accelerated rate of turnover of calcium in the skeleton, which can be reduced by surgically removing these glands. When this is done, the resorption of the bones is halted, with a subsequent decline in the accretion and exchangeable fractions of the skeleton (table 3.7).

Vitamin D is another substance which influences the metabolism of the skeletal minerals, and giving this vitamin to rachitic rats increased all aspects of the kinetics of bone functions (table 3.6). The net increase in bone formation was attributed to the effect of the vitamin upon the uptake of ions from the intestine. The other effects were interpreted as showing that

Table 3.7   *The effect of parathyroid hormone on the kinetics of bone metabolism in man (after* [4])

Condition	Age	Weight kg	Accretion g Ca/d	Exchangeable g Ca	Resorption g Ca/d
Normal	—	—	0·5	5	
Hyperparathyroid before operation	51	53	2·2	7·8	2·2
Hyperparathyroid after operation	51	53	1·0	6·6	0

the vitamin increased the resorption of bone mineral and thus, by increasing the concentration of calcium and phosphate ions in the blood, it also increased the accretion rate of new mineral and the size of the exchangeable fraction. It was therefore suggested that the vitamin influences bone resorption when given in normal physiological concentrations.

One final example of the application of these kinetic studies shows the usefulness of the approach and the way in which the results correlate with anatomical work. The rat is unique among mammals in that the administration of oestrogens results in formation of a great amount of spongy bone in the skeleton. This was interpreted as being caused by an inhibition to the resorption of this material rather than to an overproduction of this bone. Unfortunately, the administration of oestrogens also causes the early maturation of the skeleton, with a cessation of growth, and this complicates the interpretation of kinetic studies. The results of an experiment in which Ca^{45} and oestrogens were given to young rats are, however, shown in table 3.8, which reveals a number of similarities to the normal condition

Table 3.8 *Calcium metabolism in the tibias of young rats with or without oestrogen treatment* [11]

	Upper ends		Shafts		Lower ends	
	Control	Oestrogen	Control	Oestrogen	Control	Oestrogen
Calcium content mg	47·7	58·0	68·5	50·3	24·9	22·6
Net increase mg Ca/hr	0·6	0·06	0·04	0·02	0·02	0·02
Accretion (A) mg Ca/hr	0·19	0·13	0·06	0·03	0·03	0·02
Resorption (R) mg Ca/hr	0·13	0·07	0·02	0·01	0·01	0·00
Exchangeable (E) fraction (mg Ca)	3·33	2·60	1·25	0·72	0·60	0·39
Resorption/Accretion (R/A)	0·76	0·56	0·27	0·29	0·34	0·16

as seen in table 3.4. The effect of the oestrogens can be seen in the ratio of resorption to accretion (R/A) which, by being a ratio of two rates, minimizes the effects of the reduced growth rate while illustrating changes in the relative effects of these processes. Thus, in the bone shafts, the change in bone resorption can be accounted for simply by the effects of decreased growth, and the ratio R/A is similar to that in the controls. In the ends of the tibia, however, the ratio of R/A is greatly decreased as compared with the control animals and this is completely in keeping with the anatomical picture, namely that oestrogens inhibit the resorption of spongy bone in the long bones of rats [11].

REFERENCES

[1] BAUER, G. C. H., CARLSSON, A., and LINDQUIST, B. (1955a), 'Evaluation of accretion, resorption, and exchange reactions in the skeleton', *K. fysiogr. Sällsk. Lund. Forh.*, **25**, 3–18.

[2] BAUER, G. C. H., CARLSSON, A., and LINDQUIST, B. (1955b), 'A comparative study on the metabolism of Sr^{90} and Ca^{45}', *Acta Physiol. Scand.*, **35**, 56–66.

[3] BAUER, G. C. H., CARLSSON, A., and LINDQUIST, B. (1955C), 'Some properties of the exchangeable bone calcium', *Acta Physiol. Scand.*, 35, 67–72.

[4] BAUER, G. C. H., CARLSSON, A., and LINDQUIST, B. (1961), 'Metabolism and homeostatic function of bone', in *Mineral Metabolism*, vol. 1B, eds. Comar, C. L. and Bronner, F., Academic Press, 609–76.

[5] BRONNER, F. (1964), 'Dynamics and function of calcium', in *Mineral Metabolism*, vol. 2A, eds. Comar, C. L. and Bronner, F., Academic Press, 341–444.

[6] CHIEVITZ, O. and HEVESY, G. (1935), 'Radioactive indicators in the study of phosphorus metabolism in rats', *Nature, Lond.*, 136, 754–5.

[7] FLEISCH, H. and NEUMAN, W. F. (1960), 'Quantitative aspects of nucleation in calcium phosphate', *J. Amer. chem. Soc.*, 82, 996.

[8] FLEISCH, H. and NEUMAN, W. F. (1961), 'Mechanisms of calcification: role of collagen, polyphosphates and phosphatase', *Amer. J. Physiol.*, 200, 1296–300.

[9] GLIMCHER, M. J. (1959), 'The molecular biology of the mineralized tissues with particular reference to bone', *Rev. mod. Phys.*, 31, 359–93.

[10] HEVESY, G. CH., LEVI, H. B., and REBBE, O. H. (1940), 'Rate of rejuvenation of the skeleton', *Biochem. J.*, 34, 532–7.

[11] LINDQUIST, B., BUDY, ANN M., MCLEAN, F. C., and HOWARD, J. L. (1960), 'Skeletal metabolism in estrogen-treated rats studied by means of Ca^{45}', *Endocrinology*, 66, 100–11.

[12] MARSHALL, J. H. (1964), 'Theory of alkaline earth metabolism', *J. Theoret. Biol.*, 6, 386–412.

[13] NEUMAN, W. F. and NEUMAN, MARGARET W. (1958), *The Chemical Dynamics of Bone Mineral*, Univ. Chicago Press, 209 pp.

[14] NORRIS, W. P. and KISIELESKI, W. (1948), 'Comparative metabolism of radium, strontium and calcium', *Cold Spr. Harb. Sym. quant. Biol.*, 13, 164–71.

[15] SOLOMON, A. K. (1960), 'Compartmental methods of kinetic analysis, in *Mineral Metabolism*, vol. 1A, eds. Comar, C. L. and Bronner, F., Academic Press, 119–67.

[16] URIST, M. R. and ADAMS, J. M. (1966), 'Effects of various blocking reagents upon local mechanism of calcification', *Arch. Path.*, 81, 325–342.

CHAPTER 4
Calcium in the Blood

The bones, the intestine, and the reproductive system (including the mammary glands in mammals), in fact, all the organs of the body that are involved in calcium metabolism during reproduction are connected by the blood system. Changes in the activity of one organ produce various influences in other parts of the body through the circulatory system. Despite this, the calcium content of the blood remains remarkably constant. This is obviously achieved by means of some homeostatic system. The efficiency of this system can be seen from the fact that in a bird, when egg laying, a quantity of calcium, equivalent to that contained in the whole circulatory system, can be removed by the oviduct every ten minutes without producing any great fluctuation in the calcium content of the blood [8].

Most of the calcium in the blood is in solution in the plasma. Cells contain only small quantities of calcium, and the amount present in the erythrocytes is generally neglible. In man, the concentration of calcium in the plasma is normally in the range of 9–11 mg %, with 10 mg % or 2·5 mM an average value. The value of 10 mg % is typical for most mammals, birds, reptiles, and amphibians when they are not in reproductive activity (table 4.1).

Analysis of the calcium in vertebrate plasma has shown that it exists in two roughly equal fractions characterized as the diffusible and the non-diffusible forms. The diffusible fraction comprises that part which will pass through a dialysis membrane, while the non-diffusible forms the retained fraction. It is not possible to estimate the two forms by a simple dialysis of the plasma against water, as the two fractions are in equilibrium with each other. For this reason, methods involving ultra-filtration or ultra-centrifugation are sometimes used to separate the protein-bound and the free fractions of plasma calcium. For most purposes, diffusible and ultra-filterable calcium can be considered to be identical. Non-diffusible, non-ultra-filterable and protein-bound calcium are also virtually identical.

In most physiological processes, the calcium ion is the most important form of this element. Diffusible calcium consists of ionic calcium together with small amounts of un-ionized calcium mainly in the form of calcium citrate, but with small fractions in combination with phosphate and bicarbonate anions. In those body fluids which contain little protein, such as the cerebrospinal fluid or the intercellular body fluids with which the plasma is in equilibrium, the calcium is virtually all in the diffusible form at a concentration of about 5 mg %. A small fraction of this may be in the form of complexes, but most is present as ionic calcium, so that these fluids resemble an ultra-filtrate of the plasma.

Table 4.1 *Concentration of calcium (mg %) in the blood of tetrapods when not reproducing* [2, 3, 15, 18]

Amphibia	
Rana catesbiana (bull frog)	11·6
Rana pipiens (leopard frog)	10·3
Reptile	
Pseudemys scripta troosti (turtle)	8·5
Thamnophis sauritus (ribbon snake)	10·9
Bird	
Gallus domesticus (domestic fowl)	10·2
Passer domesticus (house sparrow)	9·7
Mammal	
Homo sapiens (man)	10·0
Mus musculus (mouse)	9·9

The intercellular fluids form a large physiological compartment amounting to about 10 litres in a 70-kg man. They contain about 500 mg of calcium almost entirely in the diffusible form. The plasma consists of about 2·8 litres of fluid containing 280 mg calcium with approximately 140 mg in the ionic form. Calcium ions pass freely and rapidly between these two fluid systems.

The relationship between the diffusible and non-diffusible calcium has been considered to be an equilibrium based upon the dissociation of a weak electrolyte of calcium proteinate [11],

i.e.   Ca Proteinate $\rightleftharpoons$ Ca^{++} + Protein^{--}

It is therefore possible to determine a dissociation constant for the calcium form of the plasma proteins

$$\frac{[\text{Ca}^{++}] \times [\text{Protein}]}{[\text{Ca Proteinate}]} = K_{\text{Ca Prot.}} = 10^{-2 \cdot 22} \text{ (in mammals)}$$

More detailed analyses give the dissociation constants of the two main plasma proteins, albumin and globulin, in their isolated form (table 4.2).

Table 4.2   *The reaction of mammalian plasma proteins with calcium* [11, 12, 14]

	Total plasma proteins	Plasma albumin	Plasma globulin
Protein concentration (g %)	5·5–7·6	3·3–5·6	1·6–3·1
Calcium-binding ability (moles Ca/10^5 g)	—	10·5	5·6
Dissociation constant	$10^{-2·22}$	$10^{-2·43}$	$10^{-2·03}$

There is about twice the amount of albumin as there is globulin in the human plasma. Albumin also binds about twice as much calcium per gram of protein as does globulin, so that about 80% of the non-diffusible calcium is associated with this protein, whereas the other 20% is bound to globulin (table 4.3). Although the two proteins differ in the total amount of

Table 4.3   *The concentration of various calcium complexes in human serum* [14]

			mg %
Total calcium 10 mg %	Non-diffusible calcium 3·28 mg %	Albumin	2·6
		Globulin	0·68
	Diffusible calcium 6·52 mg %	Ionized	5·32
		Complexes as	
		HCO_3^-	0·64
		PO_4^{---}	0·24
		citrate	0·28
		others	?

calcium carried per gram of protein, they have approximately the same dissociation constants.

This interpretation of the relationship between the diffusible and non-diffusible calcium of the blood has important implications. If the two forms do represent the dissociation of a weak electrolyte, then variations in the total calcium content of the blood should involve both fractions. This possibility has been tested clinically in both hypoparathyroidism, where the total calcium content of the blood falls and in hyperparathyroidism where it rises above normal levels. Thus, providing firstly that the total protein concentration of the plasma does not alter, and secondly that there is no quantitative change in the ability of the plasma proteins to bind calcium, the ratio of ionized to un-ionized calcium should remain approximately constant,

$$\text{i.e.} \quad \frac{[\text{Ca}^{++}]}{[\text{Ca Proteinate}]} = \frac{K_{\text{Ca Prot.}}}{[\text{Protein}]}$$

Some deviations will occur because of the alterations in the ratio of Ca Proteinate : Protein brought about by variations in total calcium, but these changes are small and the relationship predicted on the basis of the law of mass action has been found to be true for many of the clinical conditions which have been tested [13].

There are, however, some experiments which suggest that the hormone of the parathyroid gland may influence the distribution of calcium between the diffusible and non-diffusible fractions by affecting the calcium binding properties of the serum proteins of birds and mammals (table 4.4). It is

Table 4.4 *The influence of the parathyroid hormone upon the distribution of calcium in the plasma of birds and mammals* [7, 10]. *The results have been interpreted as demonstrating that the hormone reduces the calcium binding ability of the plasma proteins so that the diffusible calcium increases at the expense of the non-diffusible. The birds were vitamin-D deficient*

Animal	Citric acid mg %	Total Ca mg %	Diffusible Ca mg %	Non-diffusible Ca mg %	Diffusible as % total Ca
Human (No. 1), hyperparathyroid	—	13·7	9·9	3·8	74
Human (No. 1), hyperparathyroid after operation	—	7·3	4·6	2·7	64
Human (No. 4), hyperparathyroid	—	12·6	3·2	9·3	74
Human (No. 4), hyperparathyroid after operation	—	5·4	2·0	3·4	63
Domestic fowl and parathyroid hormone	3·91	13·4	7·6	5·8	57
Domestic fowl (control)	3·37	13·4	6·4	6·9	48

suggested that the hormone reduces the calcium binding ability of the proteins so that there is an increase in the percentage of diffusible calcium. More work is necessary on this phenomenon, especially as the citric acid in the blood varies in some of these experiments. The citric acid content of the blood is influenced by the parathyroid hormone, so that this may account for some of the variations in the level of diffusible calcium which would not, therefore, necessarily reflect the level of ionic calcium.

A similar increase in the percentage of diffusible calcium in hyperparathyroidism has been interpreted as indicating that the sequential binding of calcium by the plasma proteins involves a stepwise process with each stage having a different formation constant. This conclusion was reached because it was found that the increase in diffusible calcium could be demonstrated *in vitro* by adding calcium ions to the blood of parathyroidectomized dogs until the total calcium level was similar to that of normal or hyperparathyroid dogs (table 4.5). Thus, the increase in the percentage of

Table 4.5 *The influence of the parathyroid hormone upon the distribution of calcium in the plasma of the dog. The percentage of diffusible calcium increases with an increase in total calcium. The results are interpreted as not being due to the hormone as a similar effect can be obtained by adding calcium to the blood of the hypoparathyroid animal* in vitro. *It is therefore concluded that the ability of the serum proteins to bind calcium decreases as the amount of calcium in the blood increases* [1]

Treatment	Total Ca mg %	Diffusible Ca mg %	Non-diffusible Ca mg %	Diffusible as % total Ca
In vivo *experiments*				
Parathyroidectomized dog	6·50	3·45	3·05	52·8
Normal dog	11·26	6·55	4·71	58·3
Hyperparathyroid dog	18·23	10·60	7·55	58·7
In vitro *experiments*				
Blood of para-thyroidectomized dog	6·89	3·26	3·63	52·3
Blood of para-thyroidectomized dog + extra Ca	10·47	4·34	6·13	58·4
Blood of para-thyroidectomized dog + additional Ca	15·61	5·79	9·82	63·1

diffusible calcium could be obtained in the absence of parathyroid hormone and it was suggested that successive calcium ions are each bound more weakly by the protein complexes. Such a phenomenon is already well known from studies on the binding of calcium by casein, where the first calcium forms a complex with a pK of 3·43 but the sixteenth calcium ion bound by the protein molecule has a pK of only 1·04 [1].

Analyses of the ability of plasma proteins to bind calcium have also been made, using data from the pregnant human. In this case the plasma of the mother has a dissociation constant which has been calculated as $pK_{Ca\ Prot.}$ = 2·11 whereas the foetus has plasma with a value $pK_{Ca\ Prot.}$ = 2·37 [4]. If the analyses upon which these calculations are based are correct, this demonstrates an increased ability of the blood proteins of the foetus to bind calcium. This has been interpreted as a way by which the foetus could preferentially remove calcium from the maternal circulation in an analogous way to the uptake of oxygen by foetal haemoglobin.

The equilibrium between diffusible and non-diffusible calcium is also greatly influenced by pH. The loss of carbon dioxide from *in vitro* samples of the blood of the fowl was sufficient to change the pH from 7·55 to 7·87 and this resulted in a decrease of 1–2 mg % in the diffusible fraction of the blood calcium [17]. This indicates a fall of about 12–24% in the level of ionized calcium and similar results have been found with human serum [9]. In both cases there appears to be a replacement of the hydrogen ions on the plasma proteins by calcium ions. It is unlikely that this process has any physiological significance although similar changes have been noted during hyperventilation [5]. For the most part, however, the phenomenon simply indicates the dynamic state of calcium in the plasma and the practical difficulties in estimating the main fractions.

It is normally possible to consider variations in the total calcium content of the blood in a meaningful way because they are directly proportional to the level of the ionic calcium in the blood. There is no doubt, however, that it is the ionic rather than the total blood calcium which is physiologically active in most processes, and it is this fraction of the blood calcium which is affected by the regulatory processes. The control of the concentration of ionic calcium in the blood is mainly brought about by the influence of two hormones. These will be discussed in more detail later. Suffice it to say that one of these is secreted by the parathyroid gland as a direct response to a fall in the level of ionic calcium in the blood. An increased secretion of parathyroid hormone produces compensatory changes which raise the level of blood calcium. Another hormone from the thyroid–parathyroid complex has the opposite effect. This substance, called calcitonin or thyrocalcitonin, acts by lowering the level of calcium in the blood. The proportional activity of these two hormones maintains the blood calcium at a remarkably stable value. A number of other influences do affect the blood calcium and the most important of these is probably vitamin D. This substance affects the absorption of calcium from the intestine and also induces the resorption of bone so that it also can raise the level of calcium in the blood if given in sufficient doses.

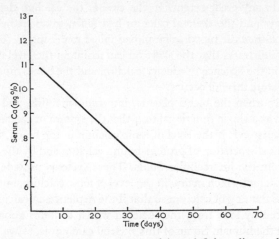

FIG. 4.1. The effect of maintaining rats on a calcium-deficient diet as shown by its influence upon the level of serum calcium (after [6]).

A further investigation of these regulatory mechanisms demonstrates a fundamental concept in calcium metabolism. The calcium level of the blood is only slightly affected by starvation, but if a calcium deficiency in the diet is maintained for a long time the level of plasma calcium does fall (fig. 4.1). Maintaining rats on diets with extreme proportions of calcium and phosphorus also influences the level of calcium in the blood in relation to the severity of the diet (fig. 4.2). In both these experiments the defective diets had to be fed for a long time before the level of calcium in the

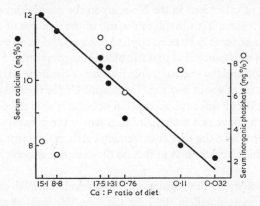

FIG. 4.2. The effect of various dietary ratios of Ca and P upon the level of serum calcium and phosphorus. The ratios of Ca and P are plotted on a logarithmic scale (after [16]).

D

blood fell to any great extent. In the case of the calcium deficient diet it took 68 days and the skeletal calcium had fallen to about half its normal mass by the time the blood calcium had fallen to 6·1 mg % (fig. 4.1). This clearly demonstrates that the skeleton can maintain the level of calcium in the blood in the absence of dietary calcium and the bones must be severely depleted before this fall occurs.

It is only when the blood plasma, intercellular fluids, and bone are all considered as a single functional unit that the system of calcium regulation can be understood. If the level of ionic calcium in the blood falls it is buffered by the dissociation of protein-bound calcium and by the migration of calcium from the intercellular fluids. These systems provide the first reserves of calcium which maintain the level of ionic calcium, but in man they contain less than 1 g of calcium so that if the depletion of calcium continues it is restored by ions from the skeleton which contains about 1,200 g of calcium in the human. Some of this skeletal calcium is, as we have already seen, overlaid by other osseous tissue and therefore relatively inaccessible. It can only be released by osteolytic activity presumably under the influence of the osteoclast and osteocyte cells. Other regions of bone, particularly the newly formed and incompletely ossified parts, are in constant interchange with the ions in the blood. This forms the exchangeable fraction of the skeleton, but since the blood is normally supersaturated with bone mineral it receives rather than donates calcium in any overall exchange of ions between the two systems.

A number of attempts have been made to relate the levels of calcium and phosphate ions in the plasma to a solubility product of bone. If this is to be done at a strict physiochemical level, then allowances have to be made for the effect of other ions in the blood upon the reactivities of the calcium and phosphate ions. This involves the use of the concept of activity coefficients, and these ideas have been applied to blood and bone by Neuman and Neuman [14] who concluded that the blood is supersaturated for bone mineral. The blood and the exchangeable fraction of the bone only tend to equilibrate at a level of about 6–7 mg % calcium. Under normal circumstances this does not occur since the resorption of bone is able to keep the level of blood calcium above this value. Animals where the parathyroid glands are subnormal or where the diet is extremely calcium deficient may approach this level of blood calcium as in fact do those in the experiment illustrated in fig. 4.1.

The physiology of the regulation of the level of blood calcium will be examined in more detail in the next chapter. For most vertebrates, however, the plasma calcium will normally be about 10 mg % or a calcium activity of 0.47×10^{-3}. Plasma inorganic phosphate is normally about

$3 \cdot 1$ mg % with a HPO_4^{--} ion activity of $0 \cdot 19 \times 10^{-3}$. Considerable variations do occur in these values, but the figures given form a basis for comparisons. In the event of either the calcium or the inorganic phosphate level of the blood increasing there will be an increased tendency for bone deposition. A decrease in one or other ion will decrease this tendency. Thus both the non-diffusible calcium of the blood and the surface chemistry of the bone tend to lead to a buffering of the ionic-calcium level of the blood and any metabolic adaptations to which we will later refer will be superimposed upon this system.

REFERENCES

[1] BREEN, MOIRA and FREEMAN, S. (1961), 'Plasma calcium distribution in relation to parathyroid function', *Amer. J. Physiol.*, **200**, 341–4.

[2] CORTELYOU, J. R. (1958), 'Parathyroid glands in amphibia', *Anat. Rec.*, **132**, 424.

[3] DESSAUER, H. C. and FOX, W. (1959), 'Changes in ovarian follicle composition with plasma levels of snakes during estrus', *Amer. J. Physiol.*, **197**, 360–6.

[4] DUCKWORTH, J. (1942), 'Calcium nutrition of the foetus', *Nature, Lond.*, **149**, 731.

[5] FANCONI, A. and ROSE, G. A. (1958), 'The ionized, complexed and protein-bound fractions of calcium in plasma', *Quart. J. Med.*, **27**, 463–94.

[6] GREENBERG, D. M. and MILLER, W. D. (1941), 'Severe calcium deficiency in growing rats. 3. Serum calcium of individual animals during development of calcium deficiency', *J. Nutr.*, **22**, 1–6.

[7] HERTELENDY, F. and TAYLOR, T. G. (1960), 'On the interaction between vitamin D and parathyroid hormone in the domestic fowl', *Biochim. Biophys. Acta.*, **44**, 200–2.

[8] HERTELENDY, F. and TAYLOR, T. G. (1961), 'Changes in blood calcium associated with eggshell calcification in the domestic fowl', *Poult. Sci.*, **40**, 108–14.

[9] HOPKINS, J., HOWARD, J. E. and EISENBERG, H. (1952), 'Ultra-filtration studies on calcium and phosphorus in human serum', *Bull. Johns Hopkins Hosp.*, **91**, 1–21.

[10] LLOYD, H. M. and ROSE, G. A. (1958), 'Ionized, protein-bound and complexed calcium in the plasma in primary hyperparathyroidism', *Lancet*, 1258–61.

[11] MCLEAN, F. C. and HASTINGS, A. B. (1935), 'The state of calcium in the fluids of the body. 1. The conditions affecting the ionization of calcium', *J. biol. Chem.*, **108**, 285–322.

[12] MCLEAN, F. C. and URIST, M. R. (1961), *Bone: An Introduction to the Physiology of Skeletal Tissue*, Univ. Chicago Press, 2nd edn., 261 pp.

[13] MCLEAN, F. C., BARNES, B. O., and HASTINGS, A. B. (1935), 'The relation of the parathyroid hormone to the state of calcium in the blood', *Amer. J. Physiol.*, **113**, 141–9.

[14] NEUMAN, W. F. and NEUMAN, MARGARET W. (1958), *The Chemical Dynamics of Bone Mineral*, Univ. Chicago Press, 209 pp.

[15] PFEIFFER, C. A., KIRSCHBAUM, A., and GARDNER, W. V. (1940), 'Relation of estrogen to ossification and levels of serum calcium and lipoid in the English sparrow, *Passer domesticus*', *Yale J. Biol. Med.*, **13**, 279–84.

[16] STOERK, H. C. and CARNES, W. H. (1945), 'The relation of the dietary Ca : P ratio to serum calcium and to parathyroid volume', *J. Nutr.*, **29**, 43–50.

[17] TAYLOR, T. G. and HERTELENDY, F. (1961), 'Changes in the blood calcium associated with eggshell calcification in the domestic fowl. 2. Changes in the diffusible calcium', *Poult. Sci.*, **40**, 115–23.

[18] URIST, M. R. and SCHJEIDE, A. O. (1961), 'The partition of calcium and protein in the blood of oviparous vertebrates during estrus', *J. gen. Physiol.*, **44**, 743–56.

CHAPTER 5

Regulatory Mechanisms: Thyroid-parathyroid Hormones and Vitamin D

The concept of the regulation of physiological processes by means of chemical signalling systems is an attractive one. It forms the basis for our ideas on hormones, which are chemical substances secreted into the blood in one region of the animal but producing an effect in some distant organ. Unfortunately, such ideas are too general to enable one to provide any precise definition of a hormone, and recently, the tendency has been to restrict the term to those chemicals which fit into systems with clearly defined homeostatic properties.

Calcium metabolism is regulated by at least two types of control system. The first of these involves the thyroid and parathyroid glands which produce several protein hormones. These are effective in regulating the calcium metabolism of an animal because, not only do they induce responses from a number of specific 'target' organs, but their rate of secretion is itself affected by the results of their own activities, i.e. there is a feedback of information from the regulated system to the regulator. In order for this system to be practicable, the hormone must be destroyed in the body as fast as the system may be required to respond, thus enabling the endocrine organ to produce the necessary variations in the concentration of the hormone. Ideally, the system should also possess an antagonist, so that regulation can be obtained in either an increasing or decreasing direction without the possibility of overshooting the required level of activity. It is because the method of regulation of calcium metabolism by means of the thyroid–parathyroid complex shows all these properties that it is unquestionably referred to as a hormonal system. The other system which influences the calcium metabolism of tetrapods involves the steroid vitamin D. This substance is synthesized in the skin of higher vertebrates and produces its effects on the intestine and skeleton of the animal. The effects, however, are not influenced by the needs of the animal, and thus do not form a regulatory system. For these reasons, vitamin D is not considered to be a hormone, and the discussion of it will be left until later.

The Parathyroids

The parathyroid glands of the mammal are small structures closely applied to the thyroid gland. They were first described by Richard Owen following his dissection of the neck region of an Indian rhinoceros. The description attracted little attention, and the glands were rediscovered two decades later by Sandstrom in 1880. Because of their close association with the thyroid gland, they became known as the parathyroids, and for a while they were simply considered as undifferentiated parts of the thyroid. It was not until the turn of the century that it was possible to show that the lethal effects of thyroidectomy operations were due to the inadvertant removal of the parathyroids. Thus the close association of the two glands which had for so long concealed the real significance of the parathyroids eventually led to the discovery of their importance.

The removal of the parathyroid glands of a dog results in hypersensitivity of the operated animal. This is followed by involuntary twitching and the contraction of large groups of muscles which throw the animal into unnatural postures until eventually it passes into tetanic seizures. These become progressively more frequent and may terminate in death. The symptoms are all indicative of a disturbance in the neuro-muscular system which is itself particularly sensitive to the level of ionic calcium in the blood. It has now been abundantly demonstrated that the parathyroid glands maintain the concentration of calcium ions in the blood at a constant level and that in their absence this falls, death resulting by tetanic seizures. The hormone of the parathyroid glands regulates the level of the calcium and phosphate ions of the blood by affecting the bones, kidneys, and intestine of mammals, and probably all tetrapods. The hormone is therefore a dominant factor in all studies of calcium metabolism, but the glands are also of interest because they are sometimes described as the only endocrine organs which are not common to all vertebrates. They are absent from fish, and it has been suggested that in these animals the control of calcium metabolism is governed by the large quantities of vitamin D found in their bodies [48]. In the amphibia, the glands are often described as arising during metamorphosis, and this is taken as an explanation of its absence from neotenous forms such as Typhlomolge, Necturus, and Proteus [20]. Other reports suggest that the gland is present in anuran tadpoles and shows cytolysis at the time of metamorphosis [48]. In the birds and mammals, there is some evidence that the parathyroids are not only present but are actually active in the developing offspring. Thus the glands are of great importance during reproduction, for they not only control the calcium metabolism of the adult but as will be seen later they are also involved in the development of some embryos.

Development and Structure

The parathyroid glands arise during embryology by a separation of solid masses of tissue from the extremities of the pharyngeal pouches. The ventral corners of the third and fourth pouches are involved in the formation of these glands in amphibians, reptiles, and birds. The derivative of the second pouch has been considered to be involved in the formation of the amphibian gland, but it normally disappears early in development and there is no evidence for it being involved in the formation of the parathyroids of any other vertebrate [20]. In mammals, the endocrine tissue forms from the dorsal regions of the third and fourth pouches. Some attempt has been made to associate the ultimobranchial bodies of teleosts with a parathyroid-like function. The evidence for involving these derivatives of the fifth gill pouches is rather indirect, so that for the moment, fish will be considered to be devoid of parathyroids [21].

Most vertebrates have two pairs of parathyroid glands. In amphibians, such as *Rana catesbiana*, they are about 1 mm in diameter, and lie close to the external jugular vein. Histologically, they consist of a compact mass of elongate parenchyma cells usually arranged in whorls. The structure is notable mainly for the relatively poor vascular supply, and for the rather clear cytoplasm of the cells [45]. During the winter months, the amphibian parathyroids appear to degenerate, and extensive destruction of the cells occurs [14, 54]. The cells regenerate in the spring from some surviving cells which remain just beneath the fibrous connective tissue that surrounds the gland. Electron micrographs have confirmed a seasonal variation in the parathyroids but related it to the different ultrastructure of active and inactive cells [26a].

The reptilian parathyroids have not been as extensively studied as those of other vertebrates. Normally, there are two pairs of glands, but there is some variation, and it is reported that in the crocodile only the derivative of the third pouch persists at the time of hatching [21]. The reptilian parathyroids consist of cords of cells which are all of one type and invested with capillaries [6a]. Either one or two pairs of glands are present in birds posterior to the thyroid, although in some species, such as the domestic fowl, they all tend to fuse together. The glands are composed of one type of cell, the so-called 'chief cells' [23]. A similar cellular organization is found in the rodents [27], but most mammals have two types of cell in the parathyroid glands. The 'chief cells' compose the mass of the gland and are roughly cuboid in shape. Scattered between them are the less numerous 'oxyphil cells', which are strongly eosinophilic, and in the electron microscope can be seen to be densely packed with mitochondria [53]. The mammalian parathyroid glands are normally associated with the thyroid gland and may even be embedded in it making parathyroidectomy difficult. This leads to difficulties in interpretation, because there are numerous examples in physiological experiments when it has become necessary to suggest that accessory parathyroid tissue exists away from the main glandular structure. The absence of any outstanding cytological characteristics makes it difficult to identify these accessory tissues [46], although there is evidence for their existence in amphibians [45] and birds [36].

The Control of Parathyroid Secretion

It has frequently been observed that diets with a low content of calcium lead to a hypertrophy of the parathyroid glands. The effect seems to be due to variations in the concentration of serum calcium, and if diets are prepared which differ greatly in the total amounts and ratios of calcium and phosphate ions, it is possible to show an almost perfect correlation between

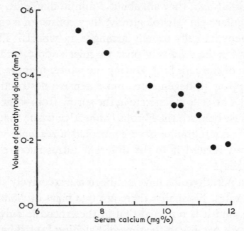

FIG. 5.1. The relationship between the concentration of serum calcium and the volume of the parathyroid glands of rats (after [47]).

the volume of the parathyroid glands and the serum-calcium level of the rat [47] (fig. 5.1). Similar results have been obtained with birds, where low calcium diets can produce up to a six-fold increase in the size of the parathyroid glands of the domestic duck [3]. When embryonic parathyroid glands are cultured *in vitro*, both the secretory and the mitotic activity of the tissue are under the direct control of the concentration of ionic calcium (table 5.1). This would indicate that the synthesis and release of parathyroid hormone is stimulated by low levels of serum calcium, an interpretation which is confirmed by perfusing decalcified blood through the parathyroid glands of a dog, when it can be shown that the effluent contains a substance with all the characteristic properties of the parathyroid hormone [38]. Clearly then, a low level of serum calcium stimulates the release of the hormone and presumably a high concentration of calcium inhibits its secretion. These concepts of parathyroid control have been neatly tested by Talmage and Toft, who found that the number of osteoclasts in a bone appeared to be directly correlated with the quantity of parathyroid hormone in the blood. They used this relationship to assess the effects of washing out the peritoneal cavity of rats with various solutions which would equilibrate with the ions in the blood. They found that a peritoneal

Table 5.1   *The effect of calcium ions upon the parathyroid glands of rats and chicks maintained in tissue culture. In embryonic tissue the cells divide more frequently in low calcium media, and in both animals low calcium solutions stimulate cytoplasmic growth which results in increased hormone secretion into the culture medium* [41]

Source of parathyroid gland	Calcium content culture medium $(_mM/l)$	Mitoses/1000 cells	Ratio cytoplasm/nucleus in cultured cells
13 d. chick embryo	1·0	1·3	2·18 ± 0·14
13 d. chick embryo	3·2	0·6	1·27 ± 0·07
Adult rat	0·7	rare	1·83 ± 0·04
Adult rat	2·1	in	1·39 ± 0·04
Adult rat	2·7	adult tissue	1·19 ± 0·04

lavage which was rich in calcium lowered the number of osteoclasts in the bone, whereas a solution rich in phosphate ions had little effect (fig. 5.2). Apparently the secretion of the parathyroid glands is suppressed by high levels of calcium, and it is this ion, rather than phosphate, which influences the gland's activity. A radioimmunoassay has recently been devised for estimating the quantity of parathyroid hormone in the plasma and it has been shown that there is a reciprocal relationship between the amount of the hormone and the concentration of calcium. Thus the release of the hormone is directly controlled by the concentration of plasma calcium although it was also shown that magnesium could act like calcium in repressing the release of the hormone [45a].

If parathyroid hormone is injected into a mammal or a bird, there is a rise in the calcium ion concentration of the blood. The maximum response occurs within about 3 hours in birds [40], but is considerably slower in mammals. If the parathyroid glands are removed or destroyed, the calcium level of the blood falls rapidly. From this it can be inferred either that the hormone is rapidly destroyed in the body or that it is antagonized by some other system. Both these possibilities would increase the efficiency of the parathyroid system of control of calcium metabolism, and both have been investigated.

Two organs have been implicated as possible inactivators of the mammalian parathyroid hormone. On the basis of autotransplantation experiments, it was suggested that the liver destroyed the hormone [16], but experiments in which the hormone was incubated with various organs prior

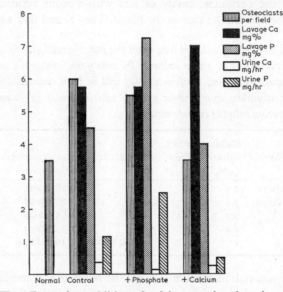

FIG. 5.2. The effects of an addition of calcium or phosphate ions to a solution being used to wash out the peritoneal cavity of rats. Note that the addition of calcium ions represses the activity of the parathyroids as measured by the number of osteoclasts per unit area of bone and by the decrease in the excretion of phosphate by the kidney (after [52]).

to its assay, showed that the kidney was much more effective and was capable of completely destroying the activity of the hormone (table 5.2). It is now generally accepted that the parathyroid hormone is inactivated by the body, so that the calcium level of the blood can only be maintained if the hormone is continually being secreted. A number of estimates have been made as to the rate of secretion of the hormone in mammals and a value of about 1 USP unit */kg body wt/hr is an average, with a variation of about

* 'USP unit' is the unit accepted by the United States Pharmacopeia. In the case of parathyroid hormone one unit is $\frac{1}{100}$ the amount required to raise the calcium content of 100 cc of dog blood by 1 mg within 16–18 hours of administration.

Table 5.2   *The activity of parathyroid extract after incubation with various organs of the rat. Note the complete inactivation of the hormone by the kidney (recalculated from [37])*

Treatment	Activity %
60 USP units parathyroid extract	100
60 USP units after incubation with kidney	0
60 USP units after incubation with heated kidney	55
60 USP units after incubation with muscle	73
60 USP units after incubation with liver	80
60 USP units after incubation with plasma	40

tenfold, depending upon the assumptions involved and the species being considered [32].

In 1962 Copp, Cameron, Cheney, Davidson, and Henze published a paper which added another factor to the understanding of the control of the calcium level of the blood. They showed by means of an ingenious experiment that if the thyroid–parathyroid complex of a dog was perfused, using blood with a very high calcium content, then there was a fall in the calcium level of the rest of the animal's blood, and this fall was actually faster than occurred if the thyroid–parathyroid structure was surgically removed from the animal (fig. 5.3). The surgical removal of an endocrine organ is obviously the most severe method for ensuring that that organ ceases to release its hormone into the blood, so that the more rapid fall in

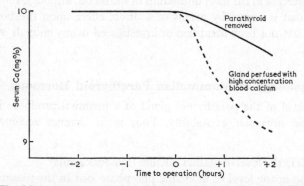

FIG. 5.3. The fall in the concentration of serum calcium in the dog following parathyroidectomy or after the perfusion of the gland with blood containing a high concentration of calcium. The increase in the rate at which the serum calcium falls after the second treatment is interpreted as evidence for a 'calcium depressing' hormone, calcitonin (after [7]).

the calcium level of the blood following perfusion of the gland could not be explained as simply a cessation of parathyroid activity but must reflect the activity of some other hormone which actively lowers the calcium level of the blood. This new hormone was called calcitonin, and it was thought to be secreted by the parathyroid gland [7]. In the few years since its original discovery, calcitonin has attracted much attention. There seems to be no doubt that the hormone does exist and that it antagonizes the effects of the other parathyroid hormone. There is some doubt, however, as to whether calcitonin is secreted by the parathyroid [8] or whether it originates in the thyroid, when it is sometimes called thyrocalcitonin [6, 51]. At the present time there appear to be three possibilities. Either different species produce the hormone from different glands, i.e. the dog and sheep from the parathyroid, and pigs, goats, rats, cows, rabbits, and monkeys from the thyroid; or, all species produce it from the thyroid and experimental difficulties have led to the erroneous conclusion that the hormone originated in the parathyroid. This is currently the most widely held view, particularly since a purified polypeptide with all the properties of the hormone can be isolated from the thyroid of many mammals [21a] and there is some histochemical evidence that the so-called C cells of the thyroid are the sites of hormone synthesis [38a]. There is, however, one final possibility, namely, that the hormone is a thyrocalcitonin but that the release of this hormone from the thyroid is normally controlled by a secretion of the parathyroid [19]. This latter suggestion has been questioned [17a] but it deserves further study for it is actually capable of explaining most of the experimental results so far obtained. Little is known about the way in which thyrocalcitonin produces a decrease in the level of calcium in the blood, although the evidence suggests that it occurs by means of a direct effect upon the bones. The hormone has not been identified or investigated in any animals other than mammals.

The Physiology of Mammalian Parathyroid Hormone

The removal of the parathyroid gland of a mammal produces increased neural and muscular excitability. Four main changes accompany this effect:

1. A fall in the level of plasma calcium (hypocalcaemia).
2. A rise in the level of inorganic phosphate ions in the plasma (hyperphosphataemia).
3. An initial increase [49] and then a decrease in level of urinary calcium (hypocalciurea).
4. A decrease in the level of urinary phosphate (hypophosphaturea).

Injection of the hormone produces the opposite effects (fig. 5.4). Thus the hormone influences the concentration of both calcium and phosphate ions, suggesting that bone might be involved in the regulatory processes, while the kidney also plays an important role by altering the composition of the urine. A fruitful controversy occurred during the 1930s between those who considered the renal effect to be the primary response to the hormone (theory 1) [1], while others considered that bone was the main target organ (theory 2) [30]. The controversy can be depicted schematically as follows:

$$\text{(Theory 1)} \qquad\qquad\qquad \text{(Theory 2)}$$

Excretion of phosphate $\rightleftharpoons$ [Ca] × [PO$_4$] $\rightleftharpoons$ Bone salt formation
　　by the kidney 　　　　　　 in blood 　　　　　　 or destruction

The fact that the hormone raises the calcium level of the blood could be attributed either to an increased excretion of phosphate ions by the kidney which would induce the ionization of more calcium or, alternatively, the hormone could act directly on the bone, leading to its resorption and an increase in the calcium content of the plasma.

It is now generally accepted that the parathyroid gland regulates the concentration of ionic calcium in the blood and extracellular fluids of the body primarily by affecting the resorption of bone, but this is a relatively slow response. The renal effect of the hormone provides a faster acting system and assists in the dissolution of bone by excreting excess phosphate ions [43]. The hormone also appears to increase the uptake of calcium from the intestine, so that the result of the responses of these three organ systems is to produce a co-ordinated reaction which increases the calcium content of the body fluids (table 5.3).

Table 5.3　*The effects of parathyroid hormone (after [43])*

	Onset of response	Sensitivity of response	Magnitude of response
Bone	slow	insensitive	unlimited
Kidney	rapid	sensitive	limited
Intestine	intermediate	?	limited

(a) The Effect on Bone

Most work supports the concept proposed by McLean [29, 30] that the ionic calcium in the blood is maintained at a constant level by means of a feedback system working through the effects of the parathyroid hormone upon bone tissue. Bone mineral exists in two physiological compartments as an exchangeable and a non-exchangeable form corresponding roughly to a surface layer of newly formed but incompletely mineralized bone and a deeper-lying relatively inert fraction respectively. The normal concentration of calcium in the plasma is about 10 mg %, but this falls after parathyroidectomy to about 6 or 7 mg % which is thought to be the equilibrium value of blood calcium with the exchangeable fractions of bone. Clearly, then, the parathyroids are responsible for maintaining the plasma calcium at a level above that of the equilibrium value for bone, and this apparent supersaturation is presumably due to cellular activity in the bone tissue. These concepts have been investigated by using radio-isotopes to label the different fractions of bone and then washing out the peritoneal cavity of the animal with various solutions with which the body fluids can come into ionic equilibrium. The experiments have been performed on nephrectomized rats from which the parathyroid glands were removed at various times after the injection of Ca^{45}. When the body fluids of these animals were sampled with the peritoneal lavage technique, it was found that if the Ca^{45} was administered less than 24 hours before parathyroidectomy, then the loss of Ca^{45} into the washings was the same in the parathyroidectomized rats as in the controls (table 5.4). This suggested that

Table 5.4   *The effect of parathyroidectomy on the removal of total bone* Ca *and* Ca^{45} *by the peritoneal lavage of nephrectomized rats. The radio-isotope was injected either 18 hours or 2–3 weeks prior to the experiment. Note that in all cases parathyroidectomy reduces the total amount of calcium removed, but that it only modifies the removal of the radio-isotope when this has been injected for several weeks. This is interpreted as demonstrating that during the first 24 hours, the Ca^{45} resides in the surface layers of the bone which are in physico-chemical equilibrium with the body fluids. Only after 2–3 weeks, when the Ca^{45} has accumulated in the deeper layers of the bone, is the parathyroid gland necessary for its release (data from* [50])

Time since Ca^{45} given	Treatment	Ca^{45} removed as % of controls	Total Ca removed as % of controls
		%	%
18 hours	Controls	100	100
	Parathyroidectomy	100	73
14–21 days	Controls	100	100
	Parathyroidectomy	67·5	66

in the short time since the injection of the Ca^{45} the radio-isotope had accumulated only in the regions of exchangeable bone, and the movement of calcium in and out of this fraction is not directly affected by the loss of the parathyroid gland. When the experiment was repeated 2–3 weeks after the injection of Ca^{45}, it was found that parathyroidectomy decreased the amount of Ca^{45} appearing in the peritoneal washings. This indicates that in the 2–3 weeks since the injection of the radio-isotope, it had passed from the surface layers of exchangeable bone into the inner parts of the bones of the skeleton by the continual accretion of additional minerals. As the hormone increased the release of the Ca^{45} from the bone when it was in this situation but not when it was in the surface layers, it was concluded that the parathyroid hormone acts by increasing the resorption of mineral from the non-exchangeable fraction of the bone [50].

The process by which the parathyroid hormone affects the bone calcium and makes it available to the extracellular fluids is not known. Most of the evidence suggests that osteoclastic activity is stimulated by the hormone, so that both the organic material and the inorganic salts are destroyed simultaneously by the cells [32]. The organic matrix is presumably digested by an enzyme [56] and the inorganic mineral is dissolved by a lowered pH and the presence of such organic acids as citrate and lactate [33].

There appear, therefore, to be two processes by which calcium and phosphate ions can be released from bone. One of these is probably a simple physico-chemical equilibrium which only produces a net movement of ions in the bone-to-blood direction when the concentrations of calcium and phosphate ions fall to the level associated with parathyroidectomy. This process must therefore be of minor importance in most normal physiological conditions when the calcium and phosphate ion concentrations are such as to favour the deposition of bone mineral from the blood. This continual loss of ions from the blood to the skeleton would, in fact, rapidly deplete the blood were it not for the reversal of the process by means of the activities of the osteoclasts. The resorption of bone mineral by these cells constitutes the second process by which calcium and phosphate ions may pass out of the skeleton. In this case, the ions are liberated into the blood against a concentration gradient and so produce the supersaturation of the blood (p. 17). The extent of the osteoclastic resorption of bone is regulated by the parathyroid hormone, and as this activity of the parathyroid gland is itself regulated by the concentration of ionic calcium in the blood, i.e. by the effects of its own activity, it produces a 'feedback system'. This self-regulating system is therefore to a large extent quite separate from the physico-chemical equilibrium system, and it is interesting to note that they are not only different in their physiology but are also localized in different regions of the bone.

Some objections have been raised regarding the details of these concepts

[34] and there is some evidence which suggests that calcium may be preferentially removed from bone mineral (table 5.5), but on the whole

Table 5.5 *The effect of parathyroid hormone on the composition of rat bones. Note the preferential loss of calcium* [18]

	Phosphate	Calcium	Ca/P ratio
Control rat	18·63	30·99	1·67
Rat after 10–30 units hormone	18·38	27·56	1·50
Rat after 40–70 units hormone	17·96	25·70	1·44
Rat after 100–200 units hormone	17·86	23·86	1·30

there is general agreement that the parathyroids induce bone resorption and so raise the concentration of both calcium and phosphate ions in the blood. The kidneys assist in the process of bone resorption by removing phosphate ions from the blood and so preventing the two ions being re-deposited as bone mineral.

(b) Kidney

Injections of parathyroid hormone produce a rapid and clearly demonstrable increase in the loss of phosphate ions from the body into the urine (fig. 5.4). In this way, the hormone indirectly assists in allowing the calcium level of the blood to rise, and there are some indications that the hormone may also increase the reabsorption of calcium from the kidney tubules and thus directly assist in raising the level of plasma calcium [26] (fig. 5.4). There is no doubt, however, that the main effect of the hormone upon the kidney is to increase the excretion of phosphate ions, although the actual region of the renal tubule that is affected and the cellular events which are involved in this process are matters of current controversy. The main point at issue is whether the hormone produces an increased secretion of phosphate ions into the tubule or whether it inhibits a reabsorption process.

The pioneering experiments on this subject are difficult to interpret, as many of the crude parathyroid extracts that were used contained contaminants which increased the glomerular filtration rate. These preparations therefore varied both the quantities of phosphate ions passing through the kidney as well as affecting the tubular excretory process. With the more highly purified samples of parathyroid hormone now available it is possible to produce an increased excretion of phosphate without producing any changes in glomerular filtration rates (fig. 5.5).

In the dog, numerous determinations of the excretion and reabsorption of phosphate ions by the kidney indicate a constant level of phosphate

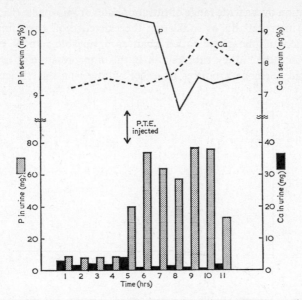

FIG. 5.4. The effect of injecting parathyroid extract into a human suffering from hypoparathyroidism. Note that the hormone preparation raises the level of serum calcium while reducing the excretion of calcium in the urine. The serum-phosphorus level falls and its excretion in the urine increases (after [1]).

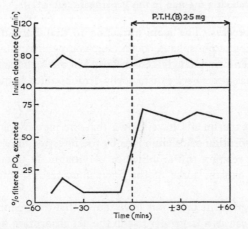

FIG. 5.5. The effect of parathyroid hormone upon the excretion of phosphate by the kidney. Note that the purified hormone used in this experiment did not affect the glomerular filtration rate (as measured by inulin clearance) so that the increased excretion must indicate a direct effect upon the transport of phosphate by the renal tubules (after [43]).

E

re-absorption over a wide range of filtration rates of phosphate (fig. 5.6). It is easiest to interpret this as indicating the existence of a maximal rate of reabsorption of phosphate rather than as a variable rate of phosphate secretion into the kidney tubules [2]. If this interpretation is correct, the parathyroid hormone produces its effect by lowering the efficiency of the

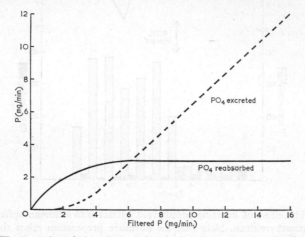

FIG. 5.6. The quantity of phosphate reabsorbed and that excreted by the kidney of the dog. The constant rate of reabsorption at varying loads has been interpreted as evidence for an active mechanism of reabsorption with a maximum capacity of about 3 mg/min in this experiment (after [2]).

reabsorption process. The main attraction to the alternative concept, of tubular secretion of phosphate, comes from comparative studies where this process has been convincingly demonstrated in birds and amphibians [28]. This process has never been satisfactorily demonstrated in mammals.

(c) Intestine

A number of experiments have shown that the parathyroid hormone increases the absorption of calcium ions by the intestine. The effect appears to be small in relation to the influence of vitamin D upon this process, and this may explain some of the anomalous results obtained in these studies [32].

Balance experiments upon rats have shown that treatment with parathyroid hormone causes a large increase in the net absorption of calcium from the intestine and a similarly large increase in the positive balance of these animals. The hormone was effective on animals fed with both normal and low phosphorus diets, but it had little effect upon animals fed a low calcium diet, presumably because of the small amount of calcium which was

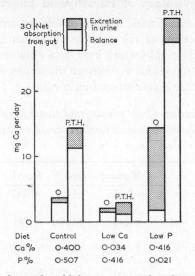

FIG. 5.7. The effect of parathyroid hormone on the absorption, excretion, and balance of calcium in rats fed on various diets. The rats were restricted to the experimental diet for eight weeks prior to the balance experiments. 50 USP units of the hormone were then injected subcutaneously twice daily for three days. Note how the hormone increases the absorption and balance of calcium in rats on normal or low phosphorus diets. The hormone also reduces the loss of calcium in the urine of rats on the low phosphorus diet (after [15]).

available (fig. 5.7). It was not possible to corroborate these results using the same technique and radio-isotopes but other experiments *in vitro* have confirmed the findings. In a solution containing physiological amounts of ionized calcium (1·25 mM) everted sacs of the small intestine (see p. 63) of the rat are able actively to transport Ca^{45} from mucosal to serosal surfaces against a concentration gradient. Parathyroidectomy three or more hours before the isolation of these intestinal sacs resulted in a decreased ability to develop and maintain this gradient (table 5.6). The addition of parathyroid hormone to the preparations *in vitro* had no effect.

Table 5.6 *The effect of parathyroidectomy on the ability of everted sacs of rat intestine to develop and maintain a concentration gradient of* Ca^{45} [42]

Treatment	Time	Serous/mucosal ratio of Ca^{45}
Normal	1 hour	2·5 → 4·4
Parathyroidectomized	1 hour	1·5 → 2·5

Comparative Physiology of Parathyroid Function

In recent years a considerable amount of information has been obtained regarding the functions of the parathyroid glands of other vertebrates [20, 21]. Most of the results which have been obtained from experiments with these other tetrapods have confirmed the results obtained from mammals, and this information is summarized in table 5.7. There are, however, a

Table 5.7   *The functions of the parathyroid glands in various tetrapods. Note that the parathyroid hormones injected are all prepared from mammalian sources*

Effect of	Mammal	Bird	Reptile	Amphibian
Parathyroid hormone on plasma calcium	+[32]	+[40]	+[6a]	+[11]
Parathyroid hormone on plasma phosphate	−[32]	−[48a]	o [6a]	−[11]
Parathyroid hormone on urinary phosphate	+[32]	+[28]	+[6a]	o [11] or +[6a]
Parathyroid hormone on resorption of urinary calcium	+[43]	+[5]	no data	+[11]
Parathyroid hormone on bone resorption	+[30]	+[48a]	+[6a]	−[13, 25] +(indirect [57] evidence)
Parathyroidectomy on plasma calcium	−[43]	−[4]	−[39] or o [6a]	−[9, 14, 55] but species differ [+12]
Parathyroidectomy on plasma phosphate	+[43]	+[48a]	result variable	
Parathyroidectomy on urinary phosphate	−[43]	−[48a]	—[6a]	+[10, 12]

+, depicts increased effect; −, decreased effect; o, no effect.

number of interesting, though rather confusing, variations in the responses of amphibians and reptiles to parathyroid hormone which are so different from those obtained with mammals as to warrant further discussion.

In the amphibian *Rana pipiens,* both the plasma and the urine show a rise in their phosphate content following parathyroidectomy. This hyperphosphaturea is in contrast to the hypophosphaturea found in mammals after the removal of the glands [10]. The injection of mammalian parathyroid hormone did not alter the phosphate content of the frog urine [11], and the time relationships of the changes following parathyroidectomy suggest that the rise in plasma phosphate concentrations was not caused by an increased reabsorption of this ion from the kidney [12]. These results are difficult to explain. It has been found, however, that sham operations on turtles produce hyperphosphaturea and as 'sham' controls were not used in the frog experiments it seems likely that the hyperphosphaturea observed was due to the general operation rather than to a loss of the parathyroid glands [6a].

It has also been reported on two separate occasions that parathyroid hormone has no effect on bone reabsorption in *Xenopus laevis* [25] and may even increase calcium deposition in the bones of *R. pipiens* [13]. It is important to realize, however, that these results were obtained by the injection of large doses of mammalian rather than amphibian hormones, and there is some evidence that the hormone may be species specific [32], or at least may be required in very large doses in order to produce a comparable effect [6a]. A different technique was therefore used by Yoshida and Talmage in an attempt to stimulate the frog's own parathyroids to resorb its bones. Specimens of *R. catesbiana* were subjected to the method of peritoneal lavage previously described, and it was shown that more calcium could be removed from intact frogs than from those which were parathyroidecto-mized. It was concluded that the resorption of bone in frogs was partially under the control of the animal's parathyroid glands [57]. There is some evidence that different species of amphibians may show varying degrees of dependence upon the parathyroid glands, for removal of these structures produced no ill effects upon *R. ridibunda* [48], whereas parathyroidectomy of *R. catesbiana* resulted in a fall of serum calcium from 11·9 mg % to 7·76 mg % with tetany attacks and death occurring within three days [55]. In reptiles there is evidence that the serum-calcium level responds to parathyroidectomy or to the injection of large doses of mammalian hormone in a similar way to other vertebrates and the hormone causes increased osteoclastic activities in at least the young of the turtle *Graptemys pseudogeographia*. There is, however, difficulty in showing that the reptile responds to the hormone by varying its phosphate metabolism [6a].

In birds, the injection of parathyroid hormones increases the excretion of phosphate ions in the urine, as in mammals. The evidence suggests, however, that this is due to an increased secretion of this ion by the kidney rather than by a reduction in its reabsorption [28].

Vitamin D

The parathyroid hormone and vitamin D have a number of similar physiological effects, and there has been much speculation as to whether they function in related ways or whether one is essential for the other to be effective. None of these speculations is supported by sufficient experimental data to provide a basis for a common interpretation of the regulation of calcium metabolism.

Vitamin D is a steroid derivative which occurs in several forms. The natural vitamin is cholecalciferol or vitamin D_3. It is produced by the action of ultra-violet light upon 7-dehydrocholesterol which is normally present in the skin of tetrapods. In the human, the vitamin is absorbed by the skin as it probably is also in amphibia [31]. In other mammals, the absorption may be greatly assisted by licking the fur [17], and in birds,

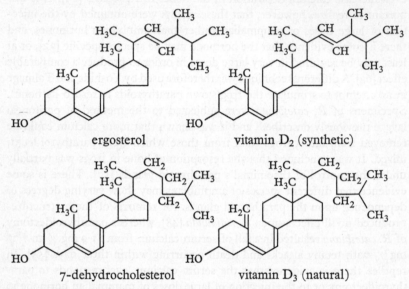

ergosterol   vitamin D_2 (synthetic)

7-dehydrocholesterol   vitamin D_3 (natural)

FIG. 5.8. The structure of vitamins D_2 and D_3 and their precursors.

there is considerable evidence that the preen gland may contain precursors of the vitamin which are spread over the feathers and then absorbed, after ultra-violet irradiation, at a later preening [24]. Vitamin D_3 is also found in enormous quantities in fish liver, although its origin is, in this case, unknown. A similar substance, ergocalciferol or vitamin D_2, is formed by irradiating ergosterol [fig. 5.8], and in mammals it has a similar potency to the natural vitamin.

Vitamin D has a number of physiological effects which Nicolaysen and Eeg-Larsen [35] distinguished as primary and secondary. The main primary effects are firstly to increase the absorption of calcium from the alimentary tract, and secondly, to influence the bones by increasing the production of citric acid.

The intestinal effect now appears to be due to the fact that the vitamin decreases a diffusion barrier in the walls of the intestine and hence increases the availability of calcium ions to the mucosa cells. Certainly, the main effect of the vitamin is to increase the absorption of calcium and decrease the loss via the faeces. By increasing the absorption of calcium, vitamin D is also able to raise the calcium content of the blood and assist in bone formation. In the absence of the vitamin, either because it is not available in the diet or because it is not formed in the skin, bone formation may be deficient and rickets occur. The vitamin also appears to be involved in the formation of citric acid and in bone resorption, so that if excessively large doses (50,000 or more I.U./day in humans) are given, the bone minerals are destroyed and the calcium concentration of the blood rises. It is because of this similarity of action that the vitamin is sometimes considered either to be synergistic with parathyroid hormone or to be essential for the action of the hormone [33]. There are, however, some basic differences between the ways in which calcium metabolism is regulated by the vitamin and by the hormone. The vitamin is an insensitive system in so far as the severity of its effects are simply dependent upon the amount which is formed in the skin or ingested in the diet, and as such are not related to the needs of the animal. The parathyroid hormone, on the other hand, is a closely regulated system in which the amount secreted is directly determined by a feedback system monitored by the concentration of ionic calcium in the blood. It is therefore directly related to the needs of the animal.

Relatively little is known about the requirements of embryos for vitamin D, but eggs and milk both contain the vitamin and are, in fact, two of the relatively few natural foods which provide a source of this material. The amount of the vitamin which is found in the yolk of the domestic fowl appears to reflect the bird's own content, for it is higher in the summer than in winter (table 5.8). If the yolk is irradiated with ultra-violet light the vita-

Table 5.8 *Vitamin-D content of various organs and secretions* [31, 44]

| | Vitamin-D content | | |
	I.U./l	I.U.	Precursors as % of steroid content
Cow milk	24	—	—
Human milk	4	—	—
Yolk of domestic fowl (Feb.)	—	25	—
Yolk of domestic fowl (April)	—	49	—
Yolk of domestic fowl (June)	—	70	—
Yolk of *Rana temporaria*	—	—	0·5

min content can be increased up to twenty-fold. Amphibian eggs also contain precursors of vitamin D [31]. In the mammal, the vitamin readily crosses the placenta, but its concentration in the foetal blood and liver is not increased by giving the mother supplementary sources [22]. Milk contains small amounts of the vitamin (table 5.8).

REFERENCES

[1] ALBRIGHT, F. and REIFENSTEIN, E. C. (1948), *Parathyroid Glands and Metabolic Bone Disease*, Williams and Wilkins, 393 pp.

[2] BARTTER, F. C. (1961), 'The effect of the parathyroid on phosphate excretion', in *The Parathyroids*, eds. Greep, R. O. and Talmage, R. V., Thomas, 388–403.

[3] BENOIT, J. (1950), 'Les glandes endocrines', in *Traité de Zoologie*, ed. Grassé, P., **15**, *Oiseaux*, Masson, 290–334.

[4] BENOIT, J., STICKER, P., and FABIANI, G. (1941), 'Technique et résultats de la parathyroidectomie chez le Canard domestique', *C.R. Soc. Biol., Paris*, **135**, 1600–1602.

[5] BUCHANAN, G. D. (1961), 'Parathyroid influence on renal excretion of calcium', in *The Parathyroids*, eds. Greep, R. O. and Talmage, R. V., Thomas, 334–52.

[6] CARE, A. D. (1965), 'Secretion of thyrocalcitonin', *Nature, Lond.*, **205**, 1289–91.

[6a] CLARK, N. B. (1965), 'Experimental and histological studies of the parathyroid glands of fresh water turtles', *Gen. comp. Endocrinol*, **5**, 297–312.

[7] COPP, D. H., CAMERON, E. C., CHENEY, BARBARA A., DAVIDSON, A. G. F., and HENZIE, K. G. (1962), 'Evidence for calcitonin – a new hormone from the parathyroid that lowers blood calcium', *Endocrinology*, **70**, 638–49.

[8] COPP, D. H. and HENZIE, K. G. (1964), 'Parathyroid origin of calcitonin – evidence from perfusion of sheep glands', *Endocrinology*, **75**, 49–55.

[9] CORTELYOU, J. R. (1958), 'Parathyroid glands in amphibians', *Anat. Rec.*, **132**, 424 (Abst.).

[10] CORTELYOU, J. R. (1960), 'Plasma and urine phosphorus changes in totally parathyroidectomized *Rana pipiens*', *Anat. Rec.*, **137**, 346 (Abst.).

[11] CORTELYOU, J. R. (1962a), 'Changes in plasma and urine calcium and phosphorus of *Rana pipiens* subsequent to different dose levels of Paroidin', *Amer. Zool.*, **2**, 400 (Abst.).

[12] CORTELYOU, J. R. (1962b), 'Phosphorus changes in totally parathyroidectomized *Rana pipiens*', *Endocrinology*, **70**, 618–21.

[13] CORTELYOU, J. R., HARGIS, G. K., and LEHRER, L. (1962), 'Influence of mammalian parathormone on bone composition in the frog *Rana pipiens*', *Amer. Zool.*, **2**, 400–1 (Abst.).

[14] CORTELYOU, J. R., HIBNER-OWERKO, A., and MULROY, J. (1960), 'Blood and urine calcium changes in totally parathyroidectomized *Rana pipiens*', *Endocrinology*, **66**, 441–50.

[15] CRAMER, C. F., SUIKER, A. P., and COPP, D. H. (1961), 'Parathyroid

influence on calcium and phosphorus absorption by the gut', in *The Parathyroids*, eds. Greep, R. O. and Talmage, R. V., Thomas, 158–66.

[16] DAVIS, R. and TALMAGE, R. V. (1960), 'Evidence for liver inactivation of parathyroid hormone', *Endocrinology*, **66**, 312–14.

[17] DAVSON, H. and EGGLETON, GRACE (1962), *Principles of Human Physiology*, (Starling) 13th edn., Churchill.

[17a] FOSTER, G. V. (1966), 'Thyrocalcitonin: Failure to demonstrate a parathyroid releasing factor', *Nature, Lond.*, **211**, 1319–1320.

[18] GEDALIA, I. and KLETTER, M. (1964), 'Effects of parathyroid hormone on bone composition in rats', *Endocrinology*, **74**, 165–9.

[19] GITTES, R. F. and IRVIN, G. L. (1965), 'Thyroid and parathyroid roles in hypercalcemia. Evidence for a thyrocalcitonin-releasing factor', *Science*, **148**, 1737–9.

[20] GORBMAN, A. and BERN, H. A. (1962), *Textbook of Comparative Endocrinology*, Wiley, 468 pp.

[21] GREEP, R. O. (1963), 'Parathyroid glands,' in *Comparative Endocrinology*, eds. Euler, U. S. von and Heller, H., **1**, Academic Press, 325–70.

[21a] GUDMUNDSSON, T. V., MACINTYRE, I., and SOLIMAN, H. A. (1966), 'The isolation of thyrocalcitonin and a study of its effects in the rat', *Proc. roy. Soc.*, **164B**, 460–477.

[22] HAGERMAN, D. D. and VILLEE, C. A. (1960), 'Transport functions of the placenta', *Physiol. Rev.*, **40**, 313–30.

[23] HOHN, E. O. (1961), 'Endocrine glands, thymus and pineal body', in *The Biology and Comparative Physiology of Birds*, ed. Marshall, A. J., **2**, Academic Press, 87–114.

[24] HOU, H. C. (1930), 'Further observations on the relation of the preen gland of birds to rickets', *Chin. J. Physiol.*, **4**, 79–92.

[25] IRVING, J. T. and SOLMS, C. M. (1955), 'The influence of parathyroid hormone upon bone formation in *Xenopus laevis*', *S. Afr. J. Med. Sci.*, **20**, 32.

[26] KLEEMAN, C. R., BERNSTEIN, D., ROCKNEY, R., DOWLING, J. T., and MAXWELL, M. H. (1961), 'Studies on the renal clearance of diffusible calcium and the role of the parathyroid glands in its regulation', in *The Parathyroids*, eds. Greep, R. O. and Talmage, R. V., Thomas, 353–82.

[26a] LANGE, R. and BREHM, H. von (1965), 'On the fine structure of the parathyroid gland in the toad and the frog', in *The Parathyroid Glands*, eds. Gaillard, P. J., Talmage, R. V., and Budy, Ann M., Univ. Chicago Press, 19–26.

[27] LEVER, J. D. (1957), 'Fine structural appearances in the rat parathyroids', *J. Anat.*, **91**, 73–81.

[28] LEVENSKY, N. G. and DAVIDSON, D. G. (1957), 'Renal action of parathyroid extract in the chicken', *Amer. J. Physiol.*, **191**, 530–6.

[29] MCLEAN, F. C. (1958), 'The ultrastructure and function of bone', *Science*, **127**, 451–7.

[30] MCLEAN, F. C. and URIST, M. R. (1961), *Bone: An Introduction to the Physiology of Skeletal Tissue*, 2nd edn., Univ. Chicago Press, 261 pp.

[31] MORTON, R. A. and ROSEN, D. G. (1949), 'Carotenoids, vitamin A and 7-dehydrosteroid in the frog (Rana temporaria)', Biochem. J., 45, 612–27.

[32] MUNSON, P. L., HIRSCH, P. F., and TASHJIAN, A. H. (1963), 'Parathyroid gland', Ann. Rev. Physiol., 25, 325–60.

[33] NEUMAN, W. F. and DOWSE, C. M. (1961), 'Possible fundamental action of parathyroid hormone in bone', in The Parathyroids, eds. Greep, R. O. and Talmage, R. V., Thomas, 310–26.

[34] NEUMAN, W. F. and NEUMAN, MARGARET W. (1958), The Chemical Dynamics of Bone Mineral, Univ. Chicago Press, 209 pp.

[35] NICOLAYSEN, R. and EEG-HARSEN, N. (1953), 'The biochemistry and physiology of vitamin D', Vitamins and hormones, 11, 29–60.

[36] NONIDEZ, J. F. and GOODALE, H. D. (1927), 'Histological studies on the endocrines of chickens deprived of ultra-violet light. I. Parathyroids', Amer. J. Anat., 38, 319–41.

[37] ORIMO, H., FUJITA, T., MORU, H., and NAKAO, K. (1965), 'Inactivation in vitro of parathyroid hormone activity by kidney slices', Endocrinology, 76, 255–8.

[38] PATT, H. M. and LUCKHARDT, A. B. (1942), 'Relationship of a low blood calcium to parathyroid secretion', Endocrinology, 31, 384–92.

[38a] PEARSE, A. G. E. (1966), 'The cytochemistry of the thyroid c cells and their relationship to calcitonin', Proc. roy. Soc., 164B, 478–487.

[39] PETERS, H. (1941), 'Morphologische und experimentelle Untersuchungen über die Epithelkörper bei Eidechsen', Z. mikr. anat. Forsch., Leipzig, 49, 1–40.

[40] POLIN, P., STURKIE, P. D., and HUNSAKER, W. (1957), 'The blood calcium response of the chicken to parathyroid extracts', Endocrinology, 60, 1–5.

[41] RAISZ, L. G. (1963), 'Regulation by calcium of parathyroid growth and secretion in vitro', Nature, Lond., 197, 1115–16.

[42] RASMUSSEN, H. (1959), 'The influence of parathyroid function upon the transport of calcium in isolated sacs of rat small intestine', Endocrinology, 65, 517–19.

[43] RASMUSSEN, H. (1961), 'Parathyroid hormone', Amer. J. Med., 30, 112–28.

[44] ROMANOFF, A. L. and ROMANOFF, A. J. (1949), The Avian Egg, Wiley, 918 pp.

[45] ROMEIS, B. (1926), 'Morphologische und experimentelle Studien über die Epithelkörper der Amphibien. I. Tiel die Morphologie der Epithelkörper der Anuren', Z. Anat. Entw. Gesch., 80, 547–78.

[45a] SHERWOOD, L. M., POTTS, J. T., CARE, A. D., MAYER, G. P., and AURBACH, G. D. (1966), 'Evaluation by radioimmunoassay of factors controlling the secretion of parathyroid hormone', Nature, Lond., 209, 52–5.

[46] SMITH, G. C. (1945), 'Technique for parathyroidectomy in pigeons', Anat. Rec., 92, 81–6.

[47] STOERK, H. C. and CARNES, W. H. (1945), 'The relation of the dietary Ca : P ratio to serum calcium and to parathyroid volume', J. Nutr., 29, 43–50.

[48] STUDITSKY, A. N. (1945), 'Function of parathyroid glands in Amphibia'. *C.R. Acad. Sci. U.R.S.S.*, **47**, 444–7.

[48a] STURKIE, P. D. (1965), *Avian physiology*, Cornell Univ. Press, 2nd edn., 766 pp.

[49] TALMAGE, R. V. (1956), 'Studies on the maintenance of serum-calcium levels by parathyroid action on bone and kidney', *Ann. N.Y. Acad. Sci.*, **64**, 326–35.

[50] TALMAGE, R. V. and ELLIOTT, J. R. (1958), 'Removal of calcium from bone as influenced by the parathyroids', *Endocrinology*, **62**, 717–22.

[51] TALMAGE, R. V., NEUENSCHWANDER, JUNE, and KRAINTZ, L. (1965), 'Evidence for the existence of thyrocalcitonin in the rat', *Endocrinology*, **76**, 103–7.

[52] TALMAGE, R. V. and TOFT, R. J. (1961), 'The problem of the control of parathyroid secretion', in *The Parathyroids*, eds. Greep, R. O. and Talmage, R. V., Thomas, 224–40.

[53] TRIER, J. S. (1958), 'The fine structure of the parathyroid gland', *J. Cell. Biol.*, **4**, 13–22.

[54] WAGGENER, R. A. (1929), 'A histological study of the parathyroids in the anura', *J. Morph.*, **48**, 1–44.

[55] WAGGENER, R. A. (1930), 'An experimental study of the parathyroids in the anura', *J. exp. Zool.*, **57**, 13–56.

[56] WALKER, D. G., LAPIERE, C. M., and GROSS, J. (1964), 'A collagenolytic factor in rat bone promoted by parathyroid extract', *Biochem. Biophys. Res. Com.*, **15**, 397–402.

[57] YOSHIDA, K. and TALMAGE, R. V. (1962), 'Removal of calcium from frog bone by peritoneal lavage, a study of parathyroid function in amphibians', *Gen. Comp. Endocrinol*, **2**, 551–7.

CHAPTER 6

Intestinal Absorption of Calcium

The intestinal mucosa provides the only surface through which calcium can enter the body of the adult tetrapod. There is the possibility that amphibians might absorb calcium ions through the skin, but the sparse evidence which is available suggests that this does not happen [9]. The intestine is therefore of prime importance in all studies of calcium metabolism. Unfortunately, it is a very difficult organ to study because of its intimate relationship with both external (e.g. dietary) and internal (e.g. hormonal) variables. When considering calcium metabolism, the intestine is anything but a simple tube through which the food passes. Thus it is not uncommon to find that the faecal calcium exceeds the dietary supply, so that obviously calcium must be added to the intestinal contents as well as removed from them. This extra calcium enters the intestine with the digestive juices, and it is likely that about 500 mg Ca/day may be secreted into the intestine of the human in this way [11]. This calcium is referred to as endogenous to distinguish it from the dietary or exogenous calcium, and its presence means that it is not permissible to consider faecal calcium as being simply unabsorbed dietary calcium. Instead one has to consider four fractions:

1. Ingested calcium.
2. Secreted calcium (i.e. endogenous).
3. Absorbed calcium.
4. Reabsorbed endogenous calcium.

If one now considers that within the diet there may be various substances which react with calcium and make it physiologically unavailable, while yet other foodstuffs may increase the efficiency of absorption, the complexity of the problem can be understood. Add to this the fact that the age of the subjects, their endocrinal condition, and their previous history, all affect the efficiency of their calcium absorption, and one might despair of ever unravelling this mass of complicated influences. As it happens, however, a surprising amount of progress has been made by carefully controlled balance experiments, and by studies which involve surgically opening the alimentary canal to the outside of the animal by means of fistulas. This latter possibility of isolating parts of the alimentary canal has been carried to its logical conclusion by *in vitro* experiments with isolated segments of the intestine. These experiments provide the simplest approach to the problem of the intestinal absorption of calcium if one is prepared to accept that the results of *in vitro* experiments are a reasonable reflection of what actually happens in the animal. Because of the simplicity of their interpretation, these experiments will be discussed first and then related to experiments on the whole animal.

The technique which has been used in most of the *in vitro* experiments consists of removing a section of the intestine, everting it by rolling it over a glass rod, filling it with saline and tying off the ends with cotton. The system is modified according to the needs of the experiment, but normally the two sides of the intestinal wall are bathed with an aerated balanced salt solution. As the experiment progresses, any transport of material from mucosal (now outer) to serosal (now inner) surface results in an increased concentration of that material within the intestinal sac. Using these methods, Schachter and his colleagues have shown that calcium is transported from the mucosal to the serosal surfaces of the rat intestine against both concentration and electrical gradients. About 80% of the transported calcium is in the ionized form, so that high concentrations of ionic calcium can be found on the serosal side of the intestine (table 6.1). This suggests

Table 6.1   In vitro *experiments upon sacs of everted rat intestine. The results are expressed as the ratio of calcium (μ moles/ml) inside (serosal): outside (mucosal) the sac after incubation in aerated saline. Note the three-to four fold increase in calcium on the serosal side of the intestine indicating the transport of the ion in that direction* [14]

	Total calcium	Ionized calcium
Inside sac (*I*)	0·88	0·71
Outside sac (*O*)	0·24	0·24
Ratio *I*/*O*	3·7 (100%)	3·0 (80%)

that the calcium is transported by an active process, a finding which is confirmed by the fact that it is oxygen dependent, requires an energy source (e.g. glucose), is inhibited by metabolic poisons and is specific for calcium (table 6.2) [14]. The active process is usually considered to be a 'calcium' ion pump" but this conclusion has been questioned on the basis of experiments which indicate that there may also be an active transport of phosphate ions across the intestinal wall and it may be this process which provides the driving force for the movement of the calcium ion [6a].

The transport of calcium by everted gut sacs varies according to the age of the rat and is greatest in the young growing animal (table 6.3). This was shown to be due to a variation in the transport system rather than to increases in the length or thickness of the intestinal wall [14, 15]. There is, in fact, a lot of evidence which suggests that the efficiency of absorption is related to the needs of the animal. If this is so, then the effect of age may simply be a reflection of the needs of a growing animal. More evidence in favour of this 'adaptive' interpretation of the changes in the efficiency of

Table 6.2   *Analyses for different cations inside (I) and outside (O) the sacs of everted rat intestine after incubation. Note that only in the case of Ca^{++} is the ratio I/O greatly beyond the value of 1·0 indicating that the transport system is specific for that cation* [14]

Cation	Number of rats used	Initial cation concentration in medium	Ratio I/O for various ions	
			mean	range
Ca^{++}	7	4×10^{-5} M	6·2	4·1–9·4
Mg^{++}	4	4×10^{-5} M	0·4	0·1–0·9
Sr^{++}	9	4×10^{-5} M	1·4	1·1–1·5
Ba^{++}	4	4×10^{-5} M	1·2	1·0–1·5
K^{+}	2	4×10^{-5} M	0·8	0·9–0·6

calcium absorption has been obtained by preparing gut sacs from animals which have been kept on different diets. The results of these experiments (fig. 6.1) clearly show that calcium-deficient diets lead to a progressive increase in the efficiency of calcium transport by the intestinal wall. They

Table 6.3   *The active transport of calcium by everted gut sacs prepared from male rats of various ages. The results are expressed in the ratio of the concentrations of calcium inside and outside the sac* [14]

Age (months)	Weight (g)	Number of rats	Length of small intestine (cm)	Ratio of calcium, inside/outside
1–15	50–90	11	74±5	4·8±1·2
2–4	150–250	10	105±6	3·7±0·8
>12	400–500	7	109±6	1·9±0·8

also show that this response is very dependent upon vitamin D. In the absence of this vitamin, responses to low calcium diets are reduced [4].

The adaptation of the alimentary canal to a calcium-deficient diet is a very interesting phenomenon. The mechanism by which it occurs has resisted detection, and neither thyroparathyroidectomy, hypophysectomy nor adrenalectomy prevents this response to a low calcium diet [8]. It is therefore a very mysterious response and, for this reason, it is very gratifying to be able to reproduce it *in vitro* with a relatively simple organ system. Although the adaptive response of the intestine to low calcium diets is not affected by the surgical removal of various endocrine organs, this does not mean that the intestine is not affected in other ways by these hormones.

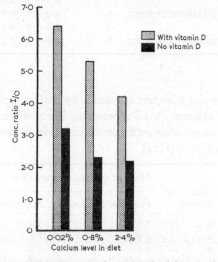

FIG. 6.1. The effect of vitamin D upon the ratio of calcium in the saline inside and outside the everted gut sacs prepared from rats fed upon various diets. Note how feeding the vitamin increases the ability of the intestine to transport calcium from the mucosal to serosal surface. Low concentrations of calcium in the diet also increase the ability of the intestine to absorb calcium. The ratio *I* (inside) /*O* (outside) represents the ability to transport calcium from the mucosal to the serosal surface (after [4]).

There is evidence that the hypophyseal and adrenal hormones do influence the ability of the intestine to absorb calcium, and a number of workers have used everted pieces of gut to show that parathyroidectomy reduces the efficiency of the active transport of calcium by the alimentary canal [4, 12]. Vitamin D is essential if the animals are to show this effect of the removal of the parathyroid glands; the converse is not true (table 6.4).

In most mammals, the absorption of calcium seems to occur mainly in the proximal part of the alimentary canal, and this has also been confirmed *in vitro*. The golden hamster seems to be an exception, however, for here most of the calcium is transported by the distal ileum (table 6.5). After

Table 6.4 *The effects of thyroparathyroidectomy on the active transport of calcium in vitamin-D-depleted and vitamin-D-treated rats. Results expressed as the concentration of calcium inside (I) and outside (O) the everted gut* [4]

Dose of vitamin D	Operation	Number of rats	Serum PO$_4$ (mM/I)	Ca (mM/I)	Ratio of concentration Ca I/O
o	Sham	7	2·8–3·7	2·6–4·0	3·9±0·7
o	Thyroparathyroidectomy	6	4·4–5·6	0·8–1·6	3·3±0·6
50,000 I.U.	Sham	7	2·8–3·5	2·5–3·8	6·4±1·3
50,000 I.U.	Thyroparathyroidectomy	6	4·4–5·3	0·7–1·8	4·8±1·2

Table 6.5 *The active transport of calcium by various regions of the alimentary canal of different species of mammal. The results are expressed as the ratio of the concentration on the serosal side (inside) and mucosal (outside) sides of everted gut sacs* [14]

Species	Number of animals	Mean of calcium concentrations, inside/outside		
		Proximal duodenum	Mid jejunum	Distal ileum
Rat	2	7·9	1·3	0·9
Rabbit	2	4·2	1·2	0·9
Guinea-pig	3	3·1	1·3	1·4
Mouse	3	1·7	0·6	0·9
Golden hamster	3	1·6	1·3	4·6

Table 6.6 *The effect of low calcium diets and vitamin D upon the ability of different regions of rat gut to transport calcium. Experiments performed on everted gut sacs and the results expressed as the ratio of concentrations of calcium inside and outside the sac* [8]

Dose of vitamin D	Region of intestine	Ratio of calcium inside/outside gut sacs of rats previously kept on various diets	
		Low calcium diet	High calcium diet
o	Duodenum	7·2±1·4	5·5±1·2
o	Ileum	0·9±0·1	0·7±0·1
200 I.U.	Duodenum	18·5±3·8	9·6±5·4
200 I.U.	Ileum	2·6±0·8	0·8±0·2

calcium deprivation, the intestine becomes adapted so that virtually the whole length of the small intestine of the young animal can transport calcium against a concentration gradient. Thus, the ileum of the rat is capable of the active transport of calcium in the mineral deficient animal, although not in a well-fed specimen. Vitamin D is again essential for this response (table 6.6). In 4–5-week-old chicks of the domestic fowl there is no regional specialization of the gut for the absorption of calcium. Instead, all parts of the intestine appear to be capable of actively transporting calcium providing vitamin D is available to the animal [2].

Vitamin D is, in fact, the greatest single factor influencing the uptake of calcium from the intestine. All forms of vitamin D are effective as is irradiation of the animal with ultra-violet light. A vitamin-D-deficient animal is rapidly replenished and an increased absorption of intestinal calcium can be demonstrated in a mammal within 1 hour of feeding the vitamin [4] (table 6.7), although the fowl seems to respond more slowly [2]. The evi-

Table 6.7   *The time required to demonstrate the effect of calciferol (vitamin D_2) on the active transport of calcium by everted gut sacs of the rat* [4]

Dose of calciferol	Hours after treatment	Number of rats	Ratio of calcium inside/outside
0	–	5	4·6 ± 0·7
50,000 I.U.	1	5	7·0 ± 1·5
50,000 I.U.	2	5	6·6 ± 1·4

dence available suggests that the vitamin affects the mechanism whereby calcium is transported across the intestinal mucosa apparently by increasing the permeability of the intestinal mucosa to calcium and making these cations more available to the active transport system in the mucosal cells [6, 13].

Another experimental technique which has produced a lot of information about the physiology of the intestine involves the use of gut fistulas. The Thiry–Vella fistula is formed by severing the intestine in two places, rejoining the main parts, and inserting the removed piece between two stab wounds in the body wall. This produces a loop of gut within the animal but opening at each end through the body wall. Once the animal has recovered from the operation, it is used to study the effect of perfusing various solutions through the loop of isolated intestine. The technique has been used to investigate the passage of calcium from the circulation into the intestine of the dog. As has already been mentioned, this is an important feature in assessing the true meaning of balance experiments. When distilled water was passed through the intestinal loop, it was found that the

F

secretion of calcium into the intestine was independent of the concentration of calcium in the plasma (fig. 6.2). This is in direct contrast to the kidney, where the quantity of calcium lost in the urine is a direct reflection of the level of plasma calcium [3]. These results underline the generally accepted view that the intestine does not provide a way of excreting calcium, but rather that any calcium lost from the body via this route is an inadvertent loss due to the inclusion of calcium ions in the digestive juices.

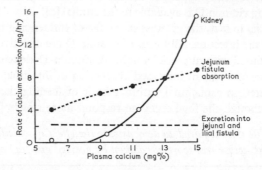

FIG. 6.2. The excretion of calcium by the kidney increases with increasing levels of plasma calcium, but the loss of calcium into Thiry–Vella fistulas of the jejunum and ileum is independent of plasma concentrations suggesting that the intestine does not act as an excretory system (after [3]).

The results which have been obtained from isolated preparations of the intestine are of great value because they demonstrate many of the features of calcium absorption in a relatively simple and well-controlled system. The results can only be accepted, however, because they confirm the findings of numerous *in vivo* experiments. Most of these have been reviewed in detail by Nicolaysen *et al.* [11], and their results may be summarized as indicating the following properties of the intact animal.

1. Calcium is lost from the blood-stream into the intestine because this ion is included in the digestive juices.
2. Calcium is absorbed at a faster rate and the net result is greater in growing as opposed to adult rats.
3. Vitamin D is undoubtedly the most important single factor in the regulation of the absorption of calcium.
4. Calcium deprivation results in an adaptation so that a greater rate and efficiency of calcium absorption occurs when calcium is next included in the diet. Thus, as soon as an animal suffers some loss of skeletal calcium, it improves the efficiency of absorption and compensates for the earlier loss by increased absorption and retention. The concept of

'skeletal saturation' has been proposed to account for this phenomenon. In the absence of 'skeletal saturation' an 'endogenous factor' is responsible for the adaptive changes found in the alimentary canal. This 'endogenous factor' is presumably some hormone which has so far evaded isolation. It does not appear to be secreted by the usual endocrine glands and Nicolaysen [10] has recently suggested that it would be logical to suppose that it is actually secreted by the bone cells themselves.

5. Vitamin D is essential for this adaptive response of the alimentary canal.

From the experiments which have been considered so far, there seems to be little doubt that the absorption of calcium by the alimentary canal involves an 'active pump' which is only effective in the presence of vitamin D. It follows, therefore, that as the calcium is absorbed for the most part in the ionic form, diets should be examined to see how they are likely to influence this. This is a difficulty in interpreting many experiments and, for this reason, this chapter has been largely based upon *in vitro* experiments. One of the important things about a diet, as far as calcium is concerned, is what percentage of calcium ions will be liberated in the alimentary canal. A number of constituents of normal diets bind calcium ions very strongly, and thus render them physiologically unavailable. One of these is phytic acid (inositol hexaphosphoric acid) which accounts for much of the organic phosphorus in cereals and seeds. It forms an insoluble salt with calcium. Some animals, such as the rat, have a phytase enzyme in the alimentary canal. Humans do not, so that when, during the Second World War it became necessary in Britain to raise the extraction of flour from 70% to 85%, the phytic acid content doubled and there was the danger of placing some of the population in negative calcium balance. The danger was overcome by adding calcium carbonate to the flour [7]. Oxalic acid has a similar effect, removing calcium ions and making them unavailable for absorption. Thus, vegetables such as spinach are far from the ideal food, for they contain so much oxalate that it not only removes the calcium ions in the vegetable but may also render other sources of calcium in the diet unavailable. Fats and fatty acids may have the same effect, forming calcium soaps, particularly when fat absorption is defective. The voluminous literature regarding the effects of phosphates upon calcium absorption is difficult to summarize. It is known, however, that calcium phosphate may precipitate in the alimentary canal if an excess of one or other ion is included in the diet [1]. Certainly in rats and many other animals, an excess of phosphorus in the diet, especially when associated with a low intake of calcium, can lead to a fall in the plasma calcium level and tetany or bone diseases. This disability can be overcome to some extent by treating the animal with vitamin D, and some mammals, including the human, seem to be less affected by excesses of phosphate in the diet [11, 7].

Milk has for a long time been appreciated not only for its high calcium content but because the calcium appears to be freely available. Recent work, particularly by Fournier, has shown that lactose is responsible for some, at least, of the remarkable properties of milk. If this sugar is added

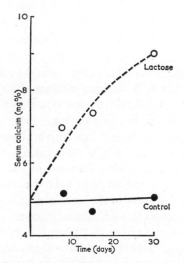

FIG. 6.3. Rats were maintained on a calcium deficient diet prior to feeding them a purified calcium diet with or without lactose. Note how the lactose increases the absorption of calcium as reflected in the increase in the concentration of serum calcium (after [5]).

to the diet, it stimulates both the absorption and retention of calcium (fig. 6.3). The effect appears to occur in the ileum and can be simulated under experimental conditions by other carbohydrates, although normally these would be absorbed in the proximal parts of the alimentary canal and would never reach the ileum. Lactose is absorbed more slowly, so that after taking a meal containing milk, it reaches the ileum and stimulates the absorption of calcium. An important aspect of this phenomenon is that the sugar and cation must be present together in the alimentary canal, and this, of course, is the normal occurrence after drinking milk [5]. Some amino acids seem to have a similar beneficial effect upon calcium absorption [16].

Milk, of course, is part of the mammalian system for the nutrition of the newborn, and it seems to some extent to be particularly well suited for taking advantage of some of the requirements for calcium absorption by the intestine. In the adult, however, the alimentary canal not only suffers the vagaries of a changing diet but can adapt to it, be stimulated by it, or be denied calcium from it. Only when one appreciates this, and the fact that all the calcium entering the body must come through this system, can one try to assess the influence of another set of variables, namely, the onset of reproduction.

REFERENCES

[1] CARTTAR, MAGDALENE, S., MCLEAN, F. C., and URIST, M. R. (1950), 'The effect of the calcium and phosphorus content of the diet upon the formation and structure of bone', *Amer. J. Physiol.*, 26, 307–31.

[2] COATES, M. E. and HOLDSWORTH, E. S. (1961), 'Vitamin D_3 and absorption of calcium in the chick', *Brit. J. Nutrit.*, 15, 131–47.

[3] CRAMER, C. F. (1963), 'Quantitative studies on the absorption and excretion of calcium from Thiry–Vella intestinal loops in the dog', in *The Transfer of Calcium and Strontium across Biological Membranes*, ed. Wasserman, R. H., Academic Press, 75–84.

[4] DOWDLE, E. B., SCHACHTER, D., and SCHENKER, H. (1960), 'Requirement for vitamin D for the active transport of calcium by the intestine', *Amer. J. Physiol.*, 198, 269–74.

[5] DUPUIS, Y. and FOURNIER, P. (1963), 'Lactose and the absorption of calcium and strontium', in *The Transfer of Calcium and Strontium across Biological Membranes*, ed. Wasserman, R. H., Academic Press, 277–93.

[6] HARRISON, H. E. and HARRISON, HELEN C. (1965), 'Vitamin D and permeability of intestinal mucosa to calcium', *Amer. J. Physiol.*, 208, 370–4.

[6a] HELBOCK, H. J., FORTE, J. G., and SALTMAN, P. (1966), 'The mechanism of calcium transport by rat intestine', *Biochim. Biophys. Acta*, 126, 81–93.

[7] IRVING, J. T. (1957), *Calcium Metabolism*, Methuen, 177 pp.

[8] KIMBERG, D. V., SCHACHTER, D., and SCHENKER, H. (1961), 'Active transport of calcium by intestine: effects of dietary calcium', *Amer. J. Physiol.*, 200, 1256–62.

[9] KROGH, A. (1938), 'The active absorption of ions in some freshwater animals', *Z. vergl. Physiol.*, 25, 333–50.

[10] NICOLAYSEN, R. (1963), in discussion, in *The Transfer of Calcium and Strontium across Biological Membranes*, ed. Wasserman, R. H., Academic Press, p. 257.

[11] NICOLAYSEN, R., EEG-LARSEN, N., and MALM, O. J. (1953), 'Physiology of calcium metabolism', *Physiol. Rev.*, 33, 424–44.

[12] RASMUSSEN, H. (1959), 'The influence of parathyroid function upon the

transport of calcium in isolated sacs of rat small intestine', *Endocrinology*, **65**, 517–19.

[13] SCHACHTER, D. (1963), 'Vitamin D and the active transport of calcium by the small intestine', in *The Transfer of Calcium and Strontium across Biological Membranes*, ed. Wasserman, R. H., Academic Press, 197–210.

[14] SCHACHTER, D., DOWDLE, E. B., and SCHENKER, H. (1960), 'Active transport of calcium by the small intestine of the rat', *Amer. J. Physiol.*, **198**, 263–8.

[15] SCHACHTER, D., DOWDLE, E. B., and SCHENKER, H. (1960), 'Accumulation of Ca^{45} by slices of small intestine', *Amer. J. Physiol.*, **198**, 275–9.

[16] WISEMAN, G. (1964), *Absorption from the Intestine*, Academic Press, 564 pp.

CHAPTER 7

Yolk Proteins and the Ovary

The physiology of the organs which have been discussed in the preceding chapters form the basis for the understanding of the calcium metabolism of most adult mammals. There are, however, two other organ systems which need to be considered before discussing the specific problems of mineral metabolism during tetrapod reproduction. These organs are the ovaries and the endolymphatic system of the inner ear for both may be important in certain animals as extra-skeletal stores of calcium for either the offspring or the reproducing female.

The ovaries are essentially the sites of origin of the primary oocytes, but among the tetrapods they perform a number of other important functions. Thus they produce a number of hormones which are involved in co-ordinating the reproductive activities, while at the same time they are the sites of yolk deposition and so influence embryonic development. The number of oocytes produced by an animal is related to the type of reproduction as is the amount of yolk included in the egg (table 7.1). Each of these aspects

Table 7.1   *Typical patterns of ovarian activity in different types of reproduction*

	Number of eggs produced	*Amount of yolk/egg*	*Type of ovulation*	*Type of reproduction*
Amphibians	many	little	multiple	larval stage
Reptiles	many	much	multiple	cleidoic egg
Birds	few	much	single	cleidoic egg
Mammals	few	little	multiple	placental

of ovarian physiology may have important repercussions upon the calcium metabolism of the female and the embryo, but this chapter will be restricted to considering four main points. The first concerns the method of deposition of yolk in the ovary, the second is related to the variations in yolk composition in the different classes of vertebrates; thirdly, there is the method

73

of ovulation; and finally, we will consider how these variations affect the overall mineral metabolism of the female.

In most vertebrates the germ cells of the female develop as far as the oocyte stage during very early life. In the mammal all the oocytes which will be used during the life of an individual are formed before or shortly after birth. They remain in this state until sexual maturity is reached, when some of them continue their development and are subsequently ovulated.

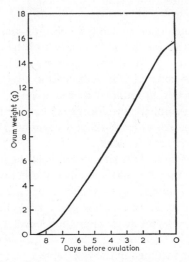

FIG. 7.1. Changes in the weight of the ovum of the domestic fowl in the nine days prior to ovulation (after [20]).

Thus, although the oocytes are formed early in life, yolk deposition is delayed until shortly before the oocytes complete their development. This process of vitellogenesis has been mainly studied in the birds and reptiles which produce large yolky eggs. In both these groups of vertebrates, the oocytes pass through a sudden change in composition as they begin to mature. The early stages are associated with a high water content (80%), but this 'hydration' stage suddenly passes into a phase of rapid growth, when there is an increased deposition of solids with the water content falling to 50%. This is the deutoplasmic stage, during which the protein content of the oocyte changes and becomes typically yolky [2, 11].

There has been considerable controversy as to the site of origin of the yolk proteins. One group of workers considers that the proteins are formed in the liver and transported in the blood to the oocyte, where they are deposited. A second group considers that the proteins are synthesized by the oocyte and various organelles have been implicated in this process.

The evidence derived from studies of birds is largely in favour of the former hypothesis. The ovary begins to enlarge 1–2 weeks before ovulation is due to occur (fig. 7.1), and during this time a new phosphate containing protein called 'vitellin' appears in the plasma [7], together with a large increase in non-diffusible calcium [8]. If the blood vessels of the liver are ligatured so as functionally to hepatectomize the domestic fowl, this new component of the plasma proteins disappears [17]. Similarly, if radioactive phosphate ($^{32}PO_4$) is injected subcutaneously into the laying fowl, it is incorporated first into the liver, and following the synthesis of vitellin, it reappears in the blood and is accumulated in the ovary (table 7.2). Vitellin

Table 7.2   *The radioactivity (c/min/γ phosphate) of the liver, blood and egg yolk of a bird after a subcutaneous injection of* 100 μc $^{32}PO_4$. *Note the initial activity in the liver followed by its transfer to the blood and accumulation in the yolk* [4]

Organ	Activity after 6 hrs	Activity after 12 hrs
Liver	164 (100%)	101·0 (62%)
Blood	38·3 (100%)	45·1 (118%)
Egg yolk	0·62 (100%)	4·1 (661%)

has been considered as the protein of yolk, but recent work suggests that it is not a single substance but a mixture of at least a phosphoprotein (phosvitin) and a lipoglycoprotein (lipovitellin). The exact state of this material and the nomenclature used to describe it is rather confusing and depends upon the methods of fractionating and analysing it. Electrophoresis of the serum of laying birds shows the presence of high concentrations of at least three new proteinaceous components. In the ultra-centrifuge they have been resolved as a small peak due to a phosphoprotein (X_1), a large peak related to a lipoglycoprotein (X_2) and an enormous lipoprotein peak (fig. 7.2). The sedimentation constants and the molecular weights of these fractions were almost exactly twice those of similar yolk fractions. It was suggested, therefore, that these complex proteins are yolk precursors, synthesized in the liver, transported in the blood, and then split into two during their passage into the oocyte (table 7.3). The transition from plasma to yolk protein appears to be a fairly simple process, as the terminal amino-acids remain the same (fig. 7.3) and the two sets of protein show similar serological properties [10].

Yolk proteins also seem to be synthesized by the liver of reptiles, and the transport of these materials to the ovary has been demonstrated in a study

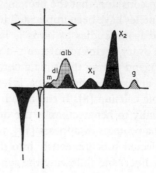

FIG. 7.2. Ultra-centrifuge patterns of plasma from oestrogenized (black) and
control (stippled) cockrels. The plasma of the oestrogenized cockerel contains
similar components to those of the normal reproducing hen. Areas under peaks
are proportional to concentrations. l, light lipoprotein; m, mucoprotein; dl, dense
lipoprotein; alb., albumen; X_1, X_1-phosphoprotein; g, globulin; X_2, X_2-
lipoglycoprotein (after [14]).

of the blood proteins of a wild population of reproducing ribbon snakes
(*Thamnophis sauritus*). Electrophoresis of the plasma proteins of these
animals showed that a new component appeared in the blood of the breeding female. The ratio of lipid to protein in this plasma component was

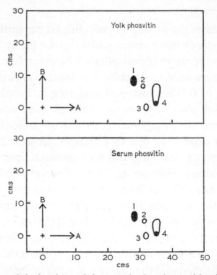

FIG. 7.3. Dinitrophenol derivatives of the terminal amino-acids of egg yolk and serum
phosvitin identified by two dimensional chromatography: (A) run in tertiary
amyl alcohol, (B) run in 1·5 M phosphate buffer at pH 6·0. 1, DNP alanine;
2, 2–4 dinitrophenol; 3, 2–4 dinitroalanine; 4, bis DNP-lysine (after [9]).

similar to that found in the yolk of mature follicules or developing eggs of this snake. The concentration of protein phosphorus was higher in the yolk (3·3%) than in the serum (1·7%), suggesting that, although the two proteins were serologically similar, a phosphorylation occurred during the transfer from the blood to the ovary [2]. Similar changes in the serum proteins of turtles (*Pseudemys scripta troostii*) could be induced by injecting oestrogens into male or immature females. Analyses of the serum of the treated animal showed that a single new peak could be demonstrated by ultra-centrifugation, although there was also a small amount of lipoprotein in this plasma. The yolk proteins of the turtle showed two peaks in the ultra-centrifuge. One of these had a sedimentation constant similar to the X_2 yolk protein of the birds, although chemically it resembled the X_1 phosphoprotein (table 7.3). In both the naturally reproducing ribbon snake and the oestrogenized turtle, the appearance of new proteins in the serum is

Table 7.3 *The calcium and protein content of the serum of oestrogenized animals compared with the composition of their egg yolks (data from [5, 13, 16])*

	Amphibian (*Rana catesbiana*)		Reptile (*Pseudemys scripta troostii*)		Bird (*Gallus domesticus*)	
	Serum	Yolk	Serum	Yolk	Serum	Yolk
Number of peaks in ultra-centrifuge	1 (X)	2	1 (X)	2	2 (X_1+X_2)	2
Sedimentation constants	S 17	S 11 little S 6	S 17	S 11 little S 5·3	S 8·5 (X_1) S 17·0 (X_2)	S 4·75 (X_1) S 10·0 (X_2)
Molecular weight	—	—	—	—	154,000 (X_1) 400,000 (X_2)	77,000 (X_1) 200,000 (X_2)
Chemical identity	Phosphoglycolipoprotein and phosphoprotein with similar sedimentation constants	— Phosphoprotein (S6)	—	S 11·0 similar to X_1 of birds	Phosphoprotein (X_1) Lipo-glycoprotein (X_2)	Phosphoprotein (X_1) Lipo-glycoprotein (X_2)
mg Ca/g mixed protein	35·0	—	55·0	—	50·0	—
mg Ca % wet weight	—	27·2	—	212·0	—	104·8
mg Ca/g yolk protein	—	0·6	—	10·6	—	6·5

associated with a swelling of the liver and hypercalcaemia. It is generally agreed that these three phenomena are all associated with a synthesis of yolk proteins in the liver and their transport to the ovary in the form of calcium complexes.

Somewhat similar phenomena can be demonstrated in amphibians, but their interpretation has been the subject of some controversy. If oestrogens are injected into the frog (*Rana catesbiana*), the liver swells and a new protein can be detected in the plasma. Ultra-centrifugation of the plasma demonstrates a single new peak, but phosphorus analyses suggest that there are actually two fractions, a phosphoglycolipoprotein and a phosphoprotein which sediment together [16]. The calcium level of the plasma is elevated in both normal reproduction [21] and after treating the immature frog with oestrogen. The new proteins in the plasma have been shown, serologically, to be similar to those in the yolk. Thus, if the frog's ovaries are used to make an anti-serum, it can be shown that the serum of the female frog has three of the four precipitation reactions shown by the water soluble fraction of the yolk (i.e. livetin). The female liver showed four precipitation reactions to the anti-serum, but the liver of the male produced only a single precipitation [5]. This evidence all tends to suggest that the liver synthesizes the yolk proteins which are then carried in the blood to the ovary. Electron micrographs of various amphibian ovaries have, however, shown yolk proteins within mitochondria [19] or cup-shaped membranous bodies [1, 6], and this has been interpreted as indicating a synthesis of yolk proteins by the mitochondria or by various yolk precursor bodies in the oocyte. Alternative suggestions have been made and in particular it seems possible that as yolk proteins have only been found in the mitochondria of the ovaries of very young animals, they represent the remains of that animal's original yolk stores and, far from being formed, they are really being utilized [6].

The evidence in the amphibia, reptiles, and birds suggests, therefore, that the yolk proteins originate in the liver, but that they may be modified in different ways in different animals by such influences as additional phosphorylation or division into two fractions during their incorporation into the oocyte. The possible activity of various organelles in this process remains to be conclusively demonstrated.

In the mammal, the quantities of yolk proteins which are formed are too small to allow easy analysis. Injecting oestrogens does not produce any additional serum proteins, hypercalcaemia, or swelling of the liver. It appears that the evolution of viviparity precludes the necessity for the transport of large quantities of egg-yolk precursors in the blood. Clearly then, there seems to be some correlation between the formation of yolk proteins and the type of reproduction shown by a particular group of animals. This relationship is well demonstrated when one considers the composition and calcium-binding ability of various yolk proteins. A sample of 100 g of wet yolk from the frog *Rana catesbiana* contains 41·7 g protein but only 27·2 mg of calcium, giving a value of 0·6 mg Ca/g protein. This can be related to a form of reproduction in which a larval form is produced without any embryologically formed bones but capable of feeding and absorbing calcium before it forms its skeleton. Yolk of the turtle *Pseudemys scripta troostii* contains only 20·4 g protein % wet weight, but it has a stronger affinity for calcium and is associated with 212 mg or 10·6 mg Ca/g protein. In the domestic fowl, 100 g of wet yolk contains 16 g of protein and 104·8 mg calcium or 6·5 mg Ca/g protein [16]. Both the reptile and bird produce cleidoic eggs from which the offspring hatch with well-ossified bones. Thus there is more than a tenfold increase in calcium/g yolk protein between the amphibians and the birds and reptiles. This may reflect an association between the composition of the yolk and the transition from the anamniotes to the amniotes. The fact that the turtle has a greater store of Ca/g protein in its yolk than does the bird is an interesting point to which we will refer again later.

Once the yolk proteins have been synthesized in the liver and deposited in the ovary, the oocyte is ready to be ovulated. In most vertebrates a number of follicles develop, and the oocytes are ovulated, as a batch. If fertilized, they give rise to a clutch of eggs or a litter of offspring.

The process of ovulation has been observed in amphibia, where it may take over 10 hours to complete [12]; in reptiles, where up to 85 oocytes may be released within an hour [3]; and in mammals, where the ovulation of the oocytes which will later form a litter follow each other with only a slight delay [18]. The common factor in all these vertebrates is the rapid ovulation of a number of oocytes within a very short time. The system in birds is entirely different. In this case, the oocytes mature one at a time. Thus there is a temporally extended series of ovulations following each other at approximately 24-hour intervals until the complete clutch is laid. This distinction between the birds and the other tetrapods is a fundamental one, for it means that whereas the processes of vitellogenesis, ovulation, and tertiary membrane secretion are discrete steps in most vertebrates, in the birds they continually overlap. Thus one avian oocyte will be ovulated shortly after the previous egg has been laid and while yolk is still being laid down in the ovary. The reason for this extended system of ovulations in the birds is not known, although it appears to be a specialization which, once attained, had a number of important implications and rendered the evolution of viviparity unlikely to occur in birds [15].

From what has already been mentioned, it will be appreciated that the composition of the yolk proteins, their deposition in the ovary, and the time relationships of ovulation, all vary in different groups of tetrapods. What remains to be shown is how these phenomena are intimately associated with the evolution of different methods of reproduction and with the calcium metabolism of the female. The transition from the anamniotes to the amniotes involves the loss of a larval stage. This change in the life history can be related to an increase in the calcium content of the yolk and the formation of embryonic bones. The yolk proteins are transported from the liver to the ovary in the form of soluble calcium complexes. Thus the non-diffusible calcium level of the blood rises during vitellogenesis and the extent of the increase is related to the evolution of new yolk proteins and the rate of yolk formation. In amphibia, the calcium associated with the yolk precursors in the serum is in the form of a phospholipid–glycolipoprotein complex and is transported and deposited in the ovary in this form. The X_1 protein, which is the fraction with the greatest capacity for binding calcium, probably did not appear in significant concentrations in the blood until vertebrates, such as the reptiles and birds, colonized the land. The X_1 phosphoprotein only appears as a separate serum protein in the birds (table 7.3) [16]. In the egg yolk of birds, the X_1 and X_2 proteins are largely insoluble, as they complex with each other [13].

The extent of the rise in the level of serum calcium caused by transporting the yolk proteins as calcium complexes is greatest in the reptiles. In the ribbon snake, at the time of ovulation, there is about sixteen times more calcium in the blood than in the blood of immature or male specimens of the same species [3]. This very large increase is probably related to the great affinity of the yolk proteins for calcium, to the large size of the oocytes of reptiles, and the fact that large numbers of them mature simultaneously. In the birds, the consecutive sequence of ovulation avoids this enormous increase in the level of serum calcium during reproduction, but at the same time it results in an elevated level of total calcium at the time when the eggshell is being formed.

It will be apparent, therefore, that the number of oocytes released, and their size, are both related to the type of reproduction. Amphibians with larval forms have only a small store of protein and calcium in their eggs, but vertebrates, which form embryonic bones, require larger mineral stores and have evolved yolk proteins with a large calcium-binding ability. The transport of these proteins from the liver, where they are synthesized, to the ovary, where they are deposited, requires the formation of calcium complexes which therefore induce a large hypercalcaemia at the time of vitellogenesis. The full effects of these increases in the level of non-diffusible calcium have not been investigated. They are, however, completely absent from eutherian mammals where the evolution of the placenta has obviated the necessity for the provision of large protein and mineral stores in the yolk.

REFERENCES

[1] BALINSKY, B. I. and DAVIS, R. J. (1963), 'Origin and differentiation of cytoplasmic structures in the oocytes of *Xenopus laevis*', *Acta. Embryol. Morphol. Exper.*, **6**, 55–108.

[2] DESSAUER, H. C. and FOX, W. (1959), 'Changes in ovarian follicle composition with plasma levels of snakes during estrus', *Amer. J. Physiol.*, **197**, 360–6.

[3] DESSAUER, H. C., FOX, W., and GILBERT, N. L. (1956), 'Plasma calcium, magnesium and protein of viviparous colubrid snakes during estrus cycle', *Proc. Soc. exp. Biol. N.Y.*, **92**, 299–301.

[4] FLICKINGER, R. A. and ROUNDS, D. E. (1956), 'The maternal synthesis of egg-yolk proteins as demonstrated by isotope and serological means', *Biochem. Biophys. Acta.*, **22**, 38–42.

[5] FLICKINGER, R. A. and SCHJEIDE, ARNE O. (1957), 'The localization of phosphorus and the site of calcium binding in the yolk of the frog's egg', *Exp. Cell. Res.*, **13**, 312–16.

[6] HOPE, J., HUMPHRIES, A. A., and BOURNE, G. H. (1964), 'Ultrastructural studies on developing oocytes of the salamander *Triturus viridescens*. II. The formation of yolk', *J. Ultrastruct. Res.*, **10**, 547–56.

[7] LASKOWSKI, M. (1938), 'The gonadotrophic hormone and the level of blood phosphorus in the hen', *Biochem. J.*, **32**, 1176–80.

[8] MCDONALD, MARGARET R. and RIDDLE, O. (1945), 'The effect of reproduction and estrogen administration on the partition of calcium phosphorus and nitrogen in pigeon plasma', *J. biol. Chem.*, **159**, 445–64.

[9] MOK, C., MARTIN, W. G., and COMMON, R. H. (1961), 'A comparison of phosvitins prepared from hen's serum and from hen's egg yolk', *Can. J. Biochem. Physiol.*, **39**, 109–17.

[10] ROEPKE, R. R. and BUSHNELL, L. D. (1936), 'A serological comparison of the phosphoprotein of the serum of the laying hen and the vitellin of the egg yolk', *J. Immunol.*, **30**, 109–13.

[11] ROMANOFF, A. L. and ROMANOFF, ANASTASIA J. (1949), *The Avian Egg*, Wiley, 918 pp.

[12] RUGH, R. (1935), 'Ovulations in the frog. I. Pituitary relations in induced ovulations', *J. exp. Zool.*, **71**, 149–162.

[13] SCHJEIDE, O. A. and URIST, M. R. (1959), 'Proteins and calcium in egg yolk', *Exp. Cell. Res.*, **17**, 84–94.

[14] SCHJEIDE, O. A. and URIST, M. R. (1960), 'Proteins induced in plasma by oestrogens', *Nature, Lond.*, **188**, 291–3.

[15] SIMKISS, K. (1962), 'Viviparity and avian reproduction', *Ibis*, **104**, 216–19.

[16] URIST, M. R. and SCHJEIDE, O. A. (1961), 'The partition of calcium and

protein in the blood of oviparous vertebrates during estrus', *J. gen. Physiol.*, **44**, 743–56.

[17] VANSTONE, W. E., DALE, D. G., OLIVER, W. F., and COMMON, R. H. (1957), 'Sites of formation of plasma phosphoprotein and phospholipid in the estrogenized cockerel', *Can. J. Biochem. Physiol.*, **35**, 659–65.

[18] WALTON, A. and HAMMOND, J. (1928), 'Observations on ovulation in the rabbit', *J. exp. Biol.*, **6**, 190–204.

[19] WARD, R. T. (1962), 'The origin of protein and fatty yolk in *Rana pipiens*. I. Phase microscopy', *J. Cell. Biol.*, **14**, 303–8.

[20] WARREN, D. C. and CONRAD, R. M. (1939), 'Growth of the hen's ovum', *J. agric. Res.*, **58**, 875–93.

[21] ZWARENSTEIN, H. and SHAPIRO, H. A. (1933), 'Metabolic changes associated with endocrine activity and the reproductive cycle in *Xenopus laevis*. III. Changes in the calcium content of the serum associated with captivity and the normal reproductive cycle', *J. exp. Biol.*, **10**, 372–8.

CHAPTER 8

Endolymphatic Sacs

In most of the higher vertebrates the skeleton contains from 96% to 99% of the calcium of the body. In the lower vertebrates, however, and in particular in the amphibia, there are large deposits of calcium associated with the inner ear. These deposits are mainly calcium carbonate, and although they are found in two distinct regions, they are given the general name of otoliths. The first region contains the statoliths, a number of calcareous deposits involved in the functioning of the sense of balance, and these are common to all vertebrates. The other region consists of a sac-like outgrowth from the inner ear, which is very small in birds and mammals but enormously enlarged in the amphibia and some reptiles. In all vertebrates, this sac is capable of producing calcareous deposits, although the precise function of this material is unknown. Both the region forming the statoliths and the sac-like diverticulum are part of the endolymphatic system of the ear.

The Structure of the Inner Ear

The inner ear or membranous labyrinth consists of a series of sacs and canals which are composed of a cellular epithelium surrounding a fluid called endolymph. The whole organ normally lies in the otic region of the skull, and it is possible to distinguish two main parts to the system. These are the utriculus and the sacculus, and they are usually connected by a narrow channel (fig. 8.1). Both structures contain areas of sensory epithelium or maculae. The utricular macula lies on the floor of that diverticulum in a horizontal plane, while the saccular macula is typically in a vertical plane. The sensory cells of both maculae are associated with large calcareous deposits or statoliths, which appear to be involved in stimulating the sense cells when the head is placed in various positions. The detection of movement is achieved by the semi-circular canals, and most vertebrates possess two vertical and one horizontal canal set at right-angles to each other. Each canal connects at both ends to the utriculus. Arising from the junction of the utriculus and the sacculus is a small tube, the endolymphatic duct. Typically this is a slender structure which extends dorsally

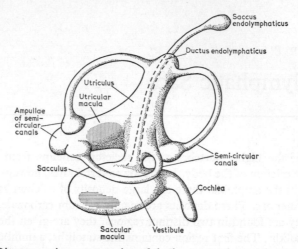

FIG. 8.1. Diagrammatic representation of the inner ear of a vertebrate.

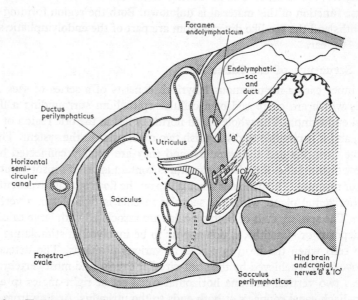

FIG. 8.2. Transverse section of a metamorphosing clawed toad (*Xenopus laevis*) showing the membranous labyrinth and perilymphatic system in the otic region of the head (after [16]).

and medially, passing through a foramen to enter the cranial cavity and terminate in a slight diverticulum, the endolymphatic sac.

The ductus endolymphaticus is present in the agnathans *Myxine* and *Petromyzon*, where it arises from the inner ear, enters the cranium, and is dilated to form a small saccus filled with poorly crystalline material. In elasmobranchs, the ductus endolymphaticus is a conspicuous structure opening to the exterior, a condition which is frequently assumed to be primitive. The duct runs almost straight to the surface, but may expand to form a large sac immediately below the surface as in *Raja*. This sac is of decreasing size in *Acanthias, Scyllium,* and *Chimaera,* but it contains crystals of calcium carbonate which can be extruded to the surface if the skin is pressed near to the opening of the ductus. An endolymphatic duct and sac have been described in many bony fish, although not all authors agree as to the homologies of these structures. Among the Dipnoi the saccus is well developed and extends into the cranium as a large bag showing many diverticulae filled with calcareous deposits [23].

The saccus endolymphaticus reaches its greatest development in some amphibia (fig. 8.2). The organ is, however, very variable in size and may be a small, club-shaped, non-vascular structure in some species, while in others it extends the whole length of the animal as a distended sac containing masses of calcareous material. According to Dempster, who examined thirty-four different species, there are six main types of endolymphatic sac in the amphibia (table 8.1). No correlation was found between the various types of endolymphatic organ and the habits of the animals.

Table 8.1 *Morphological types of endolymphatic sacs found in the amphibia* [7]

Type	Degree of fusion between sides	Vascularization	Content of $CaCO_3$	Size and degree penetration into vertebrae	Remarks	Examples
1	−ve	−ve	few or −ve	small, cranial	simple, club-like	*Necturus, Siren*
2	−ve	+ve	+ve	cranial	expanded	*Salamandra, Triturus*
3	−ve	+ve	+ve	cranial	constricted ant.	*Plethodon, Aneides*
4	+ve	+ve	+ve	cranial	—	*Ambystoma*
5	+ve	+ve	+ve	cranial and vert.	—	*Rana, Xenopus*
6	+ve	+ve	+ve	cranial and vert.	extended ant.	*Bufo, Hyla*

Among adult reptiles, the organ is small, except among a small group of mainly desert-living lizards, including most of the gekkonids, *Chaemaesaura, Xantusia vigilis,* and the iguanid *Anolis sagrae* [1, 11]. In these forms, the endolymphatic sac is well developed and passes from the cranium through an aperture in the parietal to lie as a large white structure in the neck region. This extension of the endolymphatic sac is filled with masses of calcareous material throughout life (plates 4, 5, p. 226).

In the birds and mammals, the saccus endolymphaticus is a small structure which is filled with calcareous material only during embryonic development.

The Embryology of the Endolymphatic Sac

A number of detailed descriptions have been made of the development of the vertebrate inner ear. The formation of the endolymphatic sacs of the amphibia have been particularly well studied because of the large size of these organs. Of particular importance to the present work are Whiteside's study of *Rana temporaria* [23] and Paterson's investigations of *Xenopus laevis* [16] and the Pipidae [17].

In *Rana temporaria,* a larva with a head to anus length of 4 mm shows a well-developed inner ear, which is already divided into a sacculus and an utriculus with rudimentary semi-circular canals. The ductus endolymphaticus is formed, but the saccus is represented by only a slight expansion of the distal end of the ductus. This relatively delayed development of the saccus endolymphaticus seems to be a general phenomenon. In a 10-mm larva, the saccus has enlarged in a cranio-caudal direction and can be seen to be separated into a pars anterior and a pars posterior in front and behind the ductus endolymphaticus respectively. At this stage, the saccus endolymphaticus lies in an inter-dural space above the brain, and already it contains much calcareous material. As development progresses, the two sacci meet in the midline and grow caudally over the dorsal part of the spinal cord. The system develops numerous pouches which become surrounded by many blood vessels. This degree of development has been reached by the time the 15-mm larva starts metamorphosis, and shortly afterwards the saccus begins to protrude from the vertebral canal in the region of the intervertebral foramina to form the typical calcareous sacs which overlie the spinal ganglia of the adult frog. The endolymphatic system continues to grow after metamorphosis, and more calcium carbonate is deposited as the epithelium becomes increasingly vascularized.

The wall of the saccus remains throughout its development as a single layer of epithelial cells which, apart from being slightly more flattened, are virtually indistinguishable from the ductus. The system grows slowly and continuously until it reaches its adult form. It shows no regression during its development, a fact that has led Whiteside to consider that it must represent an adult rather than a specialized larval organ.

Information on the development of the endolymphatic system in other vertebrates is relatively sparse. A most interesting observation dating back to 1841 and concerning 'the remarkable accumulation of microscopic crystals in the hind head of the snake embryo' is obviously concerned with the calcareous deposits in the endolymphatic sacs of *Coluber natrix* [3]. Similar deposits occur in the embryos of *Anguis fragilis, Lacerta viridis, Chelonia midas, Testudo graeco,* and *Crocodilus.* Calcareous deposits also occur in the endolymphatic sacs of avian and mammalian embryos, but, as in most reptiles, they are resorbed in the adult [23].

Endolymph

Both the ductus and the saccus are filled with endolymph, which is one of the most remarkable fluids known in physiology. The fact that calcium carbonate can be deposited in it is only one of its many peculiarities. The fluid has been particularly well studied in relation to the physiology of hearing, so that samples have mainly been collected from the mammalian cochlea. The small quantity of fluid available from this source has made analyses difficult, but it has been established that the endolymph has a composition unique among extracellular fluids. This is shown most clearly in the low concentration of sodium and high concentration of potassium ions which appear to be secreted across an epithelium which is practically impermeable to ions (table 8.2). In addition to the unusual composition

Table 8.2   *Analyses of endolymph and perilymph from some mammals* [4]

	Sodium (meq/l)	Potassium (meq/l)	Chloride (meq/l)	Protein (mg %)	Non-protein nitrogen (mg %)
Guinea-pig					
Perilymph	148	5	120	75	20
Utricular endolymph	26	142	110	25	21·5
Cat					
Perilymph	164	6	150	142	21
Cochlear endolymph	66	117	—	—	—

of the endolymph, it also has a potential difference of +80 mV relative to the perilymph which surrounds much of the inner ear. This potential difference and its orientation are again very unusual characteristics [5, 6].

Examination of the endolymph of other vertebrates has shown a similar distribution of potassium and sodium ions expressed here as a ratio because of the difficulties of obtaining sufficient material to determine absolute amounts (table 8.3). The actual value of the ratio of K/Na varies somewhat

Table 8.3 *The ratio of potassium to sodium ions in the endolymph of various vertebrates* [13]

Animal	Highest K/Na *value*
Frog (*Rana pipiens*)	30
Turtle (*Chrysemys picta*)	42
Lizard (*Phrynosoma cornatum*)	20
Pigeon (*Columba livia*)	3
Guinea-pig (*Cavia porcellus*)	50–100

between different experiments, possibly because of contamination from blood or perilymph. Endolymphatic potentials have also been determined in a large number of vertebrates and, on the basis of these results, Schmidt distinguishes three basic types (table 8.4).

Table 8.4 *Some properties and types of endolymphatic potentials* [20]

Type	1	2	3
Endolymphatic potential relative to perilymph	Less than 13 mV	*c.* 20 mV	50–100 mV
Effect of anoxia	Insensitive	Sensitive	Sensitive
Variation in potential throughout endolymph	All parts similar	Cochlea slightly higher than vestibule	Cochlea much higher than vestibule
Occurrence	All poikilotherms	All birds	All eutherian mammals

One final characteristic of the endolymphatic system is the presence, at least in mammals, of carbonic anhydrase in the walls of the labyrinth. The concentration of this enzyme increases from the base to the apex of the cochlea. It is present in only small quantities in the vestibule but at high concentrations in the saccus endolymphaticus (table 8.5).

Those characteristics of the endolymphatic system which have been mentioned, namely, an unusual ionic composition, the maintenance of a considerable potential difference between it and the surrounding fluids, and the presence of the enzyme carbonic anhydrase, can all be interpreted as indications of metabolic regulation of the ionic composition of the fluid. It is true to say that at the moment the significance of these characteristics is not completely understood, although it would seem natural to relate them to the sensory functions of the inner ear. They may, however, also be related to secretory activity such as that necessary to form the statoliths and other deposits of calcium carbonate. At the moment, this has not been

Table 8.5 *The concentration of carbonic anhydrase in the labyrinth of the cat's ear as compared with other organs* [8]

Organ		Units of carbonic anhydrase per g wet wt
Kidney		275
Blood		943
Inner ear:	basal turn of cochlea	1,086
	middle turn of cochlea	2,263
	apex of cochlea	3,162
	saccus endolymphaticus	3,000
	vestibule	81

demonstrated in any way, but it should be borne in mind when considering the functions of the endolymphatic sacs of various vertebrates. The results of a recent survey of the X-ray diffraction patterns of vertebrate otoliths are given in table 8.6, and it is interesting to find that different vertebrates

Table 8.6 *Crystallographic types of otoliths in the endolymphatic systems of vertebrates (after* [2])

Group	Type of crystals
Agnatha	Poorly crystalline apatite (P)
Elasmobranchii	Aragonite and calcite (C)
Dipnoi	Aragonite (C)
Teleostei	Aragonite (C)
Urodela	Aragonite (C)
Anura	Aragonite (C)
Reptilia	Aragonite and calcite (C)
Birds	Calcite (C)
Mammals	Calcite (C)

(P), calcium phosphate.
(C), calcium carbonate.

produce calcareous deposits of various types in their endolymph. The formation and type of deposit may be related to the ability of the animal to regulate the ionic composition of the fluid in which these crystals are formed. The agnatha have poorly crystalline otoliths of apatite, whereas most other anamniotes have crystals of aragonite. Most amniotes contain calcite otoliths, although the reptiles still retain some of the aragonite polymorph [2]. A number of ions are known to interfere with the formation of calcareous deposits and the series from the agnatha to the mammals could be interpreted as showing a progressive elimination of these interfering ions [21]. Little can be said about the formation of these deposits until more is known about the physiology of the endolymphatic system and a similar comment might be made regarding their function. The enormous quantity of these calcareous deposits in the amphibia has led to a great deal of speculation as to their possible significance.

The first suggestion, dating back to the nineteenth century, was prompted by the fact that in the frog the calcareous sacs protrude out between the vertebrae and overlie the spinal ganglia. At that time, the relationship of these deposits to the endolymphatic system of the ear was not understood, and it was assumed that these deposits must be a protective device similar in function to the other membranes surrounding the spinal cord [9]. This protection theory still receives a little support, but there is no experimental evidence in favour of this view nor is it very convincing in demonstrating an association between comparative anatomy and behaviour or habitat. A second theory, proposed by Hasse, suggests that the sac acts as a reservoir for endolymph when the pressure in the labyrinth becomes excessive. This again is not a very convincing suggestion because of the lack of any supporting evidence and the equal success of animals without this enormous enlargement of the endolymphatic sac. A similar theory which attempts to relate the size of the saccus to the physiology of hearing was also advocated by Hasse and has been supported by Noble. It suggests that the endolymphatic sacs transmit vibrations which impinge on the vertebral region of the animal to the sensory system of the ear. 'The sacs never extend into the neural canal of the vertebrae in urodeles and this restriction is correlated with poorly developed auditory powers in this group' [15]. This view has again been severely criticized on comparative grounds, especially now that evidence is available to suggest that urodeles have a well-developed auditory sense [16, 17].

Both the remaining theories consider that it is the calcium deposits rather than the sacs themselves that are functionally important. It has been shown that if the frog is placed in water containing carbon dioxide it is possible to dissolve completely the calcareous material in the endolymphatic sacs. The carbon dioxide has to be regulated so as not to suffocate the frogs, but with appropriate conditions it is possible to remove the deposits within about eighteen days. This experiment is of considerable importance as it demonstrates that the calcareous deposits are physiologically available to the animal, presumably via the extensive blood supply to these sacs. In Sulze's original work on this problem he used X-rays to demonstrate the disappearance of the calcareous deposits [22]. The remarkable feature shown by these radiographs is, however, not only the disappearance of the deposits from the sacs but also the presence throughout the experiment of the statoliths which are completely unaffected. Thus, not only are the calcareous deposits of the sacs available to the animal but they are also preferentially dissolved. It has been suggested on the basis of these experiments that the deposits act as a buffering system for metabolic acids. Experiments on diving frogs show that there is an anaerobic metabolism in these animals,

Table 8.7 *The effect of bone repair on the calcareous deposits in the endolymphatic sacs of starving* Rana pipiens (*data from* [19])

Number of animals	Preliminary treatment	Result	Number of animals with broken bones	Results of bone repair upon endolymphatic sacs
9	4 weeks in 0·8% $CaCl_2$ solution	Increased $CaCO_3$ in sacs	9	8 show decrease in $CaCO_3$ in sacs 1 no change
9	Tapwater	6 good deposits $CaCO_3$ 3 no deposits $CaCO_3$	9	6 decrease in $CaCO_3$ in sacs 3 no change

with the calcareous deposits possibly having a buffering action upon the organic acids released during carbohydrate metabolism [18]. This has been confirmed by forcibly submerging *Rana esculenta* for several hours, after which time the calcium level of the blood has risen by from 1·6% to 13·1% (average 5%) presumably because of the utilization of the endolymphatic deposits [10]. Not only can the material in the sacs be removed but it can also be rapidly replaced if the frog has access to calcium or strontium salts [14]. A similar result is seen in cases of hypervitaminosis D, when the bones may be resorbed and the calcium stored in the endolymphatic sacs [19].

The suggestion that the endolymphatic sacs are functionally a store of calcareous material which the animal can draw upon in times of stress has actually got a much longer history. We have already seen that Carus suggested in 1841 that the calcareous material in the sacs of the snake embryo disappeared in the adult, and he suggested that it was used to form bone in the developing animal. A similar suggestion was made by Gaupp who believed that both the adult and larval amphibian could use the endolymphatic deposits to form bone. This view has been challenged by Herter [12] who broke the leg of a frog but could find no decrease in the quantity of calcium in the endolymphatic sacs two months later. The experiment has been criticized because of inadequate controls both as to the original state of the calcareous deposits and as to the diet of the animal during the experiment. The observations have been repeated by Krause [14] who used X-radiographs to assess the calcium content of the sacs. Only one animal survived the experiments, but it was concluded that calcium had been withdrawn from the sacs to assist in repairing the bone. More recently, this work has been extended by Schlumberger and Burk. They were able to show a decrease in the calcium content of the endolymphatic sacs in 78% of the frogs whose legs were fractured (table 8.7).

Despite these experiments and observations, there is still no unifying concept for the physiology of the endolymphatic sacs of vertebrates. It appears likely that where these structures are enormously developed, they represent a major store of calcium upon which the animal may call in times of a deficiency. Thus, although the endolymphatic sacs are in many ways incompletely understood, they are structures which cannot be ignored when considering the mineral metabolism of the lower vertebrates. Furthermore, as the calcium they contain is physiologically available, it will have to be considered when appraising the calcium metabolism of these animals during reproduction.

REFERENCES

[1] CAMP, C. L. (1923), 'Classification of the lizards', *Bull. Amer. Mus. Nat. Hist.*, **48**, 289–482.

[2] CARLSTROM, D. (1963), 'A crystallographic study of vertebrate otoliths', *Biol. Bull. Wood's Hole*, **125**, 441–63.

[3] CARUS, C. G. (1841), 'Merkwurdige Anhäufung mikroskopischer Krystalle am Hinterkopfe der Schlangenembryonen', *Arch. Anatomie. Physiologie*, 216–20.

[4] CITRON, L., EXLEY, D., and HALLPIKE, C. S. (1956), 'Formation, circulation and chemical properties of the labyrinthine fluids', *Brit. med. Bull.*, **12**, 101–4.

[5] DAVIS, H. (1957), 'Biophysics and physiology of the inner ear', *Physiol. Rev.*, **37**, 1–49.

[6] DAVIS, H. (1959), 'Excitation of auditory receptors', in *Handbook of Physiology: I Neurophysiology*, ed. Field, J., American Physiological Soc., 565–84.

[7] DEMPSTER, W. T. (1930), 'The morphology of the amphibian endolymphatic organ', *J. Morph.*, **50**, 7–126.

[8] ERULKAR, S. D. and MAREN, T. H. (1961), 'Carbonic anhydrase and the inner ear', *Nature, Lond.*, **189**, 459–60.

[9] GAUPP, E. (1897–1904). Ecker, A. and Wiedersheim's R. *Anatomie des Frosches*, Vieweg, Braunschweig.

[10] GUARDABASSI, A. and SACERDOTE, M. (1949), 'Variazioni della calcemia in *Rana Esculenta* dopo immersione prolungata', *Boll. Soc. ital. Biol. sper.*, **25**, 514–16.

[11] HAMILTON, D. W. (1964), 'The inner ear of lizards. 1. Gross structure', *J. Morph.*, **115**, 255–72.

[12] HERTER, K. (1922), 'Ein Beitrag zum Kalksack Problem der Frösche', *Anat. Anz.*, **55**, 530–6.

[13] JOHNSTONE, CLARE G., SCHMIDT, R. S., and JOHNSTONE, B. M. (1963), 'Sodium and potassium in vertebrate cochlear endolymph as determined by flame micro-spectrophotometry', *Comp. Biochem. Physiol.*, **9**, 335–41.

[14] KRAUSE, K. (1935), 'Experimentelle Untersuchungen über die Funktion der Kalksackchen bei Froschlurchen', *Z. vergl. Physiol.*, **22**, 346–58.

[15] NOBLE, G. K. (1954), *The Biology of the Amphibia*, Dover Publications, 577 pp.

[16] PATERSON, NELLIE F. (1949), 'The development of the inner ear of *Xenopus laevis*', *Proc. zool. Soc. Lond.*, **119**, 269–91.

[17] PATERSON, NELLIE F. (1960), 'The inner ear of some members of the Pipidae (Amphibia)', *Proc. zool. Soc. Lond.*, **134**, 509–46.

[18] POCZOPKO, P. (1960), 'Respiratory exchange in *Rana esculenta* L. in different respiratory media', *Zoologica Poloniae*, **10**, 45–55.

[19] SCHLUMBERGER, H. G. and BURK, D. H. (1953), 'Comparative study of the reaction to injury. II. Hypervitaminosis D in the frog with special reference to the lime sacs', *Arch. Path. (Lab. Med.)*, **56**, 103–24.

[20] SCHMIDT, R. S. (1963), 'Types of endolymphatic potentials', *Comp. Biochem. Physiol.*, **10**, 83–7.

[21] SIMKISS, K. (1964), 'Phosphates as crystal poisons of calcification', *Biol. Rev.*, **39**, 487–505.

[22] SULZE, W. (1942), 'Über die physiologische Bedeutung des Kalksackchen Apparates der Amphibien', *Pflug. Arch. ges. Physiol.*, **246**, 250–7.

[23] WHITESIDE, BEATRICE (1922), 'The development of the saccus endolymphaticus in *Rana temporaria Linné*', *Amer. J. Anat.*, **30**, 231–66.

PART II

Reproductive Adaptations

CHAPTER 9

Mammalian Reproduction: (1) Pregnancy

Pregnancy Anabolism

Most mammals which are adequately fed during pregnancy retain more protein, calcium, and phosphorus than is required to form and nurture their foetuses. These animals are therefore in positive balance for many nutrients and this condition has been considered as a general phenomenon called pregnancy anabolism. This concept is based upon nutritional experiments on the rat, dog, pig, cow, and human, and although the results from all these animals are fairly consistent, pregnancy anabolism has been interpreted in two basically different ways.

First, there is the view expressed by Irving who, after reviewing the available evidence, wrote: 'It seems safe to conclude that any extra storage of calcium in the mother's body during pregnancy is due to previous deficiency, and if calcium intake has been adequate, calcium storage does not occur' [12]. A similar view considers that since many animals come into reproductive activity while they are still growing, the increased weight of the mother after parturition simply reflects a normal growth in weight upon which pregnancy has been superimposed. Opposed to these views is the suggestion that pregnancy anabolism reflects important physiological changes resulting in a 'reduction in the needs for maintenance'. This implies that the pregnant female has either a reduced metabolic rate or an increased efficiency in the use of her food. There is no evidence for a decreased metabolic rate, and, in fact, one would expect pregnancy to have quite the opposite effect because of the extra weight and requirements of the foetus (table 9.1). The evidence for an increase in the efficiency of the utilization of food has a rather better basis, being derived from experiments in which rats, cows, and pigs have been fed diets which are adjusted so that under normal circumstances they are just sufficient to maintain the weight of the animal. When this low level of nutrition is given to sows during gestation, the pregnant animal still gains weight greatly in excess of the weight of the foetuses, although the non-pregnant controls show

Table 9.1 *A calculation of the effect of pregnancy upon the metabolism of a woman weighing 54 kg at conception and 66·5 kg after delivery* [15]

	Cals/day
Basal metabolism before pregnancy	1,350
Increase in metabolism at term due to increased weight	120
Heat production uterus and contents at term	175
Metabolism breast tissue	36
Extra work of heart	80
Extra work of respiration	20
Overall increase in heat production directly related to reproduction	311

Table 9.2 *The effect of the level of nutrition and of reproductive activity on the weight of pigs* [21]

	Weight at time of mating (lb)	Weight after parturition (lb)	Gain in weight (lb)	Weight at weaning (lb)	Weight loss during lactation (lb)	Total change in weight (lb)
Low level of nutrition						
Pregnant sows	505·3	549·6	44·3	533·3	16·3	+28·0
Control sows	507·5	517·0	9·5	—	—	—
High level of nutrition						
Pregnant sows	506·4	625·0	118·6	518·7	106·3	+12·3
Control sows	508·2	594·0	85·8	—	—	—

Table 9.3 *The composition of the bodies of female rats and mice, their young and unmated control animals* [24]

	Age (days)	Weight (g)	Protein (g)	Fat (g)	Calcium (mg)	Phosphorus (mg)
Control rats	225	230	40·4	51·0	2,460	1,450
Rat after delivery	225	305	49·1	72·3	2,490	1,590
Rat offspring (9 animals)	0	52·7	5·7	0·6	159	185
Control mice	—	26·6	4·44	1·48	284	174
Mouse after delivery	—	38·6	7·16	2·76	343	216
Mice offspring (7 animals)	0	10·85	1·36	0·22	36	36

little increase (table 9.2). The small gain in the weight of the control pig is possibly due to growth. Experiments similar to these have also been performed on virgin rats and mice, where there is, of course, no possibility of previous reproductive activity leaving the animals with mineral or nitrogen deficiencies. Identical animals were used as controls, so as to indicate any general changes in the animals such as growth [24]. The results are shown in table 9.3 and indicate that after parturition, the maternal weight, protein, fat, and mineral content have all increased above those of the controls. These results are based upon the average data obtained from 36 rats and 20 mice, and in another study of the pregnant rat, only 4 specimens failed to show a positive calcium balance out of 27 individuals which were fed a variety of diets [7]. The consistency of these results suggests that pregnancy anabolism must reflect some basic physiological change, and the results of ablation operations indicates that there is a hormonal background to the phenomenon, although these experiments cannot be regarded, at the moment, as being conclusive [4].

Balance Experiments during Pregnancy

The effects of pregnancy anabolism are clearly seen in balance experiments, and the further use of these data can provide some indication of the changes which occur in mineral metabolism during gestation. The first feature which can be demonstrated is that those individuals which gain most weight during pregnancy are also the ones that lose most during lactation. It appears that the tissue laid down during pregnancy may contain a lot of fluid, for it is very labile and rapidly disappears during lactation. In the same way, animals which gain very little weight during pregnancy lose very little during lactation (table 9.2). It is also apparent that the feeding behaviour of an animal during lactation is influenced by that during pregnancy. Animals on a low intake diet during pregnancy show a much greater food consumption during lactation than well-fed animals (table 9.4).

Table 9.4 *Figures showing the relationship between food consumption during pregnancy and lactation in the pig* [21]

Food level during pregnancy	Daily food intake during pregnancy (lb)	Daily food intake during lactation (lb)
High	8·1	10·9
Low	4·3	13·7

The specific requirements of the foetus for calcium rise rapidly towards the end of pregnancy when the ossification of the foetal skeleton is occurring.

H

This is demonstrated in table 9.5, which not only shows the quantities involved during the various stages of gestation but also indicates that the requirements of the foetus differ greatly in different species. In humans, the demand is very small and there does not usually appear to be any difficulty in maintaining a positive calcium balance on most normal diets (fig. 9.1). Negative balances are, indeed, more likely to occur during the

Table 9.5 *Calcium accretion by the foetus of various mammals. Data expressed as mg calcium in foetus/kg maternal body wt/hr assuming a litter size of 1 for man and the cow, and 10 for the rat and pig (recalculated from [5, 13 and 18])*

Rat (0·25 kg)

Period of pregnancy (days)	14	15	16	17	18	19	20	21	22
Calcium content of litter (mg)	0·18	0·42	0·88	4·6	15	52	81	87	123
mg Ca/kg/hr	—	0·04	0·076	0·62	1·7	6·2	4·8	0·1	6·0

Pig (250 kg)

Period of pregnancy (days)	40	60	80	100	110	115
Increase Ca content litter (g)/day	0·1	0·4	1·2	4·0	7·2	9·8
mg Ca/kg/hr	0·016	0·06	0·20	0·66	1·20	1·63

Cow (500 kg)

Period of pregnancy (months)	5	6	7	8	9
Calcium content foetus (g)	10·1	43·2	140	375	673
mg Ca/kg/hr	—	0·09	0·27	0·65	0·82

Human (70 kg)

Period of pregnancy (months)	4	5	6	7	8	9	10
Calcium content foetus (g)	0·19	1·28	3·12	5·45	8·47	13·3	22·7
mg Ca/kg/hr	—	0·02	0·03	0·04	0·06	0·09	0·18

early rather than the late stages of pregnancy (table 9.6). Where negative balances do occur towards the end of gestation there is usually some additional complicating factor involved. Thus subject VI showed a negative balance in her 26th week of pregnancy, when the faecal loss actually exceeded her intake. This is possible because of the loss of calcium into the intestine with the secretion of the digestive juices. The negative balance occurred at a time when the dietary intake of calcium was good and urinary excretion was normal, so that it was apparently caused by a decrease in the efficiency of absorption from the intestine. The experimenters noted that 'psychological and emotional records verified the fact that subject VI was undergoing great worry and anxiety during the 26th week, a period when she gave the greatest negative calcium balance' [16]. Similar emotional disturbances have been shown to upset the calcium balance of cows and indicate the experimental difficulties in this work [10]. Occasionally, some diets are not satisfactory, and subject D (table 9.6), towards the end of gestation, consumed a diet with a high crude fibre and a low vitamin-D content during the winter months. Under these conditions she also was in negative calcium balance towards the end of pregnancy, but such results are the exception rather than the rule.

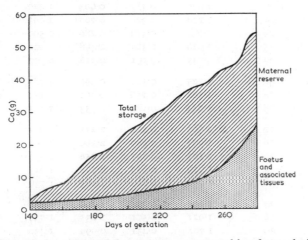

FIG. 9.1. The gain in calcium of the pregnant woman and her foetus during gestation (after [11]).

The differences between species in the need for calcium during pregnancy can be seen in table 9.5, where it is apparent, for example, that the foetuses of the rat impose a demand for calcium upon the mother which is over thirty times greater than that found in the human on a weight for weight basis. Despite this, the pregnant rat is normally in a positive balance and may actually store four or five times as much calcium in her own body as she uses to form her offspring (table 9.7). If the rat is fed a vitamin-E-free diet during pregnancy, there is a resorption of the foetus, although the mother continues to store extra minerals [7].

Relationship of Foetal and Maternal Requirements

It has long been realized that the foetus has a 'high priority' for many of the nutrients in the body of the pregnant animal. This concept has been

Table 9.6   *Calcium balance data (g/day) for five pregnant humans on normal household diets* [6, 16]

Subject number	Week of pregnancy	Ca intake	Ca output			Balance
			Urine	Faeces	Total	
A	12	0·727	0·201	0·584	0·785	−0·058
	20	1·624	0·377	1·103	1·480	+0·144
	28	1·491	0·263	1·116	1·379	+0·112
	33	1·314	0·267	0·900	1·167	+0·147
	39	1·192	0·156	0·750	0·906	+0·286
B	16	1·096	0·417	0·603	1·020	+0·076
	22	1·214	0·326	0·767	1·093	+0·121
	29	0·784	0·313	0·286	0·599	+0·185
	35	1·026	0·324	0·498	0·822	+0·204
	39	0·745	0·191	0·316	0·507	+0·238
D	30	1·125	0·121	0·961	1·082	+0·043
	34	1·182	0·150	0·961	1·111	+0·071
	38	1·044	0·122	0·953	1·075	−0·031
VI	20	2·693	0·420	2·211	2·631	+0·062
	26	1·993	0·489	2·780	3·269	−1·276
	30	2·185	0·697	1·856	2·553	−0·368
	34	1·779	0·635	0·978	1·613	+0·166
	38	1·792	0·669	1·067	1·736	+0·056
VII	14	1·694	0·524	1·390	1·914	−0·220
	26	1·921	0·501	1·235	1·736	+0·185
	30	1·708	0·431	0·999	1·430	+0·278
	34	1·761	0·525	1·073	1·598	+0·163
	38	1·600	0·404	0·962	1·366	+0·234

Table 9.7   *Calcium balance data for two pregnant rats during period of gestation* [7]

Rat number	B 149393	W 9337
Weight at parturition (g)	230	286
Weight of foetus (g)	28·1	28·7
Weight of placenta and uterus (g)	7·7	11·3
Total Ca intake (mg)	2,432	2,812
Ca excreted (mg)	2,085	2,425
Ca balance (mg)	+347	+387
Ca in foetus (mg)	65	63
Ca in uterus and placenta (mg)	3	3
Excess Ca stored (mg)	279	321

expressed in a generalized form by Hammond in his theory of the partition of nutrients [9]. This theory, shown diagrammatically in fig. 9.2, proposes that the various tissues of the body have different priorities for the incoming nutrients in the descending order brain, bone, muscle, and fat. The priority of an organ is depicted by the number of arrows, so that when the animal is experiencing adverse conditions and the level of incoming nutrients is reduced, the rate of growth of each part is reduced (by removing one arrow from each organ in fig. 9.2), so that the formation of fat stops completely. A further reduction in the supply of food decreases growth and

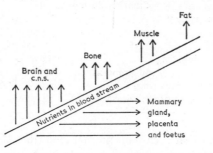

FIG. 9.2. The distribution of metabolites in relation to the needs of various organs according to Hammond's theory of the partition of nutrients (after [9]).

stops the formation of new muscle. The placenta and embryo occupy a position of high priority in this scheme, particularly during the early stages of pregnancy.

The relationship of the calcium requirements of the foetus to the supply of these ions in the maternal diet provides a good example of the association implied in Hammond's theory. In an extensive series of experiments on the rat, Bodansky and Duff [3] showed that the mineralization of the foetal skeleton was virtually independent of the diet of the mother during pregnancy (table 9.8). Thus, although the rats on diet No. 7 received over forty times as much calcium in their food as those on diet No. 26, there was virtually no difference in the calcium content of the offspring. This suggested that the pregnant rats were mobilizing the calcium reserves of their own skeletons when dietary calcium was scarce and in the case of the rats on diet No. 26, this was conclusively demonstrated, since the bodies of the foetuses contained almost five times as much calcium as their mothers consumed during pregnancy. The mobilization of these large amounts of skeletal calcium can normally be taken to involve the parathyroid glands, and the effects of these diets were therefore investigated in two ways. In the first set of experiments, the parathyroid glands were removed from the pregnant rats with the effects upon the offspring demonstrated in table

Table 9.8 *Data demonstrating that the storage of calcium and phosphorus by the foetus is independent of the diet of the rat during pregnancy* [3]

Diet number	7	27	26
Dietary calcium (mg % food)	0·49	0·122	0·017
Dietary phosphorus (mg % food)	0·49	0·245	0·245
Ratio Ca/P in diet	1·0	0·5	0·07
Weight young at birth (g)	5·0	6·3	5·7
Number young at birth	14	12	12
Weight litter (g)	70	75	68
Consumption of minerals by the mother during last 18 days of pregnancy			
Calcium (g)	1·600	0·408	0·037
Phosphorus (g)	1·600	0·819	0·536
Foetal storage of calcium (mg)	182·9	184·0	182·8
Foetal storage of calcium (% consumption)	11	45	494
Foetal storage of phosphorus (mg)	229·1	222·8	211·9
Foetal storage of phosphorus (% consumption)	14	27	39

9.9. It is apparent that even with normal food (diet No. 7) there is a fall of about 50% in the calcium content of the litter of the parathyroidectomized mothers, and with a low calcium diet (No. 26) the calcium content of the offspring of the experimental animals was less than 30% of the normal value. One particularly interesting aspect of this work is shown in the results from the high calcium diet No. 16. This diet, with its abnormally high Ca/P ratio, is usually rachitogenic, but in pregnant parathyroidectomized rats the offspring had the same calcium content as the control rats

Table 9.9 *The combined effects of various diets and of parathyroidectomy of pregnant rats upon the accumulation of minerals in the foetus* [3]

Diet number	7	27	26	16
Dietary calcium (mg % food)	0·49	0·122	0·017	1·125
Dietary phosphorus (mg % food)	0·49	0·245	0·245	0·245
Ratio Ca/P in diet	1·0	0·5	0·07	5·0
Average weight of litter (g)				
Intact mother	49·6	56·1	52·4	42·6
Parathyroidectomized	29·2	21·0	23·2	41·6
Foetal storage of calcium (mg/litter)				
Intact mother	117	136	124	71
Parathyroidectomized	50	35	35	72
Foetal storage of phosphorus (mg/litter)				
Intact mother	145	164	153	106
Parathyroidectomized	79	57	61	103

maintained on this food. This presumably implies that the maternal blood coming to the placenta had the same calcium content whether the mother possessed her parathyroid glands or whether these organs had been removed. The absorption of calcium from the intestine of rats on this high calcium diet was probably sufficient to obviate the effects of removing the parathyroid glands, although it should be pointed out that this diet was sufficiently unbalanced to reduce the deposition of foetal bone even when the mothers were normal animals.

The second way in which the role of the parathyroid glands was investigated during pregnancy involved an analysis of the blood and a measurement of the size of the glands of the rats used in the previous dietary experiments. The results are shown in table 9.10 and indicate that, on most

Table 9.10   *The influence of diet and pregnancy upon the calcium and phosphorus levels of the blood and upon the weight of the parathyroid glands of rats* [23]

Diet number	7	26	27	16
Dietary calcium (mg % food)	0·49	0·017	0·122	1·125
Dietary phosphorus (mg % food)	0·49	0·245	0·245	0·245
Normal rat				
Maternal serum calcium (mg %)	9·10	8·18	9·14	11·77
Maternal serum phosphorus (mg %)	4·67	3·90	5·13	2·50
Maternal parathyroid gland (μg)	141	265	191	124
Foetal parathyroid gland (μg)	7·7	7·7	5·3	5·6
Parathyroidectomized rat				
Maternal serum calcium (mg %)	4·65	4·06	4·24	11·5
Maternal serum phosphorus (mg %)	7·81	5·44	10·76	1·9
Foetal parathyroid gland (μg)	8·8	11·0	10·2	6·0

diets, the maternal blood is within the normal range for calcium and phosphorus concentrations. In the case of the food with the low calcium content (diet No. 26) where, it will be recalled, the foetus obtained at least 80% of its calcium from the maternal skeleton, the mother's parathyroid glands were almost twice their normal size. After parathyroidectomy, the calcium content of the maternal serum fell to about half its normal value in all except those on the rachitogenic diet No. 16. The results are therefore in close agreement with the scheme invoked to explain the effects of diet and parathyroidectomy on the deposition of minerals by the rat foetus.

In the nutritional experiments of Bodansky and Duff, diet No. 7 was considered to be quite adequate for maintaining rats during pregnancy. On this diet, the foetus was able to develop normally and utilized only 11% of the calcium consumed by the mother. Despite these minimal demands, it was found that the parathyroid glands increased in size with each pregnancy and did not revert to their original size after parturition [23]. It has also been found that pregnancy induces an osteolysis in the bones of rats [13] and both these observations would appear to imply that an increase in parathyroid activity was a normal consequence of pregnancy. A number of attempts have been made to investigate this possibility by assaying the quantity of parathyroid hormone in the blood of pregnant women. The results show a most interesting increase in the hormonal activity of the blood up to a maximum at about the 34th week of gestation (fig. 9.3).

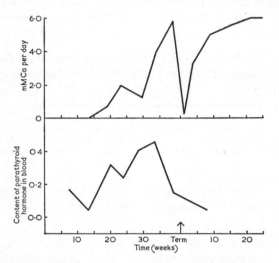

FIG. 9.3. A comparison of the calcium requirements of the foetus (*top*) and the parathyroid hormone content of the blood of the pregnant woman (*bottom*) (after [8]).

Unfortunately, the assay method used in this study was rather unreliable, involving an injection of the sample into a rabbit which was also receiving calcium by an infusion into the stomach. The quantity of parathyroid hormone in the sample was assessed by measuring the rise in the calcium content of the rabbit's blood. The results have not been checked by using more recent techniques for the isolation and estimation of parathyroid hormone, but if they are accepted at their face value, they definitely implicate the parathyroid glands as being important in mobilizing the calcium reserves of the mother, even during a normal pregnancy on a good diet. Additional evidence for this conclusion comes from investigations into the distribution of radio-isotopes fed to otherwise normally nourished rats, when it was shown that during gestation the foetus obtained about 90% of its calcium from the maternal diet and about 10% from her skeleton [25].

These experiments all suggest that the mammal has to make some adaptation in its calcium metabolism during pregnancy, and this is in keeping with the discovery that the active transport of calcium by the intestine of the rat is considerably increased during pregnancy (table 9.11). These results

Table 9.11 *The effect of pregnancy on the active transport of calcium by everted gut sacs prepared from female rats.* In vitro *experiments* [22]

Condition of rat	Weight (g)	Number of rats	Ratio calcium inside and outside gut sac
Pregnant	280–390	7	4·6 ± 1·0
Non-pregnant	240–285	7	2·0 ± 1·0

are obtained from *in vitro* experiments, and it is interesting to find that the conclusion that can be drawn from them is the same as that from balance experiments (table 9.6). This increased absorption may provide at least a partial explanation of pregnancy anabolism, although it is probably little more than just a normal response of an animal to a slight deficiency of calcium. Thus an analysis of the data from eight pregnant cows which had been treated with radio-isotopes indicated that pregnancy itself did not necessarily produce a significant increase in the intestinal absorption of calcium [5].

There is a tendency during the later stages of pregnancy for the calcium content of the mother's blood to fall [14], and this may aggravate any inclination towards hypocalcaemia. Thus, if the female is already on a diet which is deficient in calcium, the effect of pregnancy may be to exaggerate the low level of serum calcium and this may result in signs of tetany. Such occurrences are relatively rare, although they did occur in North China during the 1930s, where a number of investigations showed that much of the population had a calcium intake of only 250 mg/day. One woman on a diet containing only 170 mg Ca/day and 350 mg P/day had a serum-calcium level during her 8th month of pregnancy of only 3·6 mg %. She entered hospital in a state of tetany but responded to an adequate diet. Similar cases of tetany and osteomalacia were not uncommon in these circumstances [17].

The implications of the fall in the level of the blood calcium towards the end of gestation are not clear. It may indicate that the placenta is removing calcium from the blood at a faster rate than it can be replaced, although this seems to be unlikely, particularly when one is considering the larger mammals where the drain on the calcium reserves is relatively small. It might also indicate some activity by the mammary glands under certain circumstances, but while this may be a factor in the process, a more likely explanation comes from the observation that the diffusible level of calcium in the blood is proportionately higher in the pregnant than in the non-pregnant animal [20]. This may be possible because the level of serum proteins falls during pregnancy so that most of the fall in total calcium occurs in the non-diffusible fraction, while the diffusible calcium remains almost constant. The analyses of Andersch and Oberst [1] tend to confirm this interpretation by demonstrating that there is a good correlation between the experimental data and the redistribution of calcium which would have been expected from the fall in the level of serum proteins. This can be calculated by using the known dissociation constants for the calcium proteinate complexes of the serum (table 9.12). There is, however, the possibility of an

Table 9.12 *Changes in the concentration of serum proteins during gestation and their effect upon the level of calcium in the blood of the human* [1]

Material	Number of cases	Serum protein (g %)	Total calcium (mg %)	Filterable calcium (mg %)	Ionic calcium (calculated*) (mg %)
Non-pregnant female	8	7·22	10·5	5·2	5·0
Late pregnancy	18	6·08	9·8	5·2	5·0
Parturient female	25	6·44	10·4	5·5	5·1
Newborn (cord blood)	25	5·52	11·8	5·3	6·4

* Ionic calcium calculated by McLean and Hastings' method.

alternative explanation, for the fall in serum coincides so well with the rise in the parathyroid hormone content of the serum that it might imply a common phenomenon (figs. 9.3, 9.4). Thus they both have their greatest effect shortly before the end of pregnancy, and if these hormone analyses could be confirmed, it would imply that the fall in the total calcium of the blood did, in fact, produce a corresponding change in the concentration of ionic calcium.

If the fall in the total calcium content of the blood does indicate a depletion of the ionic calcium, one might expect dietary supplements at least partially to overcome the phenomenon. The evidence on this point is, however, rather ambivalent. Supplementing most apparently adequate diets with extra calcium and vitamin D does not overcome the fall in serum calcium which is usually interpreted as a normal and healthy occurrence during human pregnancy. The fall is, however, less likely to pass below normal levels if the pregnancy occurs during the months of greatest sunshine

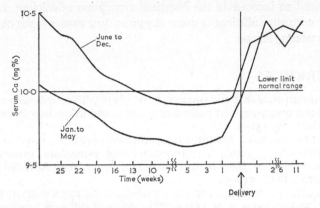

FIG. 9.4. The seasonal variations and alterations in serum calcium during human pregnancy (after [19]).

rather than during the winter (fig. 9.4), which seems to suggest that vitamin D does affect the overall situation. In the case of the pregnant ewe, there seems to be a direct correlation between the fall in blood calcium and the level of calcium in the diet (fig. 9.5).

This section may be summarized, therefore, with the comment that there is little evidence to suggest that pregnancy involves any major strain upon the calcium metabolism of the normal mammal. There may be some adaptation of the maternal body, involving a stimulation of the parathyroid

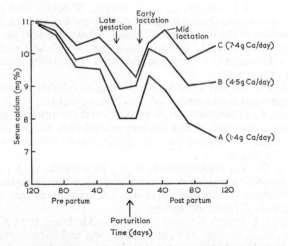

FIG. 9.5. The concentration of serum calcium in ewes during pregnancy and lactation when fed on diets containing different quantities of calcium (after [2]).

glands and an increase in the intestinal absorption of calcium, but these are not normally sufficient to cause any great disturbance to the physiology of the gestating female.

REFERENCES

[1] ANDERSCH, MARIE and OBERST, F. W. (1936), 'Filterable serum calcium in late pregnancy and parturient women, and in the new-born', *J. clin. Invest.*, **15**, 131–3.

[1a] BELANGER, L. F., ROBICHON, J., MIGICOVSKY, B. B., COPP, D. H., and VINCENT, J. (1963), 'Resorption without osteoclasts (osteolysis)', in *Mechanisms of Hard-tissue Destruction*, Amer. Ass. Adv. Sci., Washington, D.C., 531–56.

[2] BENZIE, D., BAYNE, A. W., DALGARNO, A. C., DUCKWORTH, J., HILL, R., and WALKER, D. M. (1955), 'The effect of different levels of dietary calcium during pregnancy and lactation on individual bones', *J. agric. Sci.*, **46**, 425–40.

[3] BODANSKY, M. and DUFF, VIRGINIA B. (1941), 'Effects of parathyroid deficiency and calcium and phosphorus of the diet on pregnant rats', *J. Nutr.*, **21**, 179–92.

[4] BOURDEL, G. and JACQUOT, R. (1956), 'Rôle du placenta dans les facultés anabolisantes des Rattes gestantes', *C.R. Acad. Sci., Paris*, **242**, 552–5.

[5] COMAR, C. L. (1956), 'Radiocalcium studies in pregnancy', *Ann. N.Y. Acad. Sci.*, **64**, 281–98.

[6] COONS, C. M. and BLUNT, K. (1930), 'The retention of nitrogen, calcium, phosphorus and magnesium by pregnant women', *J. biol. Chem.*, **86**, 1–16.

[7] GOSS, H. and SCHMIDT, C. L. A. (1930), 'Calcium and phosphorus metabolism in rats during pregnancy and lactation, and the influence of the reaction of the diet thereon', *J. biol. Chem.*, **86**, 417–32.

[8] HAMILTON, B., DASEL, LAURA, HIGHMAN, W. J., and SCHWARTZ, C. (1936), 'Parathyroid hormone in the blood of pregnant women', *J. clin. Invest.*, **15**, 323–6.

[9] HAMMOND, J. (1947), 'Animal breeding in relation to nutrition and environmental conditions', *Biol. Rev.*, **22**, 195–213.

[10] HART, E. B., STEENBOCK, H., SCOTT, H., and HUMPHREY, G. C. (1927), 'Dietary factors influencing calcium assimilation. 8. The calcium level and sunlight as affecting calcium equilibrium in milking cows', *J. biol. Chem.*, **71**, 263–9.

[11] HUMMEL, F. C., STERNBERGER, H. R., HUNSCHER, H. A., and MACY, I. G. (1936), 'Metabolism of women during the reproductive cycle. 7. Utilization of inorganic elements (A continuous case study of a multipara)', *J. Nutr.*, **11**, 235–55.

[12] IRVING, J. T. (1957), *Calcium Metabolism*, Methuen, 177 pp.

[13] KELLY, H. J., SLOAN, R. E., HOFFMAN, W., and SAUNDERS, C. (1951), 'Accumulation of nitrogen and six minerals in the human foetus during gestation', *Human Biol.*, **23**, 61–74.

[14] KENNY, A. D. (1961), 'Parathyroid glands and calcium metabolism', *World Rev. Nutr. Diet.*, **2**, 157–83.

[15] LEITCH, I. (1957), 'Changing concepts in the nutritional physiology of human pregnancy', *Proc. Nutr. Soc.*, **16**, 38–45.

[16] MACY, I. G., HUNSCHER, H., NIMS, B., and MCCOSH, S. S. (1930), 'Metabolism of women during the reproductive cycle. I. Calcium and phosphorus utilization in pregnancy', *J. biol. Chem.*, **86**, 17–35.

[17] MAXWELL, J. P. (1934), 'Osteomalacia and diet', *Nutr. Abst. and Rev.*, **4**, 1–8.

[18] MOUSTGAARD, J. (1962), 'Foetal nutrition in the pig', in *Nutrition of Pigs and Poultry*, eds. Morgan, J. T. and Lewis, D., Butterworth, 189–206.

[19] MULL, J. W. and BILL, A. H. (1934), 'Variations in serum calcium and phosphorus during pregnancy. I. Normal variations', *Amer. J. Obstet. Gynec.*, **27**, 510–17.

[20] NICHOLAS, H. O., JOHNSON, H. W., and JOHNSTON, R. A. (1934), 'Diffusible serum calcium in pregnancy', *Amer. J. Obstet. Gynec.*, **27**, 504–10.

[21] SALMON-LEGAGNEUR, E. and RERAT, A. (1962), 'Nutrition of the sow during pregnancy', in *Nutrition of Pigs and Poultry*, eds. Morgan, J. T. and Lewis D., Butterworth, 207–23.

[22] SCHACHTER, D., DOWDLE, E. B., and SCHENKER, H. (1960), 'Active transport of calcium by the small intestine of the rat', *Amer. J. Physiol.*, **198**, 263–8.

[23] SINCLAIR, J. G. (1942), 'Fetal rat parathyroids as affected by changes in maternal serum calcium and phosphorus through parathyroidectomy and dietary control', *J. Nutr.*, **23**, 141–52.

[24] SPRAY, CHRISTINE M. (1950), 'A study of some aspects of reproduction by means of chemical analysis', *Brit. J. Nutrit.*, **4**, 354–60.

[25] WASSERMAN, R. H., COMAR, C. L., NOLD, M. M., and LENGEMANN, F. W. (1957), 'Placental transfer of calcium and strontium in the rat and rabbit', *Amer. J. Physiol.*, **189**, 91–7.

CHAPTER 10

Mammalian Reproduction: (2) Lactation

One of the dominant features of the mammalian system of reproduction is the care of the young after birth, a phenomenon which is centred round the process of lactation. Neo-natal life is invariably a time of rapid growth with the body weight doubling in only a fraction of the time taken for gestation, while at the same time the offspring is largely or solely dependent upon the mother's milk for its nutrients. Bearing this in mind, it is not surprising to learn that the period of lactation is a time of severe strain upon the calcium metabolism of the mother. The usual sequence of events appears to be that the animal switches from the positive balance of pregnancy to a frequently prolonged period of negative balance throughout the greater part of lactation. The actual state of the calcium balance can, of course, be modified by suitable food and dietary supplements, but it seems very likely that the normal pattern of calcium metabolism involves such a negative balance after parturition.

The extent to which the strain of lactation affects the stores of nutrients in the mother's body depends on four factors. First is the actual calcium content of the milk; and this varies widely between different species. Second, there is the total volume of milk secreted per day by the mother; this being affected by both the size and the number of the offspring. Information from these two sources indicates the quantity of calcium in the milk per day and this can then be related to the overall picture determined from balance experiments. Third, there is the length of time that the young are totally dependent upon the mother, and fourth, is the all-important rate process, or the time taken for the mobilization of nutrients and their secretion in the milk. This is particularly important at the initiation of lactation, when the formation of the colostrum may give the mother little time to adapt to these new demands. Before studying each of these points separately, it should be pointed out that the human mother is rather exceptional for the small demands made on her calcium metabolism during lactation.

The Composition of Milk

Table 10.1 gives some values for the calcium content of the milk of various animals. Human milk is a relatively dilute solution of calcium when compared with that of other animals which may be up to fifteen times as con-

Table 10.1 *The calcium, phosphorus, and protein content of the milk of various animals ([6], [9], [17], [19], [20], [22], [24], [32], [33], and recalculated from [2])*

Species	Adult wt (kg)	Calcium (mg %)	Phosphorus (mg %)	Protein (g %)	Ca/P (molar ratio cf. bone 1·68)
Human	60	33	15	1·2	1·76
Horse		100	60	2·2	1·34
Cow	450	125	96	3·3	1·02
Buffalo		180	120	3·8	1·20
Goat		140	120	3·8	0·93
Pig	200	220	160	5·8	1·10
Sheep		200	150	6·0	1·07
Dog		306	204	7·1	1·20
Guinea-pig		349	272	8·1	1·03
Rat	0·250	384	226	12·0	1·36
Rabbit		517	274	13·6	1·50

centrated. Despite this, it should be realized that the calcium in human milk is at least three times as concentrated as the blood from which the mammary glands obtain it. On the same basis of comparison, rabbit milk is about fifty times as concentrated as the blood. These high concentrations of calcium do not, of course, represent ionic calcium. In cow's milk, about 67% of the calcium is present as a colloidal form of caseinate, phosphate, and citrate. Of the non-colloidal calcium, phosphoric acid is in combination with about 3% of the total calcium, citrate accounts for 18%, and 12% exists in the ionic form [20]. In the goat, 70–80% of the calcium in the milk is in combination with casein, and about 4–6% is in the ultra-filterable form [37]. The Ca/P ratio of milk is very variable, and as the two elements together form most of the skeleton of the offspring, their molar ratio is also shown in table 10.1 Bone has a Ca/P molar ratio of about 1·68. Nearly all the calcium in an animal is present in the skeleton, but considerable amounts of phosphorus are present in the soft tissues. Teleologically, therefore, one might expect milk to have ratios lower than 1·68 if there is to be maximum efficiency of utilization.

Volume of Milk Secreted per Day

The volume of milk secreted per day varies a great deal from species to species. The weight of the alimentary canal of an animal is proportional to its body weight rather than its surface [2], while the metabolic rate is generally best regarded as a function of the surface area. It follows from this that the smaller mammals have relatively smaller alimentary canals in relation to their metabolic rate than do larger animals, and these concepts are in keeping with the fact that the smaller species produce a more concentrated milk than the larger animals.

Both the composition and the volume of the milk secreted have to be known to enable one to assess the demands made by lactation, and only a limited amount of information is available in this form. The situation is

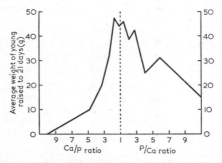

FIG. 10.1. The average weights of the offspring raised by rats fed on diets containing different ratios of calcium and phosphorus (after [8]).

made more complicated by the fact that the amount of milk produced is related to the demands made upon the mother by her offspring. This is apparent from the fact that the gain in weight of young mice is fairly constant despite variations in litter size of from 4 to 12 individuals [11], and a ewe will produce 60% more milk if she has twins instead of a single offspring [38]. In this case, both siblings survive, but never have the growth rate of single lambs. The volume of milk produced is also affected by the state of nutrition of the mother. Starving a rat for four days reduces the milk yield to zero, killing the litter, though the mother survives [2]. Similarly, varying the Ca/P ratio of the diets of lactating rats shows that there is a reduction in the weight of the litter if a large excess of either element occurs in the maternal food (fig. 10.1). The volume of milk secreted also varies throughout the period of nursing and at the start of lactation the indications are that some animals, such as the human and the guinea-pig, produce insufficient milk so that their offspring show many of the symptoms of starvation during the first few days of neo-natal life.

Some figures for the milk production of cows, humans, and pigs are

Table 10.2   *Daily loss of calcium and phosphorus in the milk of cows, pigs, and humans, (after [17], [19], [22]). Compare with the loss due to pregnancy* (table 9.5)

Species	Milk production (kg/day)	Calcium content of milk (g/day)	Calcium metabolism (mg/kg body wt/ hour)	Phosphorus content of milk (g/day)
Cow 346 (champion)	34·0	42·0	4·0	33·0
Cow 762	3·3	4·2	0·4	3·2
Pig	7·0	16·0	3·3	11·2
Human (average)	0·85	0·28	0·2	0·13
Human (high producer)	3·0	1·0	0·7	0·45

shown in table 10.2. Cow 346 is a champion milker and has ten times the loss of calcium in her milk when compared with a less prolific cow. The average value for milk production in the human is 850 mls, although many women can secrete as much as 3 litres/day. The calcium lost per day via the milk is also shown in table 10.2 for each of these instances.

Balance Experiments

Estimates of the 'calcium loss' from the body are obviously useful but incomplete when only based upon a knowledge of the calcium content and volume of secreted milk. They do not take into account the efficiency of the mammary glands, the adaptation of the body and, in particular, the effect of previous pregnancies and lactations. Balance experiments are the only readily available means of estimating these overall effects.

Medical advisors in both Britain and the United States recommend a daily intake of 0·8 g calcium for a mature adult, while the lactating woman is advised to ingest 2·0 g of calcium in her food. The increase of 1·2 g Ca/day is about four times what the average woman might be expected to lose directly via her milk, although some women with a high production of milk may approach a loss of about 1 g. The evidence available suggests that many women in the Western civilization do not have this intake of calcium during lactation. This is not, however, a matter for concern in most circumstances, for the efficiency of calcium absorption depends upon both the other constituents of the diet and the adaptation of the body to the normal diet of the subject. Thus, a Chinese wet nurse achieved calcium equilibrium on a daily intake of only 0·4 g calcium [21], and although her milk secretion was only about half that of the average Western woman, the conclusion seems justified that the calcium requirement depends very much upon the individual's physiological state (table 10.3).

I

Table 10.3 Calcium balance during lactation. Data for three Western (U.S.A.) and one Eastern (China) women maintained on normal diets. Data for two cows included for comparison. Results in mg/day (after [17], [19], [21])

Species	Human										Cow	
Subject number	VI (U.S.A.)			VII (U.S.A.)			VIII (U.S.A.)		4 (Chinese)		VI	VII
Lactation cycle	A	B		A	B		B					
Week of lactation	60	7	27	50	7	26	7	27	12	14*		
Intake	2,966	2,817	3,390	3,920	3,360	3,832	3,620	4,424	408	408	28,000	29,000
Output	2,762	3,237	5,544	3,434	3,414	4,581	4,977	6,265	686	377	37,100	30,400
Milk	577	1,239	1,295	284	706	841	474	527	154	106	6,300	9,900
Faeces	1,989	1,923	3,849	2,829	2,637	3,668	4,369	5,612	522	258	30,000	20,000
Urine	196	75	400	321	71	72	134	126	10	13	800	500
Balance	+204	-420	-2,154	+486	-54	-749	-1,357	-1,841	-278	+31	-9,100	-1,400

* Vitamin D supplement given during this and previous week.

In order to assess the effect of a calcium deficiency during lactation, Hytten and Thomson [18] assumed that in a 'hypothetical extreme instance' half of the average output of calcium in the woman's milk was obtained by resorption of her skeleton. This amounted to 0·15 g Ca/day which, during a 180-day lactation, involved a loss of about 27 g of calcium or some 2·5% of the skeleton. Such a loss is relatively small and unlikely to influence the mother's health adversely, unless pregnancy and lactation occur repeatedly without time for the body to recover its losses. If such cumulative losses do occur, they could lead to a chronic depletion of the skeleton and even some indications of tetany.

In an extended series of balance experiments, Macy and her co-workers investigated the effects of prolonged reproductive activity. A number of women were selected because they had not only had several successful pregnancies in a short time but also produced large quantities of milk. The studies were conducted in the homes while the subjects consumed their usual diets and carried on with their normal duties. Two women were studied through two consecutive lactations (A and B in table 10.3), pregnancy occurring almost immediately after the cessation of the first lactation. A third subject was studied through a single lactation cycle. Balance experiments were carried out during short periods in early, mid, and late lactation [17, 26].

The subjects were all found to be in negative calcium balance until towards the end of lactation when milk production declined (table 10.3). Faecal excretion played a dominant role in influencing the calcium balance, and at times it even exceeded the intake (e.g. subject VIII at 7 and 27 weeks; subject VI at 27 weeks; cow VI). The intake of calcium always increased after early lactation, although no instructions were given to the women on this matter. In all cases, the intake of calcium was quite high and well in excess of the loss via the urine and milk. It is to be concluded, therefore, that the alimentary canal plays a dominant role, but there appears to be a limit to the amount of calcium that can be absorbed by it. Because of this, the greater part of the calcium for the milk often has to be obtained by a resorption of the mother's bones [17]. It should be noted that the resorbed calcium may amount to as much as 1 g or more per day, so that if this continued throughout the whole of the lactation it would involve a loss of about 15% of the skeleton.

In a further study subject VII was investigated during her 4th pregnancy in 5 years [16]. This woman appeared to be particularly well adapted with regard to her calcium metabolism. She was studied for the last 145 days of pregnancy and from the 10th to 53rd days of lactation. She was on a good diet with adequate vitamin D. The results of this study (table 10.4) showed that there was a progressive decrease in the loss of calcium via the urine from a level of 0·37 g/day during pregnancy to 0·14 g/day during early lactation, and only 0·065 g/day after the 33rd day of milk production. Similar results have been obtained by other workers and interpreted as indicating an adaptation to the increased demands for calcium. During this 4th pregnancy, the mother stored 29·0 g of calcium in excess of her needs for the foetus, but about 21·0 g were lost during 43 days of lactation. This is a rate of loss of 0·5 g Ca/day and corresponds to about the rate of resorption of the skeleton of a normal adult in the absence of any physiological adaptations (Chapter 3).

Table 10.4 *Balance data on human subject VII during pregnancy and early lactation (g. Ca/day)* [16]

	Pregnancy	Lactation
Intake	3·09	3·18
Loss	2·67	3·65
Faeces	2·30	2·86
Milk	—	0·65
Urine	0·37	0·14

Calcium gained during last 145 days of pregnancy	53·0 g
Calcium in foetus	24·0 g
Therefore net gain by mother	+29·0 g
Calcium lost during 43 days of lactation	21·0 g

Similar experiments have been performed upon lactating cattle (table 10.3). In this case, it should be noted that two cows were fed identical food, but the low milk producer (cow VI) had a negative calcium balance of 9·1 g/day, while the high milk producer (cow VII) had a calcium loss of only 1·4 g/day. Again most of the loss was through the faeces. About 2% of the cow's skeleton is in the labile form, so that about 156 g of calcium are available 'exchangeable calcium'. With a negative balance of 9·1 g/day, this compartment of calcium would be depleted in 18 days, so it appears that the animal must resorb other parts of its skeletal reserves in order to maintain itself during lactation. Direct analyses of the skeletons of sheep and rats have shown that the ends and cancellous parts of the bones contributed to this calcium, the shafts being almost unaffected [1, 39]. As will be seen later, there are indications that the rate of this resorption may be critical in some instances.

One of the complications in assessing the results of balance experiments upon lactating animals is the difficulty in determining whether the changes in calcium metabolism are a true reflection of the reproductive activity.

Thus, many animals start to reproduce while they are still growing and, unless it is known that this is the animal's first litter, there is the additional possibility that the changes observed may be complicated by the continuation of a mineral deficiency from a previous period of reproduction. These objections have been overcome by using virgin rats and mice with controls of similar ages [33]. The results of such a study are shown in table 10.5. As

Table 10.5 *Composition of the bodies of rats and mice as influenced by pregnancy and lactation (calcium content in mg)* [33]

	After delivery			After lactation			Overall effect
	Control	Mother	∴ Gain	Control	Mother	∴ Loss	
Rat	2460	2490	+30	2660	2380	−310	−280
Mouse	284	343	+59	292	230	−121	−62

At end of lactation the calcium content of litter is 1,090 mg in rat and 318 mg in mouse.

Therefore, (1) Skeletal calcium lost during lactation by rat $= 12 \cdot 5 \%$

Skeletal calcium lost during lactation by mouse $= 35 \cdot 3 \%$

(2) Total calcium donated to young (as % adult skeleton) in rat $= 44 \%$

Total calcium donated to young (as % adult skeleton) in mouse $= 110 \%$

in the human, the amount of calcium stored during pregnancy is only a fraction of that which is lost during lactation. The extra calcium must, of course, be obtained from the skeleton.

The loss of calcium from the body during lactation can be reduced in the human by increasing the intestinal absorption of calcium by means of vitamin-D supplements. Cod-liver oil and yeast have been most commonly used with the results shown in tables 10.3 and 10.6. Cattle seem to

Table 10.6 *Calcium retention during lactation before and after supplementing the human diet with cod liver oil and yeast (mg/day)* [26]

Subject	VI	VII	VIII
Retention on normal diet	−33	−12	−23
Retention on diet with supplements	+7	−6	−7

be largely resistant to the effects of vitamin D in these circumstances unless massive doses are given [14]. Thus, although vitamin D may favour the reduction of a negative calcium balance during lactation, it is not normally a critical factor. The composition of rat milk is not disturbed if the diet is deficient in vitamin D, although the mothers may become severely hypocalcaemic under these conditions (table 10.17) [35].

Total Calcium Lost to the Milk during Lactation

If one assumes that the normal period of lactation in the human is about six months, then the total calcium lost by the mother represents only a small fraction of that present in her skeleton. A champion cow (*Rutger's Pogis Cutie*) can, however, secrete about eighteen times her own body weight of milk during one lactation, and a total quantity of calcium greater than that contained in her own skeleton [19]. Most of this calcium does not come from the skeleton, of course, but from ingested food. Thus, although the figures seem very large when expressed in this way, they probably do not represent too much of a drain upon the individual. Lactation, however, may be a serious strain upon the mother in the small mammals. Rats regularly lose up to 20% of their bone mass in the rearing of a litter [13], and repeated pregnancies and lactation were shown by Goss (see [30]) to be capable of removing 70% of the skeletal minerals of rats fed on a low calcium diet. These influences are demonstrated in table 10.5 where, even under normal conditions, the rat loses 12·5% and the mouse 35·3% of its skeleton during lactation. The total calcium donated by the mother (i.e. calcium from her diet + calcium from her skeleton) amounted to 44% of her total body content in the rat and 110% in the case of the mouse. Thus, the mouse is comparable to a prize Jersey cow in this respect.

Disturbances in the Rate of Calcium Metabolism – Parturient Paresis

Lactation is thought to be induced indirectly by the changes in the oestrogen and progesterone levels of the blood that occur following the delivery of the young [12]. Lactogenesis commences around the time of parturition during a period when the female body is undergoing enormous hormonal and biochemical changes. One of these changes involves a sudden variation in the rate of calcium metabolism, which may increase severalfold in the transition from gestation to lactation. If the body is unable to cope with this change, the concentration of the blood calcium temporarily falls. These changes are very clearly seen in the dairy cow, where the blood calcium falls from a normal level of about 10 mg % to about 8·5 mg % shortly after parturition. There is little doubt that this fall is due to the start of milk production, for surgical removal of the udder produces a cow whose blood calcium is virtually unaffected by parturition (table 10.7). The body normally adapts to this new rate of metabolism so that the blood calcium level returns to normal within a few days. Occasionally, however, the body appears to be unable to cope with the increased demand for calcium, so that the cow goes into a state of paralysis. This disease is called parturient paresis

Table 10.7 *Blood serum calcium (mg %) before and after parturition in cows with intact or surgically removed udders. Average values for 5 cows* [3]

	Days pre-partum			Day of parturition			Days post-partum		
	3	2	1	1–3 hrs	5–7 hrs	9–11 hrs	1	2	3
Intact	10·9	10·8	10·4	8·8	8·7	8·6	8·5	8·9	9·7
Without udder	9·9	10·4	10·3	10·2	9·9	10·3	10·7	10·9	11·0

or milk fever, and it is particularly common in Jersey cows which are producing their second or subsequent offspring. The disease is characterized by low levels of blood calcium and phosphorus, and by an increase in the magnesium content of the blood. The cow enters a state of paralysis with a

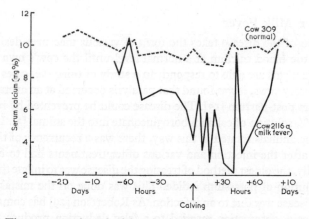

FIG. 10.2. The concentration of calcium in the blood of a normal cow as compared with one suffering from milk fever at the time of parturition (after [3]).

loss of consciousness that frequently terminates in death. Analysis of the blood during parturient paresis shows that the calcium level may fall as low as 2 mg % (fig. 10.2), presumably because the mammary glands are removing calcium from the blood to form the colostrum, at a time when it cannot be replaced quickly enough. In normal cows the extent of the fall in the level of plasma calcium is correlated with the amount of calcium secreted into the milk on the day when lactation starts (table 10.8). This

Table 10.8   *The effect of age upon the volume of milk produced and upon the level of calcium and inorganic phosphate in the plasma of cows at parturition (after [28a])*

Age of cow (years)	Plasma constituents at time of parturition		Volume and composition of milk during first day	
	Calcium (mg %)	Inorganic phosphate (mg %)	Calcium (g/24 hr)	Total phosphorus (g/24 hr)
2	9·7	4·3	6·8	7·3
3	9·0	3·6	11·7	11·5
4	8·4	3·6	15·6	18·4
5	7·8	2·8	21·8	17·7
6–7	7·2	2·3	16·3	17·3
8–14	6·9	2·3	19·3	18·8

increases with the more voluminous milk yields of the more mature animals and may account for the fact that young cows are less prone to the disease.

Cures for Milk Fever

Prevention of the disease takes the form of various measures designed to maintain the blood calcium at a normal level until the cow's own regulatory mechanisms are able to respond. In a study of thirty-six cases of milk fever in Jersey cows, it was found that paralysis occurred at an average time of 22 hours post-partum [15]. The disease could be prevented by injecting a 20–32·7% solution of calcium borogluconate into the animal [3]. In about 25% of the animals treated in this way, there was a recurrence of the fever 22 hours after the injection and various other treatments had to be used. Historically, the oldest method of treating the disease was to inflate the udder with a solution of potassium iodide. This was done on the mistaken idea that the disease was due to an infection. As Robertson [29] has commented, 'an erroneous observation married to a false deduction produced a cure for milk fever'. The treatment is successful, presumably because the inflation of the udder prevents the secretion of milk, and a variation of the original treatment is still used in cases where cows do not respond very well to the injection of calcium solutions. It is now more usual to inflate the udder with air, and the animal frequently responds within 20 hours by an increase in blood calcium of 50% and of blood phosphorus by 330% (table 10.9).

Table 10.9 *The effect of inflating the udder of a cow suffering from milk fever upon the calcium and phosphorus levels (mg %) of its blood* [3]

	Pre-inflation	Hours post-inflation								
		$\frac{1}{2}$	$1\frac{1}{2}$	3	5	8	11	14	17	20
Ca	4·2	4·6	5·0	5·1	5·5	6·0	6·2	6·4	6·5	6·6
P	1·0	1·4	1·7	1·7	2·0	2·3	2·6	3·0	3·0	3·3

Prevention of the Disease

Much work has been performed on cows in an attempt to prevent milk fever rather than have to treat the diseased animal. The obvious method of prevention would appear to be to feed mineral supplements to the cattle before parturition. This approach has not succeeded, probably because such cows are already suffering from a deficiency in their intestinal absorption of calcium.

Another cure which has been tried involves milking the cow for several days before parturition. The logic behind this practice is that the gradual initiation of lactation several days before calving would cause a less drastic demand for calcium at the critical time of delivery. An alternative practice based upon the same theory involves incomplete milking of the cow for a few days post-partum. Both methods have been singularly unsuccessful in avoiding the fall in serum calcium of normal cows at parturition or in preventing the onset of the disease (table 10.10). Thus, a better approach

Table 10.10 *The serum calcium (mg %) of normal cows after various milking treatments before and after parturition* [3]

	Days pre-partum			Day of parturition	Days post-partum		
	3	2	1		1	2	3
Milked pre-partum	10·1	10·0	9·9	8·6	8·6	9·7	10·1
Completely milked	10·2	10·3	9·9	8·3	8·4	9·1	9·6
Partially milked	10·4	10·2	9·9	8·2	8·5	9·4	10·1

would appear to be to try and stimulate the known calcium-regulating systems of the animal [4]. This has been attempted in two ways, which may be called the 'nutritional' and the 'endocrinal' approaches. According to the first theory, the disease occurs because of a deficiency in the intestinal absorption of calcium or, alternatively, because oestrogens depress the appetite [28a]. In support of these interpretations is the fact that most cows are usually in positive calcium balance at the end of pregnancy, and the ones that are not, are also often the ones that later develop milk fever [14]. The intestinal absorption of calcium can be increased by treating an animal with vitamin D, and if massive doses of 20–30 million units of this material are given to the cow a few days prior to calving, the serum-calcium level is raised and the incidence of milk fever falls (table 10.11). The action of vitamin D in an animal is fairly complex, and the

Table 10.11   *Effect of feeding various amounts of vitamin D on the serum-calcium level (mg %) of normal Jersey cows during parturition* [15]

	Pre-partum		Post-partum	
	1 week	12 hrs	12 hrs	24 hrs
Controls (no vitamin D)	10·32	9·90	8·72	8·62
10 million USP units vitamin D, 3–8 days pre-partum	10·34	10·88	9·76	9·95
30 million USP units vitamin D, 3–8 days pre-partum	11·55	12·23	11·04	11·81

elevation in serum calcium that occurs in this treatment would certainly inhibit the secretion of parathyroid hormone. It is suggested, therefore, that under these conditions the blood-calcium level is maintained through parturition purely by the absorption of this element from the intestine [15]. Opponents of this interpretation point out that the doses of vitamin D used are near the toxic level, and in such massive doses, vitamin D also has a strong osteolytic effect similar to that of the parathyroid hormone.

The endocrinal way of maintaining the serum-calcium level is by the direct stimulation of the parathyroid glands. It is known that diets with a low calcium and high phosphorus content have this effect, so it is very satisfying to find that feeding such food during pregnancy does prevent milk fever in individuals that have a history of this disease (table 10.12). Apparently this artificial stimulation of the animal's parathyroid glands starts and maintains bone mobilization at such a rate that the animal is able to survive the onset of lactation without ill-effects. Studies with radio-isotopes have confirmed this effect of low calcium and high phosphorus diets upon the skeleton. The amount of bone calcium which could be mobilized was

Table 10.12 *The effect of low calcium and high phosphorus diets upon the serum-calcium level, and incidence of milk fever in Jersey cows* [4]

Ca/P ratio of diet (by weight)	% with milk fever	Serum calcium (mg %)	
		1st day post-partum	4th day post-partum
5·9 : 1	27	8·89	9·87
1 : 1	15	8·68	9·68
1 : 3·3	0	9·53	10·18

found to be directly related to the imbalance of the diet (table 10.13). This interpretation of parturient paresis suggests that it is a form of hypoparathyroidism which is aggravated by the sudden onset of lactation. When normal cows start to calve the level of calcium in the plasma falls to about 8 mg % and it is possible, by means of a radioimmunoassay method to show that this induces a two- to three-fold increase in the concentration of circulating parathyroid hormone. Cows in milk fever show a much greater hypocalcaemia and the parathyroid hormone concentration rises five- to six-fold

Table 10.13 *Effect of the Ca/P ratio of the diet upon mobilizable calcium in the bovine skeleton. Results obtained from studies with* Ca^{45} [25]

Ca/P level of diet	Specific activity		% Mobilizable bone calcium*		
	Serum	Trabecular bone	Cortical bone	Trabecular bone	Cortical bone
1 : 7	2·9	5·6	0·51	> 100	17·0
1 : 1	2·5	3·0	0·26	100	10·0
5 : 1	2·3	2·7	0·19	100	8·3
6 : 1	2·6	2·0	0·19	77	7·3

* (Specific activity bone/specific activity serum) × 100.

[31a]. Milk fever is therefore not a typical hypoparathyroidism since the gland responds to the hypocalcaemia and releases extra hormone. Presumably there must be a loss of response to the hormone by the bone and perhaps some other target organs. This would account for the fact that some of the symptoms of the disease are not those of a typical hypoparathyroid. Thus the urinary calcium and phosphorus levels in the diseased cow remain normal instead of being decreased as in hypoparathyroidism [3]. These observations should be borne in mind when interpreting the role of the parathyroid glands in milk fever. It should also be realized, however, that

the disease also involves an aggravation of a deficiency in mineral metabolism by the process of lactation and this superimposes its own demands upon the physiology of the cow.

Comparative Aspects of 'Milk Fever'

If one accepts the usual interpretation of milk fever, namely, that it is caused by the mammary glands suddenly withdrawing calcium from the blood-stream at a faster rate than it can be replaced, then one would expect the disease to be common among other mammals. This, however, is not the case. Admittedly, not very many animals have been studied during parturition but those which have been examined show no symptoms of the disease. This being so, one either has to explain why the cow is so susceptible or why other mammals are more immune. In the case of the human, an explanation is easily found. The human colostrum is similar in composition to the mature milk of humans, i.e. it is a very dilute milk as regards calcium. In addition, the human secretes only about 20 ml of milk on the first day post-partum and only 100 ml on the second day after delivery [10], so that although the child shows some symptoms of starvation, the mother certainly is not faced with a sudden loss of calcium. In the sow the situation appears to be entirely different. An adult pig weighing 100–200 kg, produces about 7 kg milk/day, involving a loss of about 16 g Ca/day during full lactation, as opposed to a loss of about 8 g Ca/day during pregnancy. Surely one would expect some symptoms of milk fever with such a doubling of the calcium metabolism? In this case, however, the colostrum has a different composition from the mature milk of the sow, and only attains this composition after several days (table 10.14). This slow increase in the calcium

Table 10.14 *Changes in the composition of the colostrum of the sow and its transition to mature milk* [22, 23]

| | Parturition | Hours after parturition | | | | | | Mature milk |
		3	6	12	18	24	30	
Calcium (mg %)	50	50	50	60	70	80	110	220
Phosphorus (mg %)	110	110	110	110	120	120	140	160
Fat (g %)	7·2	7·3	7·8	7·2	6·9	8·7	9·3	8·1
Protein (g %)	18·9	17·5	15·2	9·2	7·2	7·3	7·0	6·1
Lactose (g %)	2·5	2·7	2·9	3·4	3·9	3·9	3·9	5·0

content of the milk could explain why milk fever is never found in the pig. Certainly the cow is in just the opposite position, for here the colostrum is actually richer in calcium than the mature milk, and yet it is produced in large quantities. This may be the reason why the disease is peculiar to that single species, for calculations show that the secretion of calcium into the colostrum occurs at a faster rate than that of calcium metabolism during pregnancy (table 10.15). Similar calculations and analyses by Payne show

Table 10.15 *Calcium content (mg %) of the colostrum and mature milk of different species. The rate of calcium metabolism necessary to form this colostrum is also calculated and compared with the maximum rate of calcium metabolism during pregnancy (table 9.5). The amount of information available is limited, but is in agreement with the suggestion that only in the cow is the rate of metabolism immediately post-partum likely to exceed that during pregnancy* [20, 27, 28]

Species	Calcium content (mg %) Colostrum	Mature milk	Volume of colostrum formed in 24 hrs post-partum	Calcium (mg/24 hrs) used in forming colostrum (C)	Maximum calcium deposition (mg/24 hrs) during pregnancy (P)	Ratio C/P
			ml			
Human	31	33	20	6	310	0·02
Pig	50	220	7,000*	3,500	9,800	0·36
Cow	170	120	9,000	15,300	10,000	1·53

* Maximum value, i.e. normal rate of flow during lactation. Colostrum certainly less than this.

that in certain circumstances the transition from pregnancy to lactation may be even more severe. He gives figures of a change from 5 g Ca/day and about 2·2 g P/day in pregnancy to 19 g Ca/day and 17 g P/day in the first day of lactation [28a].

Relationship of the Parathyroids to Lactation

It has been suggested in this chapter that the parathyroids play an intimate part in lactation; first, by being the agent by which the skeletal calcium is mobilized to overcome the effects of a negative calcium balance, and secondly, by being a rate-limiting factor that may lead to parturient paresis if the demands of the mammary glands exceed the rate of adaptation to the hormone. Further evidence for these views is provided by experiments on parathyroidectomized animals.

The rat produces a milk that contains a high concentration of calcium (table 10.1). In an extensive series of experiments, the parathyroid glands of pregnant animals were removed and the rats were fed on various diets (table 9.9, p. 104). On a very high Ca/P diet (diet No. 16), the rats maintained a high serum-calcium level, despite both parathyroidectomy and pregnancy. Normally, this diet is rachitogenic, but under these conditions it provides one of the few ways of maintaining pregnant rats, presumably because on this diet it is possible for the intestine to supply all the calcium needed by the animal. On all other diets, the serum-calcium level of the rat fell. Rats normally survive parathyroidectomy remarkably well, but it was found that whereas they frequently lived throughout their pregnancy, they died during parturition. The description of the symptoms are particularly revealing. Two to four days before term, many of the rats developed tremors of the paws which later became more pronounced, with a simultaneous stiffening of the body and tail. The rats either recovered from these attacks or followed one of two sets of symptoms. In a few, the tremors became more severe and led to tetany, unconsciousness, and death, but more commonly, the rats passed into a state of lethargy and coma. These events normally commenced after the onset of labour, and death usually occurred before the young were delivered, although in some cases the young were born after a very prolonged labour of 1–2 days, with the mother dying later [5]. Of 62 parathyroidectomized rats, 24 succumbed at the end of the first pregnancy, although they were quite normal until 2–3 days before term. Similar experiments have been performed upon dogs, although they are not such good subjects, as parathyroidectomy is normally fatal in this species. Cases are known, however, where pregnant bitches have survived the operation until term, when they have succumbed to tremors and convulsions.

Table 10.16 *The weight gain and survival in litters of rats with parathyroidectomized mothers* [7]

	Weight of offspring (g)			% Survival offspring		
	4th day	15th day	21st day	4th day	15th day	21st day
Sham operated (controls)	10·9	27·8	38·4	100	100	100
Parathyroidectomy on 4th day lactation	10·2	15·4	20·9	100	87	84

If parathyroidectomy is performed after lactation has started, there are no symptoms of tetany in the rat [7]. Instead, it is found that the young gain less weight and die more frequently than in control litters (table 10.16). This suggests that the loss of the parathyroids has a direct effect upon the secretion of milk and reduces the quantity produced. Further studies of this problem indicate that the fall in milk production is also associated with an increase in the 'calcium to total solid' ratio of the milk (table 10.17). Injecting parathyroid hormone produces the opposite effect [36]. As a working hypothesis, it is suggested that the parathyroid hormone regulates the passage of calcium from the blood to the milk, but more evidence is needed to substantiate this [35], particularly as this effect cannot be demonstrated in some cattle [34]. The composition of milk does not appear to be impaired by an absence of vitamin D from the diet of the rat, although the levels of serum calcium and phosphorus fall (table 10.17).

Table 10.17 *Calcium and phosphorus levels in milk and serum of rats under various treatments* [35]

Treatment	Serum (mg %)		Milk (mg %)		Milk Ca: total
	Ca	P	Ca	P	solid ratio (mg/g)
Sham operated	6·02	6·09	322	244	9·51
Parathyroidectomized	3·95	11·48	497	354	12·39
Diet + vitamin D	9·30	6·31	262	210	8·74
Diet − vitamin D	5·74	4·69	304	241	8·96

Lactation, then, is generally a period of negative calcium balance the severity of which will depend upon the composition and volume of milk secreted. If the young are nursed for long periods of time or if pregnancies follow each other very closely this may result in large losses of calcium from the skeletal reserves and continued stimulation of the parathyroid glands. This possibility will obviously be reduced if good dietary supplies of calcium and phosphorus are available together with vitamin D. The transition from pregnancy to lactation is, however, potentially a critical one if the demands of milk formation have not been reduced by the evolution of a decrease in either the volume or the calcium content, of the colostrum. This is perhaps the most likely explanation for parturient paresis which appears to occur in cows when there is a deficiency in the response to their parathyroid hormone system. Thus cows in milk fever appear to be unable to respond to the sudden and unusually large demand by the mammary glands for calcium ions, with the result that a hypocalcemia develops which may be fatal.

REFERENCES

[I] BENZIE, D., BAYNE, A. W., DALGARNO, A. C., DUCKWORTH, J., HILL, R., and WALKER, D. M. (1955), 'The effect of different levels of dietary calcium during pregnancy and lactation on individual bones', *J. agric. Sci.*, **46**, 425–40.

[2] BLAXTER, K. L. (1961), 'Lactation and the growth of the young', in *Milk, the Mammary Gland and Its Secretion*, eds. Kon, S. K. and Cowie, A. T., Academic Press, **2**, 305–61.

[3] BLOSSER, T. H. and ALBRIGHT, J. L. (1956), 'Urinary calcium excretion and blood calcium levels in the bovine near the time of parturition', *Ann. N.Y. Acad. Sci.*, **64**, 386–97.

[4] BODA, J. M. and COLE, H. H. (1956), 'Studies on parturient paresis in cattle', *Ann. N.Y. Acad. Sci.*, **64**, 370–4.

[5] BODANSKY, M. and DUFF, VIRGINIA B. (1941), 'Effects of parathyroid deficiency and calcium and phosphorus of the diet on pregnant rats', *J. Nutr.*, **21**, 179–92.

[6] COMAR, C. L. (1956), 'Radiocalcium studies in pregnancy', *Ann. N.Y. Acad. Sci.*, **64**, 281–98.

[7] COWIE, A. T. and FOLLEY, S. J. (1945), 'Parathyroidectomy and lactation in the rat', *Nature, Lond.*, **156**, 719–20.

[8] COX, W. M. and IMBODEN, MIRIAM (1936), 'The role of calcium and phosphorus in determining reproductive success', *J. Nutr.*, **11**, 147–76.

[9] DAVIES, J. S., WIDDOWSON, ELSIE M., and MCCANCE, R. A. (1964), 'The intake of milk and the retention of its constituents while the newborn rabbit doubles its weight', *Brit. J. Nutrit.*, **18**, 385–92.

[10] EVANS, C. L. (1952), *Principles of Human Physiology*, (Starling), Churchill, 11th edn., 1210 pp.

[11] FALCONER, D. S. (1947), 'Milk production in mice', *J. agric. Sci.*, **37**, 224–35.

[12] FOLLEY, S. J. (1956), *The Physiology and Biochemistry of Lactation*, Oliver and Boyd, 153 pp.

[13] GOSS, H. and SCHMIDT, C. L. A. (1930), 'Calcium and phosphorus metabolism in rats during pregnancy and lactation and the influence of the reaction of the diet thereon', *J. biol. Chem.*, **86**, 417–32.

[14] HART, E. B., STEENBOCK, H., KLINE, O. L., and HUMPHREY, G. C. (1930), 'Dietary factors influencing calcium assimilation. 13. The influence of irradiated yeast on the Ca and P metabolism of milking cows', *J. biol. Chem.*, **86**, 145–55.

[15] HIBBS, J. W. and POUNDER, W. D. (1956), 'Effect of parturient paresis and the oral administration of large prepartial doses of vitamin D on the blood calcium and phosphorus in dairy cattle', *Ann. N.Y. Acad. Sci.*, **64**, 375–85.

[16] HUMMEL, F. C., STERNBERGER, H. R., HUNSCHER, H. A., and MACY, I. G. (1936), 'Metabolism of women during the reproductive cycle. 7. Utilization of inorganic elements (A continuous case study of a multipara)', *J. Nutr.*, **11**, 235–55.

[17] HUNSCHER, HELEN A. (1930), 'Metabolism of women during the reproductive cycle. 2. Calcium and phosphorus utilization in two successive lactation periods', *J. biol. Chem.*, **86**, 37–57.

[18] HYTTEN, F. E. and THOMSON, A. M. (1961), 'Nutrition of the lactating woman', in *Milk, the Mammary Gland and Its Secretion*, eds. Kon, S. K. and Cowie, A. T., Academic Press, **2**, 3–87.

[19] KLEIBER, M. and LUICK, J. R. (1956), 'Calcium and phosphorus transfer in intact dairy cows', *Ann. N.Y. Acad. Sci.*, **64**, 299–313.

[20] LING, E. R., KON, S. K., and PORTER, J. W. G. (1961), 'The composition of milk and the nutritive value of its components', in *Milk, the Mammary Gland and Its Secretion*, eds. Kon, S. K. and Cowie, A. T., Academic Press, 2, 195–263.

[21] LIU, S. H., SU, C. C., WANG, C. W., and CHANG, K. P. (1937), 'Calcium and phosphorus metabolism in osteomalacia. 6. The added drain of lactation and beneficial action of vitamin D', *Chin. J. Physiol.*, 11, 271–94.

[22] LODGE, G. A. (1962), 'The nutrition of the lactating sow', in *Nutrition of Pigs and Poultry*, eds. Morgan, J. T. and Lewis, D., Butterworth, 224–37.

[23] LUCAS, I. A. M. (1962), 'Aspects of the nutrition of young pigs', in *Nutrition of Pigs and Poultry*, eds. Morgan, J. T. and Lewis, D., Butterworth, 238–254.

[24] LUCKEY, T. D., MENDE, T. J., and PLEASANTS, J. (1954), 'The physical and chemical characterization of rats' milk', *J. Nutr.*, 54, 345–59.

[25] LUICK, J. R., BODA, J. M., and KLEIBER, M. (1957), 'Some biokinetic aspects of calcium metabolism in dairy cows', *Amer. J. Physiol.*, 189, 483–8.

[26] MACY, ICIE G., HUNSCHER, HELEN A., MCCOSH, SYLVIA S., and NIMS, BETTY (1930), 'Metabolism of women during the reproductive cycle. 3. Calcium, phosphorus and nitrogen utilization in lactation before and after supplementing the usual home diets with cod liver oil and yeast', *J. biol. Chem.*, 86, 59–74.

[27] MACY, ICIE G. and KELLY, HARRIET J. (1961), 'Human milk and cows' milk in infant nutrition', in *Milk, the Mammary Gland and Its Secretion*, eds. Kon, S. K. and Cowie, A. T., Academic Press, 2, 265–304.

[28] PARRISH, D. B., WISE, G. H., HUGHES, J. S., and ATKESON, F. W. (1950), 'Properties of the colostrum of the dairy cow. 5. Yield, specific gravity and concentrations of total solids and its various components of colostrum and early milk', *J. Dairy Sci.*, 33, 457–65.

[28a] PAYNE, J. M. (1964), 'Recent advances in our knowledge of milk fever', *Vet. Rec.*, 16, 1275–79.

[29] ROBERTSON, A., MARR, A., and MOODIE, E. W. (1956), 'Milk fever', *Vet. Rec.*, 68, 173–80.

[30] SCHMIDT, C. L. A. and GREENBERG, D. M. (1935), 'Occurrence, transport and regulation of calcium, magnesium and phosphorus in the animal organism', *Physiol. Rev.*, 15, 297–434.

[31] SHERMAN, H. C. and QUINN, E. J. (1926), 'The phosphorus content of the body in relation to age, growth and food', *J. biol. Chem.*, 67, 667–77.

[31a] SHERWOOD, L. M., POTTS, J. T., CARE, A. D., MAYER, G. P., and AURBACH, G. D. (1966), 'Evaluation by radioimmunoassay of factors controlling the secretion of parathyroid hormone', *Nature, Lond.*, 209, 52–5.

[32] SPECTOR, W. S. (ed.) (1956), *Handbook of Biological Data*, Saunders, 584 pp.

[33] SPRAY, CHRISTINE M. (1950), 'A study of some aspects of reproduction by means of chemical analysis', *Brit. J. Nutrit.*, 4, 354–60.

[34] TODD, A. S., FOSGATE, O. T., CRAGLE, R. G., and KAMAL, T. H. (1962), 'Parathyroid action on calcium, phosphorus, magnesium, and citric acid in dairy cattle', *Amer. J. Physiol.*, **202**, 987–90.

[35] TOVERUD, S. U. (1963), 'Calcium–vitamin D–parathyroid interrelationships in lactating rats', in *The Transfer of Calcium and Strontium across Biological Membranes*, ed. Wasserman, R. H., Academic Press, 341–58.

[36] TOVERUD, S. U. and MUNSON, P. L. (1956), 'The influence of the parathyroids on the calcium concentration of milk', *Ann. N.Y. Acad. Sci.*, **64**, 336.

[37] TWARDOCK, A. R., PRINZ, W. H., and COMAR, C. L. (1960), 'The state of calcium and strontium in goats' milk', *Arch. Biochim. Biophys.*, **89**, 309–12.

[38] WALLACE, L. R. (1948), 'The growth of lambs before and after birth in relation to the level of nutrition', *J. agric. Sci.*, **38**, 93–153.

[39] WARNOCK, G. M. and DUCKWORTH, J. (1944), 'Changes in the skeleton during gestation and lactation in the rat', *Biochem. J.*, **38**, 220–4.

CHAPTER 11

Mammalian Reproduction: (3) Calcium Metabolism of the Foetus and Newborn

The ossification of the foetal bones progresses rapidly during the latter part of gestation. The actual degree of ossification of the newborn animal varies with both the chronological age and the weight of the offspring, but predominantly with the latter (fig. 11.1). The demands made by the foetus

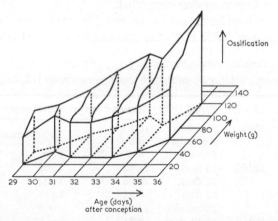

FIG. 11.1. The degree of ossification of the limb-bones of newborn rabbits. The extent of mineralization varies with both the chronological age and the weight of the foetus (after [2]).

upon the calcium metabolism of the mother are normally easily met from her diet and skeletal stores. There are, however, two aspects of mammalian reproduction which we have not yet considered, and which may be important factors in limiting the rate of bone formation. These are the efficiency of the placenta and of the mammary glands in meeting the requirements of the offspring.

Calcium Transport Across the Placenta

There is abundant experimental evidence to demonstrate that the placenta does not act simply as a passive barrier between the foetal and maternal blood-streams but that it modifies the rate of movement of various substances across its cellular layers. Substances such as the respiratory gases pass across the placenta by simple diffusion, but many metabolites are actively transported from the maternal to the foetal side of this organ. It is generally considered that calcium ions fall into this second category of substances. This view can be readily traced back to the tables of compiled data which Needham published in 1931 in the stimulating volumes of his *Chemical Embryology* [25]. It was clearly shown that in the human, cow, pig, and dog there is a higher concentration of calcium in foetal blood than in the maternal circulation. It has been implied from this data that as the foetal serum contains about 2 mg % more calcium than does the mother, the placenta must be involved in passing calcium ions into the foetal bloodstream against a concentration gradient; a phenomenon which would indicate active transport. This conclusion may be correct, but the reasoning which led to it is certainly over-simplified.

There is good evidence that in the cow (fig. 10.2), ewe (fig. 9.5), rat, rabbit, and human (table 11.1), the concentration of total calcium in the

Table 11.1 *Calcium concentration (mg %) of maternal and foetal blood of the human, rabbit, rat, and sheep during pregnancy* [18, 20, 23, 24, 29]

Species	Period	Maternal serum	Foetal serum
Man	8 months	10·1 ⎫	9·0 (premature)
	9 months	9·8 ⎭	
	Parturition	9·6	11·0
Rabbit	23 days	14·52	12·08
	24 days	12·66	13·44
	26 days	8·44	14·70
	Parturition	14·25	12·16
Rat	19–21 days	8·81	—
	Parturition	10·16	—
Sheep*	70 days	6·1	7·6
	124 days	6·1	8·2
	144 days	6·7	9·0

* Values for sheep are for 'Ca + Mg'.

maternal serum declines during the latter part of pregnancy. The full significance of this phenomenon is not clear, but it may be related to a dilution of the blood and a fall in the concentration of serum proteins in the maternal circulation (table 9.12). There are indications that the opposite trend occurs in the foetus, but this is again complicated, as will be seen later, by the fact that blood samples are usually only taken from the umbilical vein. The serum calcium concentration also tends to rise towards the end of foetal life, so that premature infants are frequently found to have lower serum-calcium levels than full-term offspring (table 11.1). This has been correlated with the high concentration of adrenocorticosteroids in the maternal circulation during the latter part of gestation and the suggestion that these hormones depress the level of serum calcium in the foetus during the 7th and 8th months of pregnancy [15]. Alternatively, Bodansky and Duff related the fall in the serum-calcium level of the mother and its rise after parturition with the opposite movement of the calcium content of the foetal serum. They suggested that the placenta influenced the blood by producing a calcium-depressing factor in the mother and a calcium-elevating factor in the foetus. This accounted for the changes during gestation and, with the loss of the placenta at parturition, the reversal of these effects [4]. There is little direct evidence for either of these theories, but they do raise the possibility that the usual experimental practice of comparing the serum of the parturient adult with the serum in the umbilical cord of the newborn animal may give a totally unrepresentative picture of the relationship of calcium between the two blood-streams during the greater part of pregnancy.

If calcium is actively moved across the placenta, it is probably transported in the ionic form. This being the case, the evidence for active transport should be based upon the occurrence of a higher concentration of ionic calcium on the foetal side of the placenta. The early work on this question was inconclusive with different techniques first suggesting that the foetal and then the maternal blood had a greater content of ionic calcium. More recent evidence seems to indicate that the two blood-streams have a similar content of diffusible calcium, although the total calcium is higher in the foetal than maternal circulation (table 11.2). This, as we have previously

Table 11.2 *Diffusible calcium (mg %) in maternal and foetal blood of the human* [1, 24]

	Total calcium	Diffusible calcium
Maternal	10·2	8·0
Umbilical cord	12·2	7·9
Maternal	10·4	5·5
Umbilical cord	11·8	5·3

seen, has been interpreted as demonstrating that the foetal serum proteins have a stronger ability to bind calcium than does the maternal blood, so that the foetus competes with the maternal system for calcium ions. This interpretation explains the higher total calcium content of the foetal blood without recourse to the concept of active transport by the placenta. Much more information is necessary before one can reach any definite conclusion, however, for although comparative studies of the dog, pig, and cow show that the developing foetus has a considerably higher concentration of serum calcium than does the mother, in the rabbit the situation is reversed (tables 11.1, 11.3).

Table 11.3   *Calcium concentration (mg %) of foetal and maternal blood in various pregnant animals* [10, 17, 18, 28]

Species	Maternal serum	Foetal serum
Dog (54 days)	11·9	< 13·6
Dog (54 days)	10·2	< 14·1
Pig (46 days)	11·2	< 17·6
Sheep (144 days)*	6·6	< 9·0
Cow	13	< 16
Rabbit (21 days)	15·7	> 13·0

* Values for the sheep are for 'Ca + Mg'.

There is little doubt that the placenta is the main avenue by which calcium enters the foetus. The analyses of a large number of human offspring showed that the calcium content of the blood in the umbilical artery averaged 10·86 mg %, while the blood leaving the placenta in the umbilical vein averaged 11·78 mg Ca % [29]. It thus appears that the blood of the human foetus can take up calcium as it passes through the placenta, but the method by which this occurs is not definitely known. A similar uptake could not be demonstrated in the foetal sheep, although the experimental conditions were rather different [18].

The classical studies of Flexner [12] showed a striking difference in the permeability of the various different types of placenta to sodium ions. The relatively complex epitheliochorial placenta of the pig allows sodium ions to pass across it at less than a hundredth of the rate shown by the thinner haemochorial placenta of man or the rat. As we shall see shortly, it is unlikely that a similar correlation exists between the structure of the placenta and the rate of transfer of calcium ions across it. This therefore implies some sort of preferential transfer system for calcium, not unlike that postulated in active transport.

In a series of interesting experiments, Comar and his associates have studied the passage of the radio-isotopes of calcium and strontium across the placenta. After injecting Ca^{45} into the pregnant cow, they found that the radio-isotope was partitioned between several competing systems. These were:

I A general mixing of the isotope with the body fluids together with deposition in the maternal soft tissues.
II Deposition in the bones of the mother.
III Transfer across the placenta to the foetal circulation followed by a deposition in the foetal soft tissues and bone.

The rate of distribution of the isotope was initially in the order (I) > (II) > (III). The Ca^{45} rapidly entered the foetal circulation and was easily detected 10 min after the injection, but the specific activity of the foetal blood was considerably lower than that of the mother even after 8 hours [28].

A more detailed analysis was performed upon the rat by raising the animals on a diet containing equal parts of strontium and calcium. The females were then mated, and after parturition, the litter and the mother were killed and analysed for strontium and calcium. The ratio of Sr/Ca in the maternal skeleton was 0·29 while the skeleton of her offspring had a ratio of 0·20. Clearly, the foetus was showing a preference for calcium, and further experiments were performed to try to determine the site of this discrimination [34]. Towards this end, an equimolar mixture of Ca^{45} and Sr^{89} was injected into either the pregnant rat or into her foetuses. The animals were killed after 24 hours and the bodies were analysed for the radio-isotopes. When the injection was made into the mother, 39% of the Ca^{45} and 20% of the Sr^{89} was found in the foetus. When the injection was made into the foetus, 26% of the Ca^{45} and 34% of the Sr^{89} was found in the mother. If a few simplifications and assumptions are made, it is possible to obtain some indication of the movements of these ions across the placenta.

First, it should be realized that the 26% of the Ca^{45} that was found in the mother after injecting the foetus with the radio-isotopes represented the net transfer of calcium across the placenta. Thus some of the calcium that left the foetus and entered the maternal blood-stream will have returned to the placenta and re-entered the foetus. In fact, from the experiments where Ca^{45} was injected into the mother, it appears that 39% of the maternal Ca^{45} passes into the foetus. Thus, a crude estimate of the gross movement of Ca^{45} across the placenta from foetus to dam is $(26 \times 100)/(100 - 39) = 43\%$. A similar estimate of the movement of calcium from dam to foetus gives a value of 53% gross, of which 14% moved back leaving 39% net. Estimates for the movement of Sr^{89} from foetus to dam are 43% gross or 34% net, and for the passage from dam to foetus 30% gross or 20% net. These values are obviously only approximate, but they show that the ratio of Ca^{45}/Sr^{89} moving from foetus to dam is 1·00, while for dam to foetus it is 1·76. In other words, the placenta shows little discrimination between the movement of Ca^{45} and Sr^{89} in the direction from the foetus to the mother, but it does discriminate with a preference for calcium in the movement of ions from the mother to the foetus. Such evidence is not conclusive, but the preferential movement of Ca^{45} as opposed to Sr^{89} would be in keeping with an active transport of calcium across the placenta into the foetus [34].

The same conclusion may be reached from experiments with the rabbit. A mixture of Ca^{45} and Sr^{85} was injected into the pregnant animal and the average level of these ions in the foetus and the mother was determined. The results are given in table 11.4 and show that the ratio in the foetus as compared with that in the mother was 2·8/1·3 or 2·1 in favour of calcium. A discrimination against Sr^{85} in favour of Ca^{45} has also been demonstrated in the placentae of the sheep and the human [6].

It is possible to calculate from the figures given in table 11.4 the rate at which calcium passes across the placenta in relation to the rate of

Table 11.4 *The transfer of Ca^{45} and Sr^{85} across the placenta of the rabbit. Results in brackets refer to range of data* [34].

Foetal weight (fresh)	$23 \pm 1·7$ g
Foetal ash (% fresh wt)	$16·3 \pm 0·3$
Calcium content (mg) foetus	80 ± 5
Average level Ca^{45} maternal plasma	0·11% dose/ml
Average level Sr^{85} maternal plasma	0·11% dose/ml
Ca^{45} transferred to foetus	2·8% dose
Sr^{85} transferred to foetus	1·3% dose
Calcium content maternal plasma	13·4 mg %
Total calcium crossing placenta (mg Ca/total foetal load/min)	$0·12 \pm 0·01$
Calcium transferred/day/foetus	24·3 mg (14·4 → 34·3)
Calcium accretion/day/foetus	13·5 mg (11·4 → 16·2)
Safety factor	1·8 (1·3 → 2·1)
Sr^{85}/Ca^{45} in maternal plasma	1·01
Sr^{85}/Ca^{45} in foetus	0·49

calcium accretion by the rabbit foetus. Average values show that each foetus receives about 24·3 mg Ca/day across the placenta while it uses about 13·5 mg Ca/day. Dividing 'the supply' by 'the requirements' gives what has been defined as the safety factor; in this case 1·8. The extent of this safety factor appears to vary to some extent with the size of the litter. The highest values occurred with a small litter of 7 when each foetus was laying down 16·2 mg Ca/day and receiving 34·3 mg Ca/day; a safety factor of 2·1. In a rabbit with a litter of 13 foetuses, two of which were undergoing resorption, each embryo received 14·4 mg Ca/day and laid down 11·4 mg Ca/day; a safety factor of only 1·3. The size of the safety factor also varies with the time of gestation and in the rhesus monkey it is estimated to be about 6 for the 124-day-old foetus and up to 10 in the 153-day-old animal [19]. In the guinea-pig, which like the rabbit has a haemochorial type of placenta, it has been shown that the transfer of phosphate across the placenta may have a safety factor of only 1·0. The safety factor is not, however, an absolute physiological entity but rather a convenient way of visualizing the normal events in relation to the rate at which calcium or other ions pass back and forth across the placenta in relation to the speed at which they are used. Thus, although the safety factors are of considerably interest, there is no reason to think that they may not be modified if, for example, the demand for calcium increased.

The transfer of sodium ions across the placentae of a variety of mammals shows a direct correlation with the number of cellular layers in the organ (table 11.5). Thus, the multi-layered epitheliochorial placenta of the sow

Table 11.5 *Sodium transfer across the mammalian placenta (after [13] from various sources)*

Species	Placental type	Sodium transferred (mg/placenta/hr)	Safety factor
Pig	Epitheliochorial	0·026	3·5
Goat	Syndesmochorial	0·41	100
Cat	Endotheliochorial	0·69	39
Guinea-pig	Haemochorial	6·1	60
Rabbit	Haemochorial	6·8	39
Man	Haemochorial	4·0 − 7·0	1100

has a low transfer rate and a low safety factor. The thin haemochorial placenta of man and the rabbit has a high rate of transfer for sodium ions and a correspondingly large safety factor. It is obvious that the transfer of calcium ions is not going to give a similar series, for the haemochorial placenta has a safety factor of only 1 to 2. Thus the absence of a correlation between structure and permeability again suggests that calcium is actively transported across the placenta.

The indication that the transfer of calcium across the placenta has such a low safety factor needs to be confirmed in other animals. At the moment it looks as if it could be a limiting factor in the supply of calcium and phosphorus to the foetus, particularly in an animal such as the sow which has quite a large turnover of calcium during pregnancy and forms an epitheliochorial placenta. In this respect some interesting observations have been made upon the concentration of calcium in the foetal membranes of this animal (table 11.6). The amniotic fluid has a relatively constant composi-

Table 11.6   *Calcium content of various foetal membranes and fluids* [10]

Species and foetal age	Amniotic fluid (mg %)	Allantoic fluid (mg %)	Tissues (mg/100 g)	
Human				
84–182 days	—	—		
105 days	7·7	—	Amniochorion	143
119–126 days	7·35	—		
Term	8·0	—	Amniochorion	14·2
Pig				
19–21 days	—	5·83	Endometrium	9·3
			Chorio-allantois	9·9
46 days	9·69	29·7	Endometrium	10·6
			Amniochorio-allantois	123
Term	—	—	Placenta	60·8
Rabbit				
21 days	10·9	26·2	Amnion	99·7
			Allantois	28·1

tion both during development and from one species to another. This is not so for the allantoic fluid, where both the rabbit and the pig show an accumulation of calcium. The high concentration of calcium appears to be maintained in solution by the presence of considerable quantities of citric acid. It has been suggested that the allantoic fluid is a product of the foetal mesonephros [8], but it may be formed in other ways or at least modified by the activity of the foetal membranes. The chorio-allantois of the pig can certainly transfer sodium outwards to the maternal tissues and this may be related to the movement of calcium ions in the opposite direction [7]. Thus, large potentials exist across the placenta with the foetal side being negative, and this could provide an electrochemical gradient for the movement of calcium [35a]. Certainly a high concentration of calcium occurs in the pig chorio-allantois from the 21st to 46th days of gestation. This deposition of calcium is a temporary phenomenon and it disappears later as the rate of calcium utilization increases, so that the concentration may be quite low at term. Thus the deposition of calcium in the placenta of the pig appears to be a transient store associated with the transport of calcium to the foetus. Similar stores occur in the placentae of deer and sheep and they are also resorbed as the foetuses develop [37]. In this they differ from the deposits of calcium which occur in the placentae of, for example, the human, cat, or rodent, where the mineral deposits only occur towards term and are usually interpreted as signs of degeneration. There is another reason for considering that the transport of calcium across the placenta of the pig may be a critical factor in the development of the foetus. Analyses of the skeleton of the foetus show that the degree of mineralization of the bones, as measured by the ratio of Ca/N falls after about 65 days of gestation and only starts to increase again after birth (table 11.7). The full significance

Table 11.7 *The degree of mineralization of the humerus (as measured by the ratio Ca/N) of the pig during gestation and lactation* [9]

Period	Ca/N
46 days gestation	1·39
65 days gestation	3·40
90 days gestation	3·06
Newborn	2·57
20–45 days	2·75
65–143 days	3·83
1 year	4·32

of changes in the ratio of Ca/N in bones is still being discussed [37], but it appears that in the pig foetus the growth of the skeleton may outstrip the supply of calcium coming across the placenta [9]. Thus the placenta is obviously important in affecting the entry of metabolites into the foetus, but it also performs a number of other functions. One of these is the isolation of the foetal regulatory mechanisms from those of the mother. This is particularly well demonstrated with the parathyroid hormone and its relation to calcium metabolism. The histology of the parathyroid glands of the foetus have been studied in detail in the human. The cells differentiate at an early stage, and it has been suggested that they show signs of endocrine activity by the middle of the gestation period [26]. Numerous workers have noted, however, that pregnancy does not protect the mother from the effects of parathyroidectomy, which indicates either that the amount of hormone produced by the foetus is very small or that it does not enter the maternal circulation.

In the pregnant rat it can be shown that the size of the maternal parathyroid glands can be increased or decreased, depending upon the availability of calcium in the diet. On a calcium-deficient diet, the glands almost double in size, but the size of the parathyroids of the foetus are unaffected. If a calcium-rich diet is fed to the mother, the foetal parathyroids decrease in size (table 9.10). The simplest interpretation of this data is that the para-thyroid hormone does not pass across the placenta, for when the glands are large and apparently very active in the mother, they are unaffected in the foetus. When the calcium level of the mother's serum is high, the foetal parathyroids are suppressed. Apparently hypercalcaemia is transmitted to the foetus, but hyperparathyroidism is not. If the parathyroid glands are removed from the mother and the level of her serum calcium falls, the foetal parathyroids are then stimulated. Similar conclusions may be reached from experiments on the injection of parathyroid hormone into the circu-lation of either the pregnant bitch or her foetuses [17]. When 80 units of parathyroid extract were injected into the bitch, it produced a typical ele-vation of the calcium content of the mother's serum (table 11.8). If one

Table 11.8   *The effect of injecting parathyroid extract into the circulation of either the pregnant bitch or her foetuses* [17]

Stage of pregnancy (days)	Dog number	Maternal weight (kg)	Foetal weight (g)	Dose given (units)	Serum calcium (mg %)			
					Injected foetus	Non-injected foetus	Bitch before treat-ment	Bitch after injection
Injection into foetus								
Near term	1	12·1	145	120	18·2	12·6	11·1	11·3
					14·8	12·1		
					16·2	12·5		
					18·4			
54	2	16·7	77	100	17·2	13·8	11·9	12·0
					18·6	13·6		
					17·3	13·6		
Injection into mother								
56	6	8·5	154	80		13·5	9·9	15·7
						13·6		
						14·3		
						13·8		
54	7	9·5	210	80		14·4	10·2	15·6
						14·0		
						12·9		
						15·0		

assumes that normally the foetal serum is about 2 mg % more concentrated than the maternal serum (as in dogs 1 and 2), then the normal level of foetal calcium in dog 7 should be 12·2 mg %. When the bitch was killed and the foetus examined 24 hours after the injection of the hormone, the foetal serum had an average content of 14·1 mg Ca %. The interpretation could be that, after the injection, either the hormone or the calcium passed in increasing amounts from the serum of the bitch to that of the foetus. In view of the experiments on the rat, the second hypothesis must be favoured. When the hormone is injected into the foetus, the calcium level of the serum rises to a very high level, although the serum of the bitch is unaffected. As the quantity of hormone injected into the foetus was even greater than that previously given to the mother the fact that the adult did not respond must mean that the hormone did not enter the bitch's circulation to any appreciable extent. Thus it would appear that although the foetus receives its calcium across the placenta, and an increase in the content of the maternal serum produces a corresponding increase in the foetal serum (table 11.9),

Table 11.9 *The serum-calcium level (mg %) of the human foetal circulation is greater than that of the mother, but related to it. Data show values for serum calcium in the two circulations* [22]

Venous blood of mother (range)	8·5 → 8·99	9·0 → 9·49	9·5 → 9·99	10·0 → 10·49
Cord blood of foetus (average)	10·32	10·83	11·58	11·86

the two systems are regulated separately, since parathyroid hormone does not cross the placenta to any extent in either direction.

Calcium Metabolism of the Newborn

The dependence of the mammalian offspring on its mother for nutrients does not end with the loss of the placenta, for parturition is followed by nursing and the young are again largely dependent upon their mother for food which thus again affects their skeletal growth.

In most adult mammals, the soft tissues, when freed of fat, have a constant and similar composition. The skeleton differs in constitution as it is mainly calcium phosphate, but it also has a constant composition, so that the variations in the proportions of different elements in the bodies of different species of mammals are fairly small. Those variations which do occur are mainly due to differences in the ratio of skeletal to soft tissue weight [21]. There is, in fact, a characteristic chemical composition for the fat-free adult mammal. The foetus and newly born animal do not share this constancy of composition, and Moulton has developed the concept of 'chemical maturity' to denote the attainment of the adult state. Thus, the rat reaches 'chemical maturity' after 50 days, the cat after 100, and the pig after 300 days, so that at the end of these periods the young of these species have attained the composition of a typical adult mammal. There are obvious exceptions to this generalization and, in particular, it has been shown that the same animal reaches chemical maturity at different times for different elements [32]. Nevertheless, it is a useful concept for comparing the composition of different species at birth. It can be seen from table 11.10 that

Table 11.10   *The composition of fat-free mammals at birth in relation to the adult composition and the concept of 'chemical maturity' (after [3], from various sources)*

Species	Water (g %)	Protein (g %)	Calcium (mg %)	Phosphorus (mg %)
Mouse	85	12·8	340	343
Rat	87	10·9	306	356
Guinea-pig	79	16·5	1,131	741
Rabbit	87	11·3	484	361
Cat	82	15·2	661	436
Pig	80	20·0	999	739
Cow	76	18·4	1,180	—
Man	82	14·1	955	558
Average adult mammal	73	21·0	1,300	750

the cow and guinea-pig produce offspring with a relatively great chemical maturity. Man and the pig are intermediate, and the rabbit, rat, and mouse are decidedly immature. The subject has been well reviewed by Blaxter [3], who points out that a high degree of chemical maturity is generally associa-

Table 11.11   *Chemical maturity of the newborn mammal in relation to the length of gestation and lactation (after [3], from various sources)*

Species	Chemical maturity (based upon protein concentration in the young as % of typical adult value) (%)	Duration pregnancy (P) (days)	Duration lactation (L) (days)	L/P
Rat	52	22	28	1·3
Rabbit	54	30	30	1·0
Mouse	61	21	21	1·0
Man	67	280	180	0·6
Cat	72	56	50	0·9
Pig	76	115	56	0·5
Guinea-pig	79	65	12	0·2
Cow	88	278	60	0·2

ted with a short period of lactation relative to the time of gestation (table 11.11). From this it might be inferred that the composition of the milk of one type of animal is closely related to the needs of the offspring of that particular species. To some extent this is true. The protein and ash content of milk are greater in the faster-growing species than in slower-maturing animals (table 11.12), although there is reason to think that the normal

Table 11.12   *The growth rate of the offspring in relation to the composition of the milk* [3]

Species	Time in days for offspring to double birth weight	Milk content protein (g %)	Ash (g %)
Man	180	1·6	0·2
Horse	60	2·0	0·4
Ox	47	3·5	0·7
Goat	19	4·3	0·8
Sheep	10	6·5	0·9
Dog	8	7·1	1·3
Rat	6	12·0	2·0
Rabbit	6	14·0	2·2

method of nursing is not necessarily the best way of ensuring an optimum rate of growth of the young. Whether maximum growth is of maximum advantage to the offspring is a matter of controversy. The question is not, however, simply an academic one, because for various reasons a large number of civilized humans have taken to feeding their offspring on the milk of other species. The cow is the usual choice, and since this animal produces a milk which is much richer in almost all its components than human milk, it might be expected to produce some changes in the rate of development of the bottle-fed infant as opposed to the breast-fed child. The phenomenon has been investigated in some detail, so that it provides a unique source of information on the question of the extent to which the physiology of the offspring is dependent upon or adapted to the physiology of its mother's mammary glands.

During the first few days after birth, the human baby which is being

Table 11.13   *Average weight of milk secreted by the human in the days after delivery* [11]

Day	1	2	3	4	5	6	7	200
Milk secreted (g)	20	97	211	326	364	402	478	950

breast-fed receives very little milk (table 11.13). The serum-calcium level of the offspring falls during this period (fig. 11.2) while the phosphorus content tends to rise if the fasting continues for more than 36 hours [5]. This is normally interpreted as indicating tissue resorption in response to

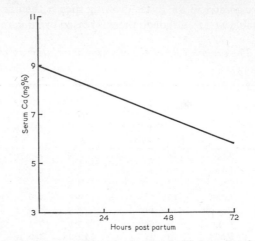

FIG. 11.2. The level of serum calcium in the blood of infants in relation to the time between birth and their first feeding (after [5]).

starvation [36]. After the first few days of this minimal nutrition, the baby begins to receive more and more human milk. The serum-calcium level then begins to rise, while the phosphorus content normally falls (table 11.14). As

Table 11.14 *The concentration of calcium and inorganic phosphorus (mg %) in the serum of the umbilical cord and/of the human infant on different diets* [5]

	Cord blood	Infant with no food	Infant fed cow's milk	Infant fed human milk
Serum calcium	10·59	7·99	8·49	8·99
Serum phosphorus	6·62	7·29	8·27	6·82

the body grows, the rate of formation and ossification of the bones does not keep pace with the development of the rest of the body, so that the percentage of calcium in the body actually falls for a period of several months (fig. 11.3). This has been interpreted as being due to an inadequate intake of minerals, and Stearns commented that 'studies of the relation between calcium intake and retention indicate that a direct relation exists between the two at all levels of milk intake studied and offer no evidence that the maximum possible retention of calcium has been attained at any stage during infancy' [33]. In support of this, it was calculated that the percentage composition of the bottle-fed baby indicated a much greater retention of calcium than in the breast-fed baby. Thus feeding cow's milk, with its higher content of calcium and phosphorus, reduces or completely overcomes [30] the fall in the percentage of calcium in the newborn infant (fig. 11.3). This effect is probably not due solely to a greater intake of calcium but

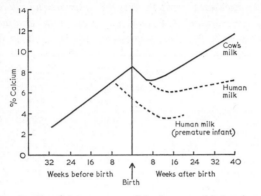

FIG. 11.3. Changes in the calcium content of the foetus and infant in relation to their time of birth and diet (after [33]).

rather to a variety of causes as more detailed balance experiments have shown. Both the breast-fed human and the suckling piglet excrete only traces of phosphorus in their urine, while other newborn animals, such as the kitten and calf, excrete large amounts of phosphorus but only small amounts of calcium (table 11.15). This strongly suggests that a deficiency

Table 11.15 *The concentration of calcium and phosphorus (mg %) in the urine of suckling animals in relation to the composition of the mother's milk* [36]

Species	Milk			Urine		
	Calcium	Phosphorus	Ca/P	Calcium	Phosphorus	Ca/P
Human infant	33	15	2·2	4·4	0·4	11
Piglet	220	160	1·4	27·6	9·5	2·9
Calf	125	96	1·3	4·4	20·0	0·22
Kitten	—	—	0·5	2·3	25·6	0·09

of one or other element in the milk is acting as a limiting factor to ossification, so that the excess of the other ion has to be excreted. Thus a phosphate deficiency limits bone formation in the human and pig, while a

L

calcium inadequacy affects the kitten and calf. These concepts have been tested in two ways.

Balance experiments on breast-fed and bottle-fed humans show that when cow's milk is given, the extra phosphorus increases the retention of calcium from 42·8% to 58·9% (table 11.16). The effect may not be com-

Table 11.16 *Balance experiments performed upon breast-fed and bottle-fed infants. Average data from 22 babies fed either breast milk containing 26·7 mg % Ca and 16·3 mg % P, or reconstituted milk containing 101 mg % Ca and 76·2 mg % P. Results expressed in mg/kg/24 hrs* [30]

	Calcium		Phosphorus	
	breast-fed	bottle-fed	breast-fed	bottle-fed
Intake	36·0	135·0	20·0	103·0
Total loss	20·6	55·2	2·7	52·0
Urine	4·4	2·4	0·5	34·9
Faeces	16·2	52·8	2·2	17·1
Absorption	19·8	88·2	17·8	85·9
Retention	15·4	79·8	17·3	51·0
Absorption (% intake)	54·9	61·0	89·0	83·2
Retention (% intake)	42·8	58·9	86·5	49·5

pletely due to the elimination of a phosphate deficiency, since the lactose and protein content of milk also affect the absorption of calcium. Vitamin D similarly affects the retention of calcium and cow's milk is richer than human milk in all these organic fractions. The importance of phosphate is, however, clearly shown by the reduction in the excretion of calcium in the urine of breast-fed infants when they are given a phosphate supplement to their diet (table 11.17). The kitten, like the breast-fed human, is unable to

Table 11.17 *The decrease in urinary excretion of calcium (mg/kg/day) when breast-fed babies are given a phosphate supplement to the diet* [30]

	Urinary calcium	Urinary phosphorus
Breast-fed	4·43	0·46
Breast-fed + phosphate supplement	2·07	20·0
Bottle-fed	2·40	34·9

maintain the calcium concentration of its body during neo-natal growth, and shows a decrease in the degree of ossification of the long bones during the first few weeks after birth. The ration of Ca/N in the bones only begins to increase when the true suckling period is over [35]. If the kitten is given a supplement of calcium phosphate through a stomach pump during the first week of life, the fall in the degree of calcification of the bones is arrested but not converted into an increase (table 11.18).

Table 11.18 *The change in the ossification of the long bones of the kitten during the neo-natal period when given a supplement of calcium phosphate. The degree of ossification is given by the Ca/N ratio* [31].

| Bone | Newborn | 1 week old | |
		No supplement	CaHPO$_4$ given
Femur	4·5	3·7	4·0
Humerus	4·7	4·0	4·7

It might be concluded from these observations that the growth and ossification of the skeleton of the newborn animal is frequently repressed, because the mother provides milk to her offspring which is poorly adapted to their needs. Thus the human infant grows faster and ossifies its skeleton more rapidly when fed upon cow's rather than human's milk. The situation is more complicated than this, however, as can be seen from a study of serum calcium during neo-natal life.

The medical literature contains an enormous number of analyses of blood taken from the umbilical cord at birth. A comparison of these values with the calcium content of the 1–3-day-old infant shows an apparent fall during neo-natal life which has been interpreted as a hypoparathyroidism of the newborn. This is a mistaken conclusion and the real situation has only been revealed by the careful analyses of Hallman and Salmi. Virtually all previous workers had analysed the venous blood which oozes from the cut cord and which is easily collected, but this is blood coming from the placenta and it contains extra calcium. Analyses of blood from both the umbilical artery and vein showed that the two differ considerably. The blood from the umbilical artery is probably more representative of the foetal circulation and it had an average calcium content of 10·9 mg % whereas blood from the jugular vein of the 1–3-day-old infant had an average of 10·8 mg Ca % (table 11.19). On the basis of these analyses, there is no reason to consider hypoparathyroidism and hypocalcaemia as a normal condition of the newborn. It is important to stress this, because hypocalcaemia does occur in certain instances in the human baby, particularly when they are bottle-fed.

Cow's milk has a lower Ca/P ratio than human milk, so that bottle-fed infants receive high concentrations of phosphorus in this food. It has already been shown that this has the beneficial effect of increasing their calcium retention, but it also has other effects. In particular, it tends to increase the concentration of serum phosphorus in the child with the result that the serum calcium level becomes correspondingly depressed and may occasionally even fall to a level where 'neo-natal tetany' occurs [14]. One infant studied in this condition had a serum-calcium level of 6·8 mg % and a phosphorus level of 8 mg %. When given an injection of parathyroid hormone, the serum calcium rose to 11·7 mg %, the phosphorus level fell to 6 mg %, and the convulsions ceased [27].

Table 11.19 *Analyses of plasma calcium (mg %) from the umbilical blood vessels, the jugular vein of the newborn infant (1–3 days) and the mother* [16]

Case	Umbilical blood Vein	Umbilical blood Artery	Jugular vein newborn	Maternal vein
1	10·5	9·0	9·2	10·2
2	11·6	10·4	11·2	10·4
3	11·4	10·6	10·7	10·5
4	12·6	11·3	11·0	10·0
5	13·0	12·3	11·2	11·7
6	12·8	12·0	11·5	10·1
7	11·7	11·3	11·1	9·8
8	14·0	11·7	10·3	11·7
9	11·1	10·8	10·5	9·1
10	12·2	11·4	11·6	9·9
11	11·5	11·1	11·5	9·3
12	11·3	10·2	10·8	10·3
13	11·1	10·3	9·6	9·3
14	12·0	11·2	11·2	8·8
15	11·8	10·5	10·8	10·5

A recent study in the north-east of the United States of America has shown that about 80% of mothers bottle feed their children, and yet a study of 16 cases of neo-natal tetany admitted to Massachusetts General Hospital showed that in all instances the infants had been bottle-fed with preparations containing low Ca/P ratios (table 11.20). The effect of these diets was demonstrated in an independent study of the parathyroid glands of autopsied infants. Out of 15 infants studied, 8 had been bottle-fed and had hypertrophied parathyroids whereas the 7 which had been breast-fed had normal parathyroid glands [14]. In most cases, feeding human infants on products derived from cow's milk may lead to hypocalcaemia and hyperphosphataemia without producing signs of tetany (table 11.21), but any limitation in the parathyroid or renal function of the child will undoubtedly be aggravated by these diets and may lead to neo-natal tetany.

It is apparent, therefore, that the composition of the milk of a particular species may indeed be adapted to some extent to the needs of the offspring.

Table 11.20 *Diets fed to infants which resulted in 16 cases of neonatal tetany* [14].

Product	Ca/P ratio	Number cases with neo-natal tetany
Human milk	2·26	0
Cow's milk	1·27	2
Evaporated milk formula	1·05 → 1·27	5
Cow's milk product 'I'	1·05	3
Cow's milk product 'II'	1·00	6

Other diets may lead to a more rapid mineralization of the skeleton, but in so doing may disturb the physiology of the newborn animal. Thus the mammalian system of reproduction appears to contain a number of at least potential bottlenecks in mineral metabolism. The mineralization of the foetal skeleton is limited in some instances (e.g. pig) by the rate of transfer of calcium and phosphorus across the placenta, while the ossification

Table 11.21 *Relation of diet to P intake, serum Ca and serum P in newborn infants without signs of tetany* [14]

Infant	Milk Diet	Average P intake (mg/sq m/day)	Serum P (mg %)	Serum Ca (mg %)
B.G.	Breast	205	7·6	8·6
L.G.	Breast	190	6·9	8·8
B.K.	Bottle	1,020	12·9	6·2
T.M.	Bottle	981	10·3	6·1

of the bones of some neonatal animals (e.g. human) may be restricted by the composition of their mother's milk. These factors may have long-term effects upon the offspring, for it has been shown in the rat that if the young are well fed during the first three weeks of life, they continue for the rest of their lives to be larger than less well-nursed rats, even though they are all given a free access to food once they are weaned [38]. Thus there is no doubt that the association between the mother and her offspring is both extremely intimate and extremely complex, with some of the details of placental and mammary physiology and the way in which they affect both animals still being poorly understood

REFERENCES

[1] ANDERSCH, MARIE and OBERST, F. W. (1936), 'Filterable serum calcium in late pregnant and parturient women, and in the newborn', *J. clin. Invest.*, **15**, 131–3.

[2] APPLETON, A. B. (1929), 'The relation between the rate of growth and the rate of ossification in the foetus of the rabbit', *C.R. Ass. Anat. Bordeau*, 24th meeting, 3–25.

[3] BLAXTER, K. L. (1961), 'Lactation and growth of the young', in *Milk, the Mammary Gland and Its Secretion*, eds. Kon, S. K. and Cowie, A. T., Academic Press, **2**, 305–61.

[4] BODANSKY, M. and DUFF, V. B. (1939), 'Regulation of the level of calcium in the serum during pregnancy', *J. Amer. med. Ass.*, **112**, 223–9.

[5] BRÜCK, E. and WEINTRAUB, D. H. (1955), 'Serum calcium and phosphorus in premature and full term infants', *Amer. J. Dis. Child.*, **90**, 653–68.

[6] COMAR, C. L. and WASSERMAN, R. H. (1964), 'Strontium', in *Mineral Metabolism*, eds. Comar, C. L. and Bronner, F. L., Academic Press, **2A**, 523–72.

[7] CRAWFORD, J. D. and MCCANCE, R. A. (1960), 'Sodium transport by the chorio-allantoic membrane of the pig', *J. Physiol.*, **151**, 458–71.

[8] DAVIES, J. and ROUTH, J. I. (1957), 'Composition of the foetal fluids of the rabbit', *J. Embryol. exp. Morph.*, **5**, 32–9.

[9] DICKERSON, J. W. T. (1962), 'The effect of development on the composition of a long bone of the pig, rat and fowl', *Biochem. J.*, **82**, 47–55.

[10] ECONOMOU-MAVROU, V. and MCCANCE, R. A. (1958), 'Calcium, magnesium and phosphorus in foetal tissues', *Biochem. J.*, **68**, 573–80.

[11] EVANS, C. L. (1952), *Principles of Human Physiology*, (Starling), 11th edn., Churchill, 1210 pp.

[12] FLEXNER, L. B. and GELLHORN, A. (1942), 'The comparative physiology of placental transfer', *Amer. J. Obstet. Gynec.*, **43**, 965–74.

[13] FUCHS, F. (1957), *Studies on the Passage of Phosphate between Mother and Foetus in the Guinea-pig*, E. Munksgaards, Copenhagen.

[14] GARDNER, L. I., MacLACHLAN, ELSIE A., PICK, W., TERRY, MARY L., and BUTLER, A. M. (1950), 'Etiologic factors in tetany of newly born infants', *Pediatrics*, **5**, 228–40.

[15] GITTLEMAN, I. F., PINCUS, J. B., SCHMERZLER, E., and SAITO, M. (1956), 'Hypocalcaemia occurring on the first day of life in mature and premature infants', *Pediatrics*, **18**, 721–9.

[16] HALLMAN, N. and SALMI, I. (1953), 'On the plasma calcium in cord blood and in the newborn. A preliminary report', *Acta paediatr.*, *Stockh.*, **42**, 126–9.

[17] HOSKINS, F. M. and SNYDER, F. F. (1933), 'The placental transmission of parathyroid extract', *Amer. J. Physiol.*, **144**, 530–6.

[18] KAISER, I. H. and CUMMINGS, J. N. (1958), 'Plasma electrolytes of the pregnant ewe and foetal lamb', *Amer. J. Physiol.*, **193**, 627–33.

[19] MCDONALD, N. S., HUTCHINSON, D. L., HEPLER, MARILYN, and FLYNN, ELIZABETH (1965), 'Movement of calcium in both directions across the primate placenta', *Proc. Soc. exp. Biol. N.Y.*, **119**, 476–81.

[20] MCISAACS, P. (1928), 'Studies on calcium metabolism. 3. Comparison in calcium metabolism of doe and litter in the rabbit', *J. exp. Biol.*, **5**, 248–51.

[21] MOULTON, C. R. (1923), 'Age and chemical development in mammals', *J. biol. Chem.*, **57**, 79–97.

[22] MULL, J. W. (1936a), 'Variations in serum calcium and phosphorus during pregnancy. 3. The effect on the foetal circulation', *J. clin. Invest.*, **15**, 513–15.

[23] MULL, J. W. (1936b), 'Variations in serum calcium and phosphorus during pregnancy. 4. Effect on the body stores as shown by the ash of rats', *J. clin. Invest.*, **15**, 515–17.

[24] NICHOLAS, H. O., JOHNSON, H. W., and JOHNSTON, R. A. (1934), 'Diffusible serum calcium in pregnancy', *Amer. J. Obstet. Gynec.*, **27**, 504–10.

[25] NEEDHAM, J. (1931), *Chemical Embryology*, Cambridge Univ. Press, 3 vols, 2021 pp.

[26] NORRIS, E. H. (1937), 'The parathyroid glands and the lateral thyroid in man: their morphogenesis, histogenesis, topographic anatomy and prenatal growth', *Contr. Embryol. Carneg. Instn.*, **26**, 247–94.

[27] PINCUS, J. B. and GITTLEMAN, I. F. (1936), 'Infantile tetany', *Amer. J. Dis. Child.*, **51**, 816–22.

[28] PLUMLEE, M. P., HANSARD, S. L., COMAR, C. L., and BEESON, W. M. (1952), 'Placental transfer and deposition of labelled calcium in the developing bovine fetus', *Amer. J. Physiol.*, **171**, 678–86.

[29] SALMI, I. (unpublished) quoted by RAIHA, C. E. (1954), 'Tissue metabolism in the human fetus', *Cold. Spr. Harb. Sym. quant. Biol.*, **19**, 143–51.

[30] SLATER, JEAN E. (1961), 'Retentions of nitrogen and minerals by babies 1 week old', *Brit. J. Nutrit.*, **15**, 83–97.

[31] SLATER, JEAN E. and WIDDOWSON, ELSIE M. (1962), 'Skeletal development of suckling kittens with and without supplementary calcium phosphate', *Brit. J. Nutrit.*, **16**, 39–48.

[32] SPRAY, CHRISTINE M. and WIDDOWSON, ELSIE M. (1950), 'The effect of growth and development on the composition of mammals', *Brit. J. Nutrit.*, **4**, 332–53.

[33] STEARNS, G. (1939), 'The mineral metabolism of normal infants', *Physiol. Rev.*, **19**, 415–38.

[34] WASSERMAN, R. H., COMAR, C. L., NOLD, M. M., and LENGEMANN, F. W. (1957), 'Placental transfer of calcium and strontium in the rat and rabbit', *Amer. J. Physiol.*, **189**, 91–7.

[35] WEIDMANN, S. M. and ROGERS, H. J. (1958), 'Studies on the skeletal tissues. 5. The influence of age upon the degree of calcification and the incorporation of ^{32}P in bone', *Biochem. J.*, **69**, 338–43.

[35a] WIDDAS, W. F. (1961), 'Transport mechanisms in the foetus', *Brit. med. Bull.*, **17**, 107–111

[36] WIDDOWSON, ELSIE M. (1962), 'Metabolic relationship of calcium, magnesium and phosphorus in the foetus and newly born', *Voeding*, **23**, 62–71.

[37] WIDDOWSON, ELSIE M. and DICKERSON, J. W. T. (1964), 'Chemical composition of the body', in *Mineral Metabolism*, eds. Comar, C. L. and Bronner, F., Academic Press, **2A**, 2–247.

[38] WIDDOWSON, ELSIE M. and KENNEDY, G. C. (1962), 'Rate of growth, mature weight and life span', *Proc. roy. Soc. B.*, **156**, 96–108.

CHAPTER 12

Calcium Metabolism in the Laying Bird

One of the diagnostic features of birds is that they reproduce by laying eggs, which are then incubated and eventually hatch as chicks. The phenomenon is so commonplace that one tends to regard it as the essence of normality. It is as well at the outset, therefore, to consider the other possibility, namely, that avian reproduction is the most specialized system that occurs in the tetrapods.

Birds have three distinct characteristics which appear to be relevant to any general studies of their reproduction. First, they have perfected the ability to fly by increasing their surface area with feathers, while reducing their weight to a minimum. Possibly related to this weight-saving is the fact that in most female birds the right ovary and oviduct degenerate, and only the gonad on the left-hand side of the animal functions in the adult. Secondly, birds are the only group of vertebrates which do not show some form of viviparity, and possibly connected with this is the third point, that birds have perfected the heavily shelled cleidoic type of egg. It is frequently argued that the last two points are simply an extension of the first, i.e. that viviparity would so increase the weight of the bird that it would no longer be able to fly efficiently. Some calculations are therefore of interest.

A domestic fowl, without its ovary weighs about 1,900 g, and during reproduction shows an increase in weight of about 100 g due to the ovary (50 g) and the forming egg (50 g). About 40% of the weight of this egg will be lost during incubation, so that the chick will weigh about 30–35 g on hatching. If we consider a six-egg clutch with one egg being laid per day, the bird will carry the extra weight of its large ovary and forming eggs for about a week and during this time will weigh 2,000 g. If we now compare this with a hypothetical bird which was capable of viviparity, we obtain the following figures; weight of bird without ovary 1,900 g, weight of ovary 0·5 g, weight of six embryos just before birth 200 g. Thus the total weight is about 2,100 g. The oviduct increases in weight at the start of reproductive activity in both oviparous and viviparous reproduction, and this will therefore be ignored. The time taken for the development of the chick is about twenty-one days, but the weight of the embryo is only considerable during the last third, i.e. for about a week. It is apparent, therefore, that if a bird such as the domestic fowl produced a litter of six offspring by viviparity instead of oviparity, there would be an increase in weight of only 5% for a week. This would seem unlikely to affect the ability of a bird to fly, especially as some birds increase their weight by 5–20% by the deposition of fat prior to migratory flights [53].

Why, then, have birds never evolved a system of viviparous reproduction when this occurs, at least occasionally, in all other vertebrate groups? The answer appears to be that the birds have a very unusual system of ovulation. It has been pointed out in Chapter 7 that birds release their oocytes in a temporarily extended sequence, whereas other vertebrates release the oocytes of a clutch virtually simultaneously. Because of this, viviparity, if it ever arose in birds, would be a very complicated process, for each embryo in the oviduct would be of a different age with different physiological requirements and with a different time for parturition. The anatomical and hormonal requirements for such a system would seem to be formidable. Why, then, did such a system of ovulation ever evolve? Any answer to this question is, of course, pure conjecture, but it is worth considering our previous argument in the light of a more typical type of ovulation. If the birds reproduced in a similar way to the reptiles, then a 1,900-g animal with a 50-g ovary producing six 50-g eggs would, if they were all produced simultaneously, increase its weight by 350 g. This compares with the 100 g increase in weight which actually occurs in the fowl and the 200 g increase which would occur with viviparity. It seems at least a possibility, therefore, that birds adopted the temporally extended sequence of ovulation as a means of reducing the increase in weight at reproduction, and once having adopted this system, the evolution of viviparity became almost impossible. Another possible explanation for the avian system of ovulation is that with the development of homeothermy there was an increase in the metabolic rate of the embryo which made it difficult to retain cleidoic eggs within the oviduct for very long, and therefore they were formed quickly, one at a time [52]. Admittedly, these are all conjectures, but they underline the one hard fact that needs to be stressed. Birds have a unique system of ovulation; the oocytes are released singly and the tertiary membranes are fully formed and the egg laid before the next ovulation occurs. The time interval between ovulation and oviposition is very short and the shell of the avian egg is well calcified. Thus, not only do we have to consider the metabolism of large quantities of calcium but, because of the type of ovulation, we also have to consider the short time-factor involved and therefore a rapid rate of metabolism.

Changes in the Metabolism of Birds at the Time of Reproduction

The calcium metabolism of birds is affected by numerous dietary factors. These include the use of grit which influences the efficiency of the absorption of the food because of its grinding action in the gizzard. If in addition the grit is soluble, it may also serve as a calcium supplement, although most poultry breeders give these separately. The level of calcium in the diet is important, and there is good evidence that the ratio of calcium to phosphorus in the food affects the absorption of these ions, although the situation is complicated by the fact that seed eaters obtain much phosphorus in the form of phytic acid which is not completely available to the bird. Phytic acid also renders some calcium unavailable to the bird. The literature on this subject has been reviewed on a number of occasions and will not be considered in detail here [60, 72].

Undoubtedly, vitamin D is the most important single factor affecting the absorption of calcium from the alimentary canal, and there is some evidence that the preen gland of birds produces a precursor of this vitamin which, after being spread on the feathers and irradiated, is apparently assimilated when the feathers are next preened. Thus it is claimed that if the gland is removed from young domestic fowl, they develop rickets, despite normal feeding and sunshine. Furthermore, normal birds are stated to have feathers which, if fed to rats, show antirachitic properties (table 12.1).

Table 12.1 *The antirachitic value of feathers of the domestic fowl when fed to rachitic rats (data from [33])*

	Material added to diet			
State of rickets	Normal feathers (%)	Fat-extracted feathers (%)	Feathers of rachitic birds (%)	None (controls) (%)
No healing	0	40	56	75
Some healing	40	60	44	25
Good healing	60	0	0	0

Attempts to repeat these experiments, using house sparrows (*Passer domesticus*) and starlings (*Sturnus vulgaris*), have failed and rickets were not produced in these species despite long-term feeding with vitamin-D-deficient diets and the exclusion of ultra-violet light [27]. It appears, therefore, that although vitamin D is undoubtedly important in the assimilation of calcium, there must be considerable variation in the requirements of different species for it. There is also an age difference, for vitamin-D-deficiencies are relatively hard to induce in mature birds, and this may at least

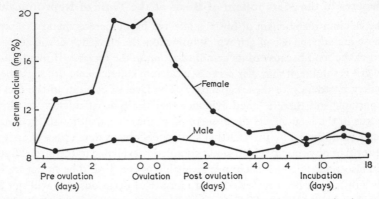

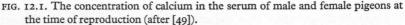

FIG. 12.1. The concentration of calcium in the serum of male and female pigeons at the time of reproduction (after [49]).

partially explain the resistance of the starlings, for these birds were frequently out of their juvenile plumage in these experiments.

Despite these variations, it is possible to show that at the time of reproductive activity a definite set of changes occurs in the calcium metabolism of the female bird. These changes were first detected in the blood of pigeons by Riddle and his associates. They found that about 108 hours before the female was due to ovulate, the level of the blood calcium rose from a normal value of about 9·3 mg % to a value of over 20 mg % at the time of ovulation. Two points were of interest. First, the male bird did not

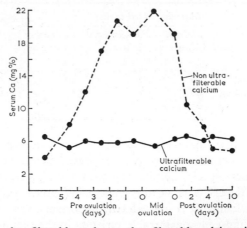

FIG. 12.2. The ultra-filterable and non-ultra-filterable calcium in the serum of laying pigeons. (The non-ultra-filterable includes what was originally described as colloidal- and non-colloidal-bound calcium) (after [43]).

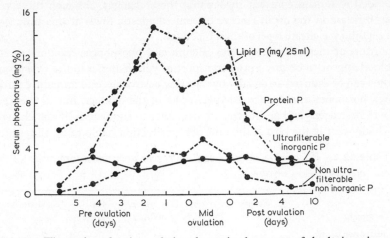

FIG. 12.3. The various fractions of phosphorus in the serum of the laying pigeon (after [43]).

show these changes, and, secondly, the changes started several days before ovulation (fig. 12.1). Thus, although the phenomenon appeared to be related to the laying of the egg, it was obviously not directly concerned with the calcification of the eggshell. Later work showed that the ultra-filterable calcium in the blood remained at a fairly constant level throughout these changes which appeared to be due to the transport of yolk proteins to the ovary as calcium complexes (fig. 12.2). Similar striking modifications were observed in other fractions of the blood in that lipid and protein phosphorus also increased, although the ultra-filterable inorganic phosphorus level remained fairly constant (fig. 12.3). The sodium level of the blood

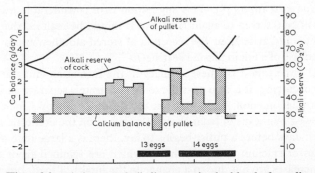

FIG. 12.4. The calcium balance and alkali reserve in the blood of a pullet on a diet rich in calcium carbonate. Note the correlation between the two and the absence of any changes in the alkali reserve of the cock (after [18]).

tended to remain constant throughout these changes, although there was an increase in the alkali reserve of some domestic fowls at this time (fig. 12.4) and the citrate level of their blood fell.

Most of these changes in the calcium and phosphorus fractions of the blood appear to be due to the transport of yolk material to the ovary, and they can be induced artificially by injecting oestrogens into immature birds. Sex hormones also induce a hypertrophy of the oviduct, but in this case both oestrogens and androgens are necessary to simulate fully the changes which occur in the bird at the time of reproduction (table 12.2). It appears,

Table 12.2   *Effect of oestrogens and androgens upon immature birds* (+ = *increase;* − = *no affect*)

Treatment	Serum Ca	Serum P	Hypertrophy of oviduct	Ca retention	Medullary bone
Oestrogen alone	+	+	+	−	?
Androgen alone	−	−	−	−	−
Oestrogen + androgen	+	+	+ +	+ +	+ + +

therefore, that androgens must also be produced by the ovaries of female birds, and this is confirmed by the fact that the growth of the comb is dependent solely upon this stimulus. Thus, as the bird comes into lay, it secretes increasing amounts of oestrogens and androgens which induce various changes in the secondary sex characteristics of the bird. These changes are seen most clearly in the pigeon or ring dove, which produce only two eggs in a clutch, with a period of about 46 hours between subsequent ovulations. In these birds it is claimed that the ovulation of the oocytes is followed by a sudden reduction in the level of circulating oestrogens, and this is immediately apparent as a decrease in the weights of the oviducts at that time [48]. This suggestion is of considerable importance and it will be referred to again later, but it should be realized that the loss in weight could arise from the secretion of stored albumen and not necessarily because of a fall in plasma oestrogens.

At the same time that these changes in the formation and transport of yolk are occurring, it is also possible to demonstrate a separate and entirely different phenomenon. This was first clearly described by Common [15], who showed by means of balance experiments upon the domestic fowl that about ten days before a pullet begins to lay, there is a large increase in the quantities of calcium and phosphorus which are retained from the diet. These increases are not due to a change in the intake of food, but rather to a decrease in the excretion of calcium (fig. 12.5). The same experiments demonstrated another odd phenomenon, namely, that when an egg was

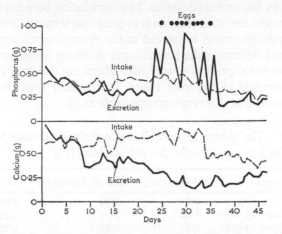

FIG. 12.5. The daily intake (broken lines) and loss (thick lines) of calcium and phosphorus in a laying pullet in relation to egg-laying (after [15]). The calcium and phosphorus content of egg are not included in this data.

laid there was a large increase in the excretion of phosphorus by the bird. This occurred not only with the first egg but at all subsequent ovipositions unless a calcium-rich diet was fed to the birds. It is apparent, therefore, that this simple balance experiment raised three important questions, some of which are still incompletely answered after more than thirty years. The problems to be considered are:

1. Where are the extra phosphorus and calcium ions stored?
2. How is the storage phenomenon integrated into the normal reproductive cycle?
3. What is the source of the excreted phosphorus?

Analyses of the carcasses of birds have shown that the oviduct does not store calcium ions, but that 97·2 to 98·7% of all the calcium in the body of a bird is present in the skeleton [17]. It would seem reasonable, therefore, to consider that the extra minerals were stored in the bones, and that if this change in metabolism was to be correlated with reproduction, it might be initiated either directly or indirectly by the sex hormones. These possibilities have been investigated in two ways. First, oestrogens were injected into male pigeons and balance experiments were performed in order to detect any possible increase in the retention of minerals. It was found that the injected birds retained an extra 30 mg Ca/day, so that over a 45-day experiment, they appeared to have retained 1·3–1·5 g more calcium than the controls [14]. An examination of the skeletons of these birds showed that there was, in fact, an average of 1·36 g more calcium in the injected birds than in the untreated males. This correlation between the balance experiments and the bone analyses is so good that it leaves little doubt that the extra minerals which are stored at the onset of reproduction are deposited in the skeleton under the influence of the sex hormones. The extra minerals are not deposited equally throughout the skeleton, but are particularly abundant in the limb bones, which more than doubled their inorganic content in these experiments (table 12.3).

Table 12.3 *The storage of calcium in the skeletons of male pigeons after receiving 0·25 mg/day oestradiol diproprionate* [13]

Treatment	Limb bones (g)	Rest of skeleton (g)	Total (g)
Nil	0·83	2·16	2·99
Injected 45 days	1·42	2·93	4·35
Injected 53 days	1·86	2·89	4·75
% increase	124	33	60·5

Although it is now generally accepted that the bird stores extra calcium and phosphorus in its skeleton, the endocrinal control of this process had to be re-evaluated in the light of more detailed work [30]. In the original work, oestrogens were injected into male pigeons so that the results would not be complicated by the presence of endogenous female hormones. Later work showed that oestrogens alone would not increase the retention of calcium and phosphorus in the domestic fowl, and it appears that androgens are also necessary. Both hormones are, in fact, produced by the ovary, and it appears that they work synergically to produce the increased retention of minerals by the bird (fig. 12.6, table 12.2). Thus the success of the original experiments, using injections of oestrogens alone, was apparently due to the fact that male birds with their own endogenous androgens were used as test animals.

The fact that female birds lay down extra stores of bone mineral prior to egg-laying strongly suggests that they will use this material during reproduction. The original observation, that egg-laying coincided with a large excretion of phosphorus, could then be interpreted as showing that calcium and phosphate ions were withdrawn from the skeleton so that the calcium could be used to form the calcareous eggshell. This being the case, the phosphate which is liberated from the bone would not be used in forming the eggshell, and this could account for the increased excretion of phosphorus at the time of egg-laying. This hypothesis received some support from the fact that the extra phosphorus which was excreted appeared

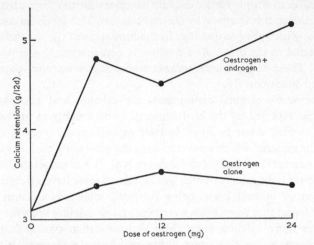

FIG. 12.6. The effect of injections of oestrogen and androgen upon the retention of calcium by the domestic fowl (after [21]).

to be urinary rather than faecal, for it was both water soluble and associated with ammonia [16]. Other experiments support this interpretation, for if the birds are given a diet rich in calcium carbonate, they no longer show a heavy excretion of phosphorus at the time of laying [71], and if the experiment is repeated on colostomized birds, there is no doubt as to the urinary source of the extra phosphorus (table 12.4).

Table 12.4 *The effect of various levels of dietary calcium upon the absorption and retention of Ca and P in colostomized birds receiving a diet containing 0·87% P and laying on alternate days [28]*

% Ca in diet	Daily intake		Absorbed		Urinary		Retention	
	Ca	P	Ca	P	Ca	P	Ca	P
	(g)	(g)	(g)	(g)	(g)	(g)	(g)	(g)
0·75	0·94	1·09	0·58	0·38	0·04	0·50	0·54	0·12
2·00	2·56	1·09	1·14	0·35	0·15	0·15	0·99	0·20
5·00	6·25	1·09	1·35	0·21	0·25	0·06	1·10	0·15

It appears, therefore, that the explanation of Common's original balance experiment is as follows. As the bird comes into reproductive activity, it starts to secrete increasing quantities of oestrogens and androgens and, under the influence of these sex hormones, extra minerals are retained by the bird and deposited in the skeleton. These skeletal minerals contain calcium and phosphate ions, and if the food is not adequate at the time of

M

reproduction to supply all the calcium necessary for the formation of egg-shell, the deficit is made good by skeletal calcium. This liberates some phosphate ions which are not involved in the formation of the eggshell and are thus excreted in the urine. As a qualitative explanation, this appears to fit the facts. There are, however, some complications when the scheme is investigated quantitatively.

In Common's original experiment, the calcium and phosphate ions which were retained by the bird appeared to be roughly in the same proportions as they occur in bone. In later experiments, however, the Ca/P ratio of the material which was retained in the pre-laying period was higher than the normal Ca/P ratio of the skeleton [16]. It was suggested, therefore, that the extra bone mineral which was laid down must have a different composition from normal bone, being relatively richer in calcium. It was similarly found that when birds were kept on low calcium diets they tended to remove more calcium from their skeletons than phosphorus, which again suggested that they were either mobilizing a store with a higher Ca/P ratio than normal bone or else they were retaining in the body some of the phosphorus liberated from the skeleton [17].

One possible explanation of these results could be inferred from experiments in which domestic fowl were given a diet rich in calcium carbonate. These birds were retaining minerals with a high Ca/P ratio during their pre-laying period, and analyses of their blood showed that at the same time there was a large increase in their blood-alkali reserve as measured by its carbon dioxide content (fig. 12.4). The alkali reserve of the blood fell during egg-laying, but always remained at a level higher than that of the male bird. It was postulated, therefore, that during the pre-laying storage period some of the calcium may have been deposited in the bone in association with carbonate rather than phosphate ions [18]. This suggestion, namely, that there was some calcium stored in the avian skeleton as phosphate (Ca_P) whereas the rest was residual calcium (Ca_R) in association with other anions, was not unlikely in view of the adsorption of ions on to crystal surfaces, and it was considered in detail by Tyler [70]. The balance data of four birds on three different diets was examined in relation to their mineral metabolism during the thirty-five days of the experiment. It was found that the bone fraction Ca_P tended to remain fairly constant while Ca_R showed large fluctuations, with a fairly large negative value on days when an egg was laid and with a large gain on non-laying days. A more detailed mathematical examination of the data showed that there tended to be a reciprocal relationship between Ca_P and Ca_R, so that if an excessive amount of Ca_R was mobilized, some of it was returned to the skeleton as Ca_P. On the other hand, an excessive deposition of Ca_R occurred only with a loss of Ca_P, the liberated phosphate presumably being excreted. This relationship between Ca_R and Ca_P is shown in fig. 12.7 and one of the results of this analysis is that it suggests that the avian skeleton has some mechanism whereby it is prevented from losing more than about 1 g Ca/day when an egg is laid and prevented from gaining more than about 1 g Ca/day during non-laying periods [70]. This analysis of the problem is of considerable historical interest as it highlighted the problem of the movement of calcium in and out of the skeletal deposits. The experiment, however, did

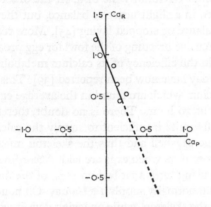

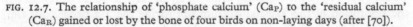

FIG. 12.7. The relationship of 'phosphate calcium' (Ca_P) to the 'residual calcium' (Ca_R) gained or lost by the bone of four birds on non-laying days (after [70]).

not include calcium-deficient diets, and there is no doubt that if it had it would probably have resulted in a resorption of more than 1 g Ca/day from the skeleton.

The division of the skeletal calcium into two fractions, identified as phosphate–calcium and residual–calcium, is not altogether satisfactory, and it appears that the excessively large Ca/P ratios obtained in some of the early balance experiments might be capable of other explanations. It has, for example, been suggested that phosphate ions might be stored within the bird or released from other tissues, so that although balance data suggest that there should be some store with an unusual Ca/P content, these additional phosphate ions obviate the necessity of it actually being directly related to the composition of the bone. It has also been pointed out that the original experiments probably used phosphorus-deficient diets, and may have accentuated the unusual Ca/P ratio found in the balance data by including the large phosphate excretion associated with the laying of the first egg [64].

Despite this, there seems a distinct possibility that the mineral stored during the pre-laying period may have various anions adsorbed on to the surfaces of the bone crystals, and this may therefore reflect the composition of the blood and the high alkali reserve of birds during this period. If this is the basis of the 'residual calcium' fraction of the bone, this could well explain its lability and possibly its reciprocal relationship with the calcium phosphate.

In the 1930s, when the classical balance experiments were being performed upon the domestic fowl, there appeared to be a limit of about 1 g/day to the retention of calcium by the bird. At the onset of reproduction, the birds were often in a slight negative balance, but they later came into positive calcium balance or stopped laying [45]. More recent experiments suggest that the intensive breeding of the fowl for egg production may have led to an increase in the efficiency of its calcium metabolism, as retentions of up to 1·83 g Ca/day have now been reported [39]. This, however, is less than the 2 g of calcium which are found in the average eggshell and which are secreted in about 20 hours. There is no doubt, therefore, that dietary sources are normally quite insufficient to supply the calcium required for the formation of the eggshell and thus the skeleton must be resorbed, to some extent, on those days when eggs are laid. According to the estimates of Tyler, who was using birds that laid on 50% of the days in the experiment, the diet would normally supply 1 g Ca/day. On non-laying days, this would be stored in the skeleton, while on laying days it would be joined by the resorption of this skeletal calcium to provide the 2 g needed for the eggshell of the fowl. If one considers that most wild birds do not receive a diet as rich in calcium as that fed to domestic species, then it is apparent that they must be even more dependent upon the resorption of their skeleton during reproduction. It should also be realized that a skeletal resorption of 1 g Ca/day by a 2-kg bird is twice the rate of resorption found in the average 70-kg human. Thus both balance data and information on the chemical kinetics of the skeleton suggest that the bone stored by birds during reproduction must have some very unusual properties.

The Occurrence of Medullary Bone

In 1916, Foote, in his investigation into the comparative histology of the femur, noted that 'in some birds, as the yellow hammer (*Emberiza atrinella*) pigeon, and white pelican (*Pelecanus erythrorhynchus*), the medullary canals are occupied by a heavy cancellous bone with small meshes and present the appearance of nearly solid bones, and yet these birds are good fliers' [26]. This strange observation, probably the most remarkable in this 240-page article, evoked no further comment. In 1934, Kyes and Potter [42] independently discovered a 'physiological marrow ossification' in pigeons, which, in its most extreme form, completely filled the femur. They pointed out that the deposition of this extra mineral in the long bones of the leg was, first, a cyclical event; secondly, restricted to the female bird; and thirdly, coincident with the maturation of the ovarian follicle (table 12.5).

Table 12.5 *Correlation of medullary bone formation with the development of the ovaries of the pigeon* [42]

Size of follicles (mm)	State of bone
< 2	No ossification in marrow cavity
> 4·5	Some ossification
10	Extreme ossification

The phenomenon was referred to as medullary bone formation, since it occurred in the medullary cavities of the skeleton, and it soon became apparent that it provided the structural basis for the extra store of minerals

Table 12.6 *Distribution of medullary bone in the skeleton of the domestic fowl as influenced by the number of eggs laid on a low calcium diet* [62]

Bone	% of total bone present as medullary bone			
	No eggs	2 eggs	4 eggs	6 eggs
Femur	21·8	32·8	33·8	39·1
Tibia	12·4	13·1	19·7	34·5
Fibula	7·9	19·0	11·9	24·5
Metatarsus	5·1	3·6	2·7	4·5
Toes	1·3	4·0	1·6	2·8
Humerus	4·6	6·8	8·6	14·7
Radius	3·6	3·6	8·4	7·9
Ulna	4·0	6·7	10·6	23·9
Metacarpals	4·3	6·5	4·5	17·9
Skull	7·2	8·3	2·0	7·5
Cervical vertebrae	7·0	10·0	9·0	13·9
Thoracic vertebrae	10·3	15·9	22·6	31·7
Lumbo-sacral vertebrae	6·7	21·8	30·1	16·3
Coccygeal vertebrae	20·5	16·0	34·0	56·8
Sternum	15·5	18·3	20·8	28·7
Clavicle	12·2	14·7	14·5	16·0
Ilium, ischium, pubis	20·8	32·0	27·4	36·5
Ribs	29·2	39·9	39·8	51·8
Coracoid	3·7	10·3	13·8	21·3
Scapula	16·1	9·8	14·1	14·7
Total skeleton	11·7	15·0	16·6	23·6

which was being simultaneously demonstrated by balance experiments. Medullary bone consists of a system of bone spicules which grow out from the endosteal surfaces and may completely fill the marrow spaces of the long bones (plate 1, p. 226). It is most clearly seen in the limb bones, but does, in fact, occur in most parts of the skeleton (table 12.6) and in all birds which have so far been investigated (table 12.7).

Table 12.7   *Birds in which changes in calcium metabolism during reproduction have been investigated (data from [51])*

Species	Calcium level of blood		Presence of medullary bone
	Male or immature female (mg %)	Reproducing female (mg %)	
Domestic fowl (*Gallus domesticus*)	12	25	+
Pigeon (*Columba livia*)	9	21	+
Ring dove (*Columba palumbus*)	9	20	not investigated
Bobwhite quail (*Colinus virginianus*)	13	29	+
Japanese quail (*Coturnix coturnix*)	—	—	+
House sparrow (*Passer domesticus*)	10	20	+
Domestic duck	11	—	+
Canary (*Serinus canarius*)	—	—	+
Canada goose (*Branta canadensis*)	—	—	+

The deposition of medullary bone starts about 10–14 days before a pullet comes into lay. This corresponds with the time when the bird starts to secrete extra sex hormones and to retain extra calcium and phosphorus. It has been shown by means of radio-isotopes that the retained minerals are, in fact, deposited at this site [36]. When medullary bone is examined histologically, it can be seen that this period of bone deposition coincides with a period of intense osteoblastic activity. This osteoblastic phase becomes rapidly converted to osteoclastic activity when the bird starts to secrete the eggshell, and the medullary bone is then resorbed. When the shell is completely calcified and the egg is laid, osteoclastic activity falls and the osteoblasts are predominant. These changes have been studied in detail in both the pigeon and the fowl, but they are more clearly seen in the former, as this bird lays only two eggs in a clutch with a space of about 20 hours between the oviposition of the first and the subsequent ovulation of the second oocyte (fig. 12·8). Three points are of particular interest in these studies. First, there appears to be a time-lag of a few hours between the laying of the first egg and the cessation of osteoclastic activity. Secondly, after the laying of the second egg, osteoclastic activity continues on a diminished scale until after about 10–20 days all the medullary bone has disappeared. Finally, the rapid alternation between osteoblastic and osteoclastic activity is so great, and the different cells disappear so rapidly, that it has been suggested that the osteoblasts and osteocytes must fuse together to produce the osteoclasts. Similarly, osteoclasts may be transformed into osteoblasts when bone formation restarts. This theory is based upon

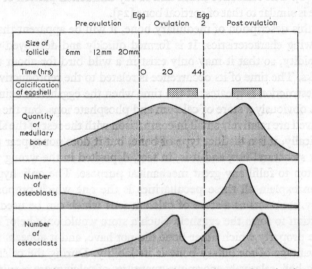

FIG. 12.8. Changes in the number of osteoblasts and osteoclasts in the medullary bone of laying pigeons in relation to the calcification of the eggshell (after [10]).

the facts that mitoses are rarely seen in bone cells, but that intermediate cell types are frequently found during the rapid changes which occur in the formation and dissolution of medullary bone. According to this theory, similar changes occur in ordinary bone but are not as clearly seen as in the rapidly mobilized medullary bone. If true, this theory would indicate that osteoblasts and osteoclasts are simply different functional states of the same cells [10].

The organic material in medullary bone differs from that of the cortical layer both in composition and structure. This is clearly seen in a histological examination of the decalcified bone, for the medullary layer binds basic dyes much more strongly, apparently because of a greater acidity in its polysaccharide components [22, 54]. Similarly, the cortical layers stain red with a haematoxylin–eosin–azure II staining method, whereas the medullary bone is blue or purple, apart from a thin layer of the most recently formed bone which is pale pink [9]. Many of the histological characteristics of medullary bone show some similarity to those which occur in the calcification of the osteon (p. 13) [57]. It differs, however, in that the collagen fibres lack an orderly arrangement and are associated with varying amounts of cementing substance. The crystals of bone mineral do not appear to be arranged on the fibre bands, and the medullary bone would appear to be too imperfectly arranged to perform any mechanical function [1]. The refractive index and X-ray diffraction pattern of medullary bone is similar to that of cortical bone [23].

From this description of medullary bone, it will be apparent that it has the following characteristics. It is formed quickly and destroyed with an equal rapidity, so that it may only exist in a wild bird for about three to four weeks. The time of its occurrence is related to the reproductive cycle, and its destruction is greatest at the time when the eggshell is being calcified. It is obviously a store of calcium and phosphate ions, but the quantities involved are relatively small in comparison with the rest of the skeleton. Histologically, it is a distinct type of bone, but it does not appear to be of any great structural use, and it is, in fact, deposited in the wrong parts of the skeleton to fulfil any great mechanical purpose. The only hypothesis which can explain all these peculiarities is the one which proposes that medullary bone acts as a store of calcium ions which can be used during reproduction to form the eggshell. Such a store would only be of use if it had some property which other bone did not have, and it appears that the great advantage of medullary bone is its lability. During the calcification of the eggshell, relatively enormous quantities of calcium are required, and it is suggested that the great advantage of medullary bone is the fact that, because of its large surface area and vascularity, it can be broken down much more quickly than cortical bone. Other suggestions have been made as to the functions of medullary bone. One of these proposes that the bones of birds have been so reduced in weight because of the requirements of flight that they can no longer act as a mineral store, i.e. if they were eroded at all this would now seriously affect their mechanical properties. This implies, therefore, a separate store of bone to be used solely as a source of minerals. A corollary to this is the suggestion that the 'mineral storage' properties of the avian skeleton are only really needed during reproduction, and therefore they are only formed and used at this time so as to avoid the extra weight to the skeleton during the rest of the year. When the kinetics of avian bone are discussed later, it will be apparent that only the first hypothesis is in agreement with the actual metabolism of calcium in the medullary bone.

The Formation of Medullary Bone

The discovery of medullary bone by Kyes and Potter related its occurrence to the activity of the ovary, and within two years it had been shown that injections of oestrogens into cock-birds did, in fact, induce the formation of this type of bone. Unfortunately, this experiment was not as conclusive as it at first appeared, and for the next ten years there was some confusion as to the actual stimulus necessary for the initiation of medullary bone. The difficulties arose for two reasons. The first was that oestrogens, besides inducing medullary bone, also cause the formation of yolk proteins which are transported through the blood in association with calcium. This produces a hypercalcaemia which was at first mistaken as an aspect of medullary bone formation, but careful experiments were able to show that they were not related and that each phenomenon could be induced in the absence of the other.

The second difficulty is similar to the one experienced in demonstrating that the increased retention of minerals by the reproductively active bird is due to both androgens and oestrogens. Medullary bone is only formed under the synergistic action of both these sets of hormones, but the early experimenters used oestrogens alone to induce these stores in male birds. The influence of the endogenous hormone in these experiments was eventually demonstrated, and it was shown that oestrogens would not induce medullary bone in male birds which were either not sexually active or which had been castrated [8]. Thus medullary bone can be made to form in birds by using mixtures of oestrogens and androgens in which the concentration of oestrogen is not sufficiently high to cause hypercalcaemia. Similarly, hypercalcaemia can be produced by levels of oestrogens which, in the absence of androgens, do not form medullary bone. The two phenomena are quite separate and can be demonstrated independently; hypercalcaemia requires only an oestrogenic stimulus and is related to the formation of yolk proteins, medullary bone requires both oestrogens and androgens and is related to the storing of minerals prior to the formation of the calcareous eggshell [51].

There is no doubt, therefore, that the sex hormones provide the basic stimulus for the formation of medullary bone, but there are additional complicating factors in that there is always a graded response in the way that certain bones respond to these hormones. Thus, in the pigeon, the femur always contains more medullary bone than the tibia which, in turn, is better supplied than the radius and ulna. Similar observations have been made in the duck, where it was also noticed that the appearance of the medullary bone coincided with the disappearance of fat cells from the marrow and an increase in the blood supply to these regions [5]. Further-more, immature pullets possess haemopoietic tissues only in those bones which will later also contain medullary bone [64], so that the extent of the blood supply may be at least one of the factors which might influence the quantity of medullary bone which forms at any particular site. When sex hormones are injected directly into the bones of male pigeons and drakes, the medullary bone actually forms at the point of injection [6]. The hor-mones may, therefore, have a direct and localized action on the bone cells. Any variations in the response of different parts of the skeleton must be caused either by different degrees of vascularization bringing different amounts of hormones to each bone or, alternatively, by different receptivi-ties of the bones to the hormones, i.e. a local factor. These two effects have been neatly demonstrated by breaking the metatarsus of laying and non-laying fowls. Normally these bones do not contain any medullary bone, but the influence of the fracture is to increase the blood supply, and it was found that under these conditions medullary bone formed in the region of the fracture in the laying but not in the non-laying bird. The medullary bone which did form was present in only small quantities, and it was con-cluded that the sex hormones, the blood supply, and a local factor all in-fluenced the formation of medullary bone in any particular region of the skeleton [65].

The Minerals of Medullary Bone

When medullary bone starts to form, the phosphorus-to-nitrogen ratio falls, indicating that a protein matrix is being formed prior to its minerali-zation. This ratio rises later as the bone is calcified, and fully formed medullary bone is better mineralized than cortical bone [7]. The medullary bone contains an unusual nitrogen fraction and the apatite/collagen ratio is much higher than in cortical bone (table 12.8).

Table 12.8 *The composition of medullary and cortical bone in the pigeon (Average values expressed as % dry fat-free bone)* [1]

Bone	Total N	Collagen N	Residual N	Calcium	Apatite	Apatite/ Collagen
Cortical	3·85	4·04	0	27·2	68	3·1
Medullary	3·21	1·78	1·41	27·6	69	6·9

The formation of medullary bone is generally accompanied by some degree of osteolysis of the cortical bones of the skeleton and the Haversian canals may become enlarged, although these effects are normally only pro-nounced on calcium deficient diets [5]. It has, however, been stated that nearly half of the phosphorus present in medullary bone has not come directly from the diet but from phosphorus already stored in the skeleton [29]. Similar experiments on the retention of radioactive calcium in the fowl have shown that medullary bone retains a specific activity two to three times higher than that of the plasma for as long as seven weeks after dosing the animal. It was therefore concluded that if there is a rapid turnover of minerals in the medullary bone, it must be replacing its calcium not from the diet but from the Ca^{45} which was present in the structural bone of the skeleton [36].

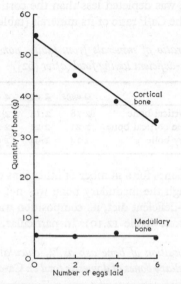

FIG. 12.9. The depletion of the bones of a laying fowl in relation to the number of eggs laid on a low calcium diet. Note how the cortical bone decreases while the quantity of medullary bone remains constant (after [62]).

In view of these suggestions and the fact that the classical balance experiments had suggested that medullary bone might have an unusual composition, Taylor and Moore [62] analysed the skeletons of domestic fowl on various calcium and phosphorus diets. After the birds had laid six eggs on a low calcium diet, it was shown that 38·4% of their skeletal calcium had been utilized to form eggshells and maintain the body, but that less phosphorus had been excreted than was calculated to have been released from the skeleton. Analyses of the bones showed that the quantity of medullary bone in the birds was relatively unaffected, but that the cortical bone of the ribs, sternum, ilium, ischium, pubis, coccygeal vertebrae, and fibula was as much as 50% depleted (fig. 12.9). These bones were termed labile, whereas the skull, metatarsus, and toes were termed non-labile as they lost relatively little mineral. The remarkable fact which emerges from these experiments is that when a bird continues to lay on a calcium-deficient diet, it is the structural bone which is depleted rather than the medullary bone. This explains the results shown in table 12.6, where it can be seen that the percentage of medullary bone in the skeleton actually increases during egg-laying on a calcium-deficient diet because the rest of the skeleton is depleted in order to maintain it.

Analyses of the ash of cortical and medullary bone showed that although the medullary bone was depleted less than the cortical bone, it did show the greatest fall in the Ca/P ratio of its minerals (table 12.9). Investigations

Table 12.9   Ca/P *ratio of minerals from labile, non-labile, and medullary bones of calcium-deficient laying fowl (after* [62])

	0 eggs	2 eggs	4 eggs	6 eggs
Labile cortical bone	2·18	2·14	2·11	2·01
Non-labile cortical bone	2·21	2·21	2·20	2·15
Medullary bone	2·14	1·94	2·09	1·84

of the ash of these bones for a number of other ions confirmed these facts, namely, that although the medullary bone was not destroyed by placing a bird on a calcium-deficient diet, its composition was changed more than that of any other bone (table 12.10). In particular, a calcium deficiency

Table 12.10   *Composition of bone ash as* % *calculated ash in labile, non-labile, and medullary bones of domestic fowl on Ca-deficient diets* [63]

	Ca	Mg	Na	K	P	CO_3	Citrate
				Non-labile			
0 eggs	37·3	0·55	0·81	0·24	16·9	4·91	2·07
6 eggs	37·3	0·63	0·83	0·35	17·3	4·18	1·80
				Labile			
0 eggs	37·1	0·61	0·78	0·59	16·9	4·36	2·63
6 eggs	35·7	0·85	1·05	1·08	18·0	3·11	1·84
				Medullary			
0 eggs	36·7	0·83	1·10	0·90	16·9	4·56	1·76
6 eggs	35·5	1·09	1·48	1·44	17·9	3·06	1·06

during reproduction was found to increase the magnesium, sodium, potassium, and phosphorus content of bone ash while decreasing the calcium, carbon dioxide, and citrate ions. It is known that during reproduction the concentration of ionic calcium in the blood tends to fall as these ions are used for the calcification of the eggshell. At the same time, the inorganic phosphate ions in the blood tend to rise as they are liberated from the bone prior to their excretion by the kidney. The concentration of citrate ions and the alkali reserve both decrease in the blood during reproduction as compared with their pre-laying levels. Thus most of the changes which occur in the composition of the bones during reproduction simply reflect the changes which are occurring in the composition of the blood at this time. This confirms the distinction between labile and non-labile bones and suggests that, although medullary bone appears to maintain its substance, it is, in fact, the most labile type of bone in the skeleton, and its composition comes nearest to reflecting that of the blood during this period of calcium stress.

In the light of these experiments, it is necessary to reconsider our ideas regarding medullary bone. There is obviously no basis for the notion that medullary bone exists to protect the structural bone from resorption during egg-laying, for in the final analysis, and in the most calcium-deficient circumstances, it is the structural bone which is destroyed, while the medullary bone is maintained in a fairly constant amount. It would seem that structural bone is unable to perform some function during reproduction which the medullary bone can, and therefore the one is converted into the other. The changes in the composition of the cortical and medullary bones suggests that medullary bone is a very labile form, and thus changes its composition more than the other bones. It therefore reflects the composition of the blood more than any of the other bones and, in doing so, loses material with a higher Ca/P ratio than normal bone and so develops a lower Ca/P ratio itself. This goes some way towards explaining the unusual Ca/P ratios found in balance experiments. More important, however, is the fact that it suggests a basis for these changes. The calcium requirements during the formation of the eggshell are so great that they can only be met by an especially labile form of bone, namely, medullary bone. Thus, in order that reproduction can continue, structural bone is converted into this form to make good any dietary deficiencies. If this hypothesis is true, it should be demonstrated by experiments upon the kinetics of bone mineral in the bird.

Kinetic Studies of Bone Minerals in the Avian Skeleton

Two attempts have recently been made to investigate the movements of Ca^{45} in the skeleton of the laying fowl. The first method used by Mueller, Schraer, and Schraer [46] uses compartmental analysis based upon data from balance experiments, together with the long-term feeding of radio-isotopes. The birds were fed on a diet containing 5 μc Ca^{45}/100 g feed for 26 days, when they were transferred to a similar though non-radioactive diet and studied for a further 30 days. At the time when the radio-isotope was removed from the food, it had the same specific activity as the eggshells which were being formed by the birds on this diet. The eggshells could thus be used as a system which automatically sampled the plasma calcium during the time when they were being formed, i.e. the specific activity of the eggshell reflected the specific activity of the blood calcium during the preceding 18–20 hours. At the end of the 56 days of the experiment the birds were killed and the total Ca and Ca^{45} content of the cortical and medullary bones was determined.

The results of the balance data are shown in table 12.11, where it can be

Table 12.11   *Balance data for domestic fowl used in Mueller, Schraer, and Schraer's radio-isotope experiment* [46]

	All birds	Laying	Non-laying
Absorption (%)	78	78	76
Endogenous excretion (% intake)	8	7	12
Retention (%)	70	71	64
Ca intake, g/bird/24 hr	2·32	2·32	2·32
Ca absorption, g/bird/24 hr	1·80	1·81	1·76
Endogenous Ca, g/bird/24 hr	0·18	0·16	0·28
Ca retention, g/bird/24 hr	1·62	1·65	1·48
Eggshell Ca, g/bird/24 hr	1·64	2·09	0
Balance ($Ca_{b+} - Ca_{b-}$), g/bird/24 hr	−0·02	−0·44	1·48

seen that the flock as a whole was in calcium equilibrium, even though the average egg production was 45 eggs/pullet/55 days. When the data are sub-divided into laying and non-laying days, it can be seen that in the former the bird retains more calcium, but is in negative balance (−0·44 g), while in the latter the bird is in positive balance (1·48 g). The increased retention on laying days is apparently due to an increased absorption and a decreased excretion of calcium, although it was assumed, in obtaining these figures, that there was no difference in the consumption of food on laying and non-laying days.

The specific activity of the eggshells formed during the experiment is shown in fig. 12.10. It rises rapidly during days 1–3 and then more slowly up to day 16, suggesting that Ca^{45} was accumulating in the skeleton during this period. From 18–26 days the specific activity of the food and the egg-shell were equal, and therefore it was assumed that the exchangeable bone calcium and the feed calcium had reached an equilibrium. The Ca^{45} was

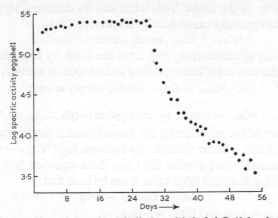

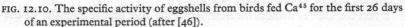

FIG. 12.10. The specific activity of eggshells from birds fed Ca⁴⁵ for the first 26 days of an experimental period (after [46]).

withdrawn from the diet on day 26, and from then on there is a curvilinear decline in the specific activity of the shell from the 27th to 35th day, after which the decline is approximately linear.

The movement of calcium in the body can be represented by the general equation.

$$*Ca_{b+} - *Ca_{b-} = *Ca_{abs} - *Ca_{shell} - *Ca_{end} \qquad (1)$$

where * represents the radio-isotope; Ca_{b+} = calcium deposited in bone; Ca_{b-} = calcium removed from bone; Ca_{abs} = calcium absorbed; Ca_{shell} = calcium used in shell formation and Ca_{end} = endogenous calcium excretion.

$*Ca_{b+} - *Ca_{b-}$ can be calculated from the balance data, and the specific activities of the feed and the eggshell. Furthermore, at the end of 16 days, the specific activity of the exchangeable fraction of the bone is equal to that of the food

$$\text{i.e.} \quad \frac{*U_{eq}}{U} = \frac{*Ca \text{ food}}{Ca \text{ content food}}$$

where $*U_{eq}$ = content of radio-isotope in exchangeable bone at equilibrium and U = calcium content exchangeable bone,

$$\therefore U = \frac{*U_{eq}}{\text{Specific activity food}}$$

From this, it is possible to calculate that the exchangeable bone amounts to approximately 4·31–4·88 g.

During the period of the experiment when the radioactivity of the bone is increasing, the quantity of radio-isotope in the bone which is being formed will be dependent upon the quantity of bone formed and the specific activity of the blood. This latter can be measured by the specific activity of the eggshell formed during this period. Thus,

$$*Ca_{b+} = Ca_{b+} . \text{ specific activity of eggshell}$$

The amount of radioactivity lost from the bone by resorption will depend upon the amount of bone resorbed and its specific activity,

$$\text{i.e. } *Ca_{b-} = Ca_{b-} . \text{ specific activity of bone}$$

Thus,

$$*Ca_{b+} - *Ca_{b-} = (Ca_{b+} . \text{ sp. act. eggshell}) - (Ca_{b-} . \text{ sp. act. bone}) \quad (II)$$

At the start of the experiment, the second term is negligible. It is then possible to obtain a linear relationship between $\log (*Ca_{b+} - *Ca_{b-})$ and time, and thus to obtain a value for Ca_{b+} from equation (II). This gives a value of $1 \cdot 02$ g, but from table 12.11 it can be seen that

$$Ca_{b+} - Ca_{b-} = -0 \cdot 02$$

and thus $Ca_{b+} = 1 \cdot 02$, and $Ca_{b-} = 1 \cdot 04$ g.

When the Ca^{45} is withdrawn from the birds' diet on the 26th day of the experiment $*Ca_{abs}$ becomes zero and equation (I) becomes

$$*Ca_{b-} - *Ca_{b+} = *Ca_{shell} \text{ and } *Ca_{end}.$$

A plot of $\log (*Ca_{b-} - *Ca_{b+})$ against time is curvilinear and a graphical analysis gives the equation

$$*Ca_{b-} - *Ca_{b+} = 157,800 \text{ } e^{-0 \cdot 292t} + 58,000 \text{ } e^{-0 \cdot 0797t} \quad (III)$$

The number of separate physiological compartments influencing a system determines the number of variables, and thus the minimum number of exponential terms in an analysis of the system [56]. It is therefore necessary during this phase of the experiment to invoke a slowly mobilized bone (Ca_s) and a fast mobilized bone (Ca_f). Thus Ca_{b+} is now composed of Ca_{s+} and Ca_{f+} while Ca_{b-} consists of Ca_{s-} and Ca_{f-}. With these additional complications, it is possible to solve the equation in an analogous way to that done in the first part of the experiment. The results of this analysis are shown in table 12.12.

Table 12.12   *Size of compartments of Ca in the skeleton of a laying bird* [46]. *Values in brackets refer to % of exchangeable bone.*

	Ca content of Exchangeable bone (U) (g)	Ca removed from bone (Ca_b-) per 24 hr (g)
Analysis from days 0–16		
Exchangeable bone	4·31–4·88	1·04 (21·3→24·1%)
Analysis from days 26–55		
Slowly mobilized bone (Ca_s)	2·55	0·23 (9%)
Rapidly mobilized bone (Ca_f)	1·87	0·79 (42%)
Sum	4·42	1·02 (23·1%)

Several points are of interest in this study. The close correspondence between the analyses of the skeleton during the time when the specific activity of the eggshell was increasing and those when the specific activity was decreasing are very good, but this latter phase can only be described in terms of a function with two exponentials, whereas the increasing phase requires a function with only a single exponential. This is a major discrepancy, but if the results of the first phase are interpreted from the parameters determined from the second phase, there is a good correlation. It would seem, therefore, that it is best to consider the skeleton to be composed of two fractions, one of which is only slowly mobilized (9%/day) whereas the other is rather smaller but almost five times more rapidly mobilized (42·2%/day). It is also interesting to find that the pullet can resorb about 1·02 g Ca/day of its skeleton, and that this corresponds to about 36% of the total calcium entering its blood-stream/day (i.e. $Ca_{abs} + Ca_{b-}$ $= 1·80 + 1·02 = 2·82$ g/day).

In this same study, it was also shown that the size of the exchangeable calcium pool is larger in birds with a negative calcium balance, and this is in agreement with the concept that medullary bone may be formed from cortical bone when the bird is on a calcium-deficient diet. Finally, it was shown that there is a highly significant correlation between the specific activity of the last eggshell and that of the medullary bone of the femur, whereas there was no significant correlation with the cortical bone. These results, therefore, are in agreement with the concept that medullary bone is rapidly metabolized and of great importance in supplying calcium for the mineralization of the eggshell. Similar conclusions have also been reached by Hurwitz [37, 38] in his studies of the kinetics of bone minerals in birds.

In his first experiments, Hurwitz used a single intravenous injection of 3 μc Ca^{45} into domestic fowl at the time when they were due to ovulate. The blood was sampled, and the birds were killed and analysed at various times after the administration of the radio-isotope. The medullary bone showed a greater uptake of Ca^{45} than other parts of the skeleton, but in all cases there was a marked reduction of activity within the first few hours. As the original injection coincided with ovulation, this fall paralleled the deposition of calcium in the eggshell. It is probable, however, that most of the Ca^{45} which was lost from the bone in this experiment simply exchanged with calcium being absorbed by the intestine and was then trapped in the calcifying eggshell. This is the only reasonable explanation for the fact that the rate of loss of radioactivity from the bones decreased with time instead of showing a proportional fall with each reproductive cycle, which is what would be expected if the Ca^{45} was liberated by resorption [37]. It appears, therefore, that the removal of calcium from the blood during the formation

N

of the eggshell so complicates the study of the distribution of radio-isotopes in the bone that it makes a kinetic analysis very complex. The experiment was therefore repeated, using birds which had been treated with Nicarbazin (4,4-dinitro-carbanilide-2-hydroxy-4,6-methyl-pyrimidine). This drug prevents ovulation by inducing yolk resorption without apparently disturbing the gonadotrophic or ovarian hormones [77]. Using these birds, it was possible to give a single injection of the radio-isotope to birds and study the distribution of the Ca^{45} without any complicating influences due to egg-laying. The distribution of radioactivity can be analysed using Bauer, Carlsson, and Lindquist's method,

$$\text{i.e.} \quad Ca_{obs}^{45} = S_t{}^{\star}E + A\int_0^t S^{\star}(t)\,.\,dt$$

where Ca_{obs}^{45} = radioactivity observed in the bone sample at the time t, $S^{\star}$ = specific activity of plasma, E = exchangeable calcium, and A = accretion rate of bone (p. 21). The results of this analysis are shown in table 12.13. It is apparent that the medullary bone has the largest uptake

Table 12.13   *Calcium exchange and accretion rate in femur segments of Nicarbazin-treated fowl* [38]

Femur segment	Ca content (mg)	Exchangeable Ca (mg)	(%)	Accretion rate (mg/hr)	(%)
Ends	655	21·50	3·3	1·50	0·22
Cortical bone	419	2·23	0·5	0·23	0·05
Medullary bone	228	9·61	5·2	0·83	0·36

of Ca^{45} due to its greater percentage of exchangeable calcium and its faster rate of accretion. The cortical bone is the least reactive part of the femur. Obviously it is not possible to determine the rate of resorption of the medullary bone using this technique because egg-laying is inhibited. This is unfortunate, as this is possibly the most interesting aspect of medullary bone physiology, and in order to assess this phenomenon Hurwitz [38] performed a long-term feeding experiment using a high calcium diet (3·8% Ca) containing 1·25 μc/100 g of feed. Domestic fowl were kept for up to fifty-four days on this diet, and were analysed after various times for total calcium and Ca^{45} in bones and plasma. It was not possible to determine a mathematically reliable turnover rate for these bones, and therefore the specific activity of the bone was compared with that of the plasma to obtain a turnover index (table 12.14). This estimate does not allow for any removal of Ca^{45} by resorption, and therefore reflects the minimum 'life span' of the tissue. It is apparent that medullary bone can be mobilized at

Table 12.14 *Relationship of bone and plasma specific activities (i.e. turnover index) of bone segments from birds on Ca⁴⁵ diet for 12 days* [38]

Bone turnover index (sp. act. bone/sp. act. plasma)	Cortical bone	Ends of bones	Medullary bone
Femur	0·07	0·34	0·68
Tibia	0·05	0·21	0·74

a rate at least ten to fifteen times faster than the cortical bone, and at least twice as fast as the ends of the bones. It was concluded that the greater part of the medullary bone must be replaced every few days, and that a turn-over rate of this magnitude greatly exceeds that of any mammal, and is probably unique. These experiments confirm the previous suggestions, namely, that medullary bone is an extremely labile tissue which can be rapidly metabolized and seems to be adapted for liberating calcium at a great rate to meet the requirements for the calcification of the eggshell. The regulation of this bone destruction is, however, an interesting problem which is a matter of current controversy.

The Control of Calcium Metabolism

In most vertebrates there is no doubt that the calcium level of the blood is under the control of the parathyroid hormone and this is undoubtedly true for birds, since calcium-deficient diets cause the calcium level of the blood

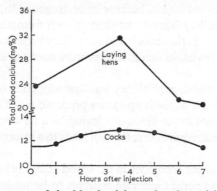

FIG. 12.11. The responses of the blood calcium of cocks and laying fowl to sub-cutaneous injections of 100 units of parathyroid extract (after [47]).

to fall, while the parathyroid glands increase in size. If parathyroid hor-mone is injected into birds, they respond quickly, and the calcium level of the blood rises and then falls to its original value within a few hours (fig. 12.11). The response is more obvious in the female than in the male, and this has led to speculation as to whether oestrogens and parathyroid hormone are synergistic in their action. This concept is quite unnecessary, however, for any change in the level of ionic calcium will produce a corresponding change in the protein-bound calcium of the blood. The oestrogen-treated bird maintains a high concentration of yolk precursors in its blood, and these bind calcium avidly, so that it is to be expected that any change in ionic calcium will produce a larger change in total calcium in the blood of the female than in that of the male birds. There is therefore no need to invoke any direct interactions between parathyroid hormone and oestrogen in this phenomenon.

Table 12.15 *Daily excretion of oestrone from laying and non-laying domestic fowl* [20]

| | μg oestrone excreted/24 hr | |
Bird number	Laying	Non-laying
R1	2·57	0·65
L2	3·86	1·21

The situation regarding the control of bone resorption is more complex. The possibility exists that because oestrogens control the formation of medullary bone they might also be involved in its resorption. This has led to the theory that following ovulation there is a fall in the level of the sex hormones in the blood which, because of oestrogen withdrawal, leads to a resorption of medullary bone at the time of shell formation. Diametrically opposed to this view is the theory that medullary bone is no different from all other tetrapod bones, in that it is resorbed under the influence of parathyroid hormone.

The 'oestrogen withdrawal' theory was first suggested by Riddle, Rauch, and Smith [48], and it depends upon two propositions. The first is that the level of sex hormones in the blood of a laying bird falls rapidly after ovulation, and the second requires that this fall leads to a resorption of medullary bone.

The quantities of sex hormones in the blood of laying birds are, unfortunately, too small to permit accurate analyses to be made. It seems likely, however, that the concentrations of these hormones do decrease after the follicle ruptures, since the weight of the oviduct falls shortly after ovulation and this organ is also maintained by an oestrogenic stimulus [48]. Similarly, the daily excretion of oestrone in the urine decreases rapidly when egg-laying ceases (table 12.15). The way in which a fall in oestrogen concentration might affect the medullary bone has been demonstrated by injecting pigeons for twenty days with an oestrogen preparation, at the end of which time the long bones were filled with medullary bone. The medullary bone was spontaneously resorbed when the injections stopped and, within fifteen days of the last treatment, the bones had reverted to their original state [12]. According to this theory, therefore, the only effect necessary for the resorption of medullary bone is a fall in the oestrogen stimulus which induces it. This accounts for its disappearance from birds at the end of reproduction.

The alternative theory suggests that medullary bone can also be resorbed by means of a stimulus from parathyroid hormone. The evidence for this view has been summarized by Taylor [59] as follows: first, parathyroid hormone acts quickly in birds and thus is capable of inducing the rapid changes which are observed at egg-laying; secondly, the extreme osteoclastic activity seen in medullary bone resorption is similar to that observed in ordinary bone treated with parathyroid hormone; thirdly, there is a fall in the level of diffusible calcium in the blood of birds during eggshell formation which could thus stimulate parathyroid activity; and finally, it explains the time lag of several hours in the change from bone resorption to bone formation which occurs following oviposition in the pigeon.

The 'parathyroid theory' postulates that medullary bone responds to similar resorptive stimuli as ordinary bone. At first sight, this unifying concept is attractive, but it does produce difficulties. It has already been mentioned that when birds are laying eggs on low calcium diets (i.e. when presumably the parathyroid glands are being greatly stimulated) the cortical bone is resorbed to reform the medullary bone. It requires a number of additional postulates to explain how this could occur, unless the medullary bone is less sensitive to parathyroid hormone than the cortical bone, and if this is the case, it is difficult to see how it could function as a labile store during eggshell formation. These difficulties do not arise with the 'oestrogen withdrawal' theory which, in some modified form appears to be the only way of explaining these observations. There are, in fact, some interesting experiments which highlight this difficulty of the parathyroid theory. When a massive dose of 750 I.U. of parathyroid hormone are injected into the laying fowl it is possible to show that a region composed of 'tubes of rarified cancellous bone occupies the space between the cortex and intramedullary deposit' [76]. It is claimed that most of the bone that is resorbed under the influence of the parathyroid hormone is removed from a region of the endosteal surface of the cortical bone. It is implied, therefore, that the parathyroid hormone either resorbs the structural bone rather than the medullary bone or alternatively affects the outer rather than the inner medullary bone which is thus left as a detached layer on the inner side of the diaphysis (plate 2, p. 226). A similar detachment of the medullary bone has been observed in laying birds which have been kept on calcium deficient diets [74] when, presumably, their own parathyroid glands have been stimulated. The observation is not as conclusive as it first appears, however, for resorption of medullary bone would leave no trace of this activity at the macroscopic level, and thus it could be argued that the hormone was indeed resorbing both types of bone. It seems at the moment, therefore, that the concept of oestrogen withdrawal fits some facts better than that of a parathyroid initiated resorption of medullary bone, but this may be partly because very little is known about the oestrogen system. In particular, more information is necessary regarding the extent of bone resorption when the oocyte is ovulated but laid without an eggshell. The oestrogen withdrawal theory would seem to necessitate either a recycling or an excretion of calcium and phosphate ions coincident with this event; for it must be assumed that ovulation leads to an almost inevitable resorption of medullary bone. Soft-shelled eggs are not accompanied by this increased excretion, and thus additional postulates are also necessary in the oestrogen withdrawal theory. It can only be concluded, therefore, that, at the moment, the mechanism governing the control of medullary bone resorption is incompletely understood, especially in the calcium-deficient bird.

Other changes also occur in calcium-deficient birds during reproduction, and in particular, the ovary decreases in size while the adrenals hypertrophy (table 12.16). Only on rare occasions do the birds go into tetany

Table 12.16 *Effect of calcium deficiency on ovary, adrenal glands, and medullary bone of laying hens* [74]. *Medullary bone assessed on scale o to* + + + +

Days on diet	Weight of ovary	Weight of adrenals	Medullary bone in tibia
	(g)	(mg)	
o	20–30	90–100	o to + + +
7	29·1	105	o to +
14	15·0	100	+ +
21	10·0	120	+ + +
28	4·3	190	+ + +

[40], although some breeds of pullets may develop a condition known as cage-layer fatigue after several months of continuous heavy egg production. This disease is characterized by the birds falling on their sides immediately

after oviposition and it may lead to death [4]. The bones of birds with cage-layer fatigue are generally thin, and it has been suggested that the disease is related to the adrenal hormones which are capable of inducing bone resorption [75].

An alternative suggestion is that normal birds only secrete gonadotrophins from the anterior pituitary while on adequate diets. When fed calcium-deficient food, the secretion of gonadotrophins ceases and reproduction stops, although it can be maintained if the hormones are given artificially (table 12.17). This 'pituitary cut-off' mechanism is thought to stop egg pro-

Table 12.17 *Average egg production of domestic fowl on a low calcium diet with or without injections of avian pituitary extracts* [66]

	Number of eggs laid		
Treatment	Days 1–5	Days 6–10	Days 11–15
Low calcium diet	3·7	1·7	0·3
Low calcium diet + pituitary injections	3·7	5·3	1·7

duction when the level of the diffusible calcium in the serum falls below normal. It thus explains the regression of the ovaries when birds are fed calcium-deficient diets for a long period of time. It is proposed that those breeds of domestic fowl which show cage-layer fatigue are specimens which have been so intensively bred for high egg production that they have lost this 'pituitary protective system', with the result that they continue to lay while in negative calcium balance and eventually collapse [66].

It has also been suggested that birds cease to lay on calcium-deficient diets because they are unable to transport the yolk proteins as calcium complexes from the liver to the ovary in the absence of dietary calcium [74]. This could account for the regression of the ovary under these circumstances, although the quantity of calcium involved in yolk transport is small in relation to the amounts available to the bird. The situation is obviously complicated with the skeleton, intestine, liver, and ovary interacting through the control system of the adrenal, pituitary, parathyroid, and gonadal hormones. The major drain on the system is undoubtedly the formation of the eggshell, and this will therefore be considered in more detail.

The Formation of the Eggshell

A radial section of a decalcified eggshell of the domestic fowl is shown diagrammatically in fig. 12.12 (*a*). It is possible to distinguish four main regions.

On the outside of the eggshell is the cuticle. This is a layer of sulphur containing protein which forms a resistant layer up to about 10 μ thick over the calcified layers of the shell. In the electron microscope it appears as a foamy structure, although its outer part is more compact [55].

Most of the thickness of the eggshell is composed of calcium carbonate in the form of calcite, the main crystals of which are orientated with their *c* axes radial (fig. 12.12 (*b*)). This is the palisade layer, and when decalcified it leaves a small amount of organic matter which forms the so-called spongy

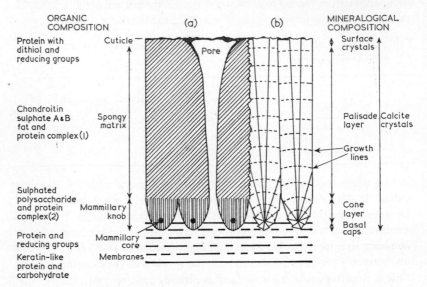

FIG. 12.12. A radial section of a stylized avian eggshell showing the structure, composition, and nomenclature of the various regions. (*a*) The decalcified shell showing the organic matrix and a pore. (*b*) The mineralized shell showing the calcite crystals which run throughout the palisade layer and the growth lines of gas inclusions (data from [50] [51] [73]).

matrix. This usually appears as a non-fibrillar mass consisting of at least 70% protein and 11% polysaccharide with some fat. Some of the polysaccharide is sulphated and about 35% of it is present as the chondroitin sulphates A and B.

The inner part of the calcified layer of the shell extends as numerous roughly hemispherical masses forming the cone or mammillary layer. It is possible to show that the organic matter of this part of the shell differs, histochemically, from the spongy matrix to which it attaches. The centre of the mammillary cone is mineralogically different from the rest of the calcareous material in the shell [68, 69] and it contains a small mass of protein known as the mammillary core. This appears to be the centre where calcification starts during the formation of the shell and studies with pola-rized light have shown that it behaves as a spherulite from which the crystals of the shell radiate (fig. 12.12 (b)). The mammillary core contains disulphide and reducing groups, and the fibres of the shell membranes run into this region.

The shell membranes are made from fibres up to 5 μ thick which are composed of a keratin-like protein coated with a mucopolysaccharide. The membranes separate into two layers which, at the blunt end of the egg, frequently surround an air space. Together, the two shell membranes form a layer about 60–70 μ thick. They attach on their outer surface to the mammillary cores of the inner part of the shell. Internally, they enclose the egg albumen.

The calcified part of the eggshell is about 300 μ thick and it is penetrated by between 7,000 and 17,000 pores. These are funnel-shaped cavities about 15–65 μ at the mouth and 6–23 μ at the inner end. They arise between the mammillary knobs and open beneath the cuticle. They appear to be respon-sible for gaseous exchange between the environment and the egg contents [51, 73].

The eggshells of different species show considerable variations in struc-ture, with the cuticle and shapes of the pores being the most variable parts. In all cases, however, they are well calcified and, being tertiary membranes, they are all secreted by the oviduct. This tubular duct can be conveniently considered as being composed of five regions. These are (1) the *infundibu-lum*, which receives the oocyte after it is shed into the body cavity by the ovary, (2) the *magnum* or albumen secreting region, (3) the *isthmus* or region which secretes the shell membranes, (4) the *shell secreting* region, sometimes unfortunately named the *uterus*, and (5) the *vagina*.

The general proportions of these regions of the oviduct are fairly similar in most birds. The egg passes rapidly through most of the oviduct until it reaches the shell-secreting region (table 12.18). It stays in this region about

Table 12.18 *Proportions of the various regions of the avian oviduct (as %* *total length) and time the egg spends in each region* [79]

Species	Infundibulum Length (%)	Time (hr)	Magnum Length (%)	Time (hr)	Isthmus Length (%)	Time (hr)	Shell forming Length (%)	Time (hr)	Vagina Length (%)
Turkey	14·8	0·25	42·6	2·5	15·3	1·25	13·5	22–24	13·6
Domestic fowl	9·6	0·25	45·0	2·5	13·4	1·25	16·9	18–20	16·1
Japanese quail	18·2	0·25	46·9	2·5	20·1	1·75	9·9	19–20	4·9

20 hours, although the calcification of the eggshell proceeds mainly in the last 15 hours. The eggshell of the domestic fowl contains about 5 g calcium carbonate which is therefore secreted at a rate of about 300 mg/hour. Histochemical studies of the oviduct are in agreement with biochemical analyses in demonstrating that the oviduct does not store large amounts of inorganic ions during reproductive activity. There is, however, an unusual accumulation of calcium ions in the isthmus region and these fall to about one-half their concentration as the egg enters this portion of the oviduct [50a]. Secretory cells at the isthmo-uterine junction show unusual triple secretory droplets and it is interesting to speculate that this may be the place where the crystal seeds of the shell may be secreted [40a]. When the egg leaves the isthmus and enters the shell-secreting region of the oviduct, the shell membranes are quite loose, but the egg becomes distended in the lower part of the oviduct by the absorption of a watery secretion. It was at one time thought that this secretion might contain the calcium and carbonate ions necessary for the formation of the shell, but analyses showed that it would take 10 litres of this solution to provide enough calcium for one eggshell [3]. The secretion is probably important in shell formation for two entirely different reasons. It continues to pass, in small amounts, into the contents of the egg throughout shell formation, and therefore is probably responsible for the formation of minute canals through the calcareous part of the shell, i.e. pores. It also distends the egg so that it becomes closely applied to the walls of the oviduct. This is sometimes considered as the stimulus necessary to start shell formation. It certainly brings the shell membranes and the walls of the oviduct into close contact, and the evidence all suggests that this enables the oviduct to remove calcium ions and some form of carbon dioxide from the blood and secrete the eggshell directly on to the shell membranes. This being the case, one would expect to find changes in the composition of the blood at this time, although these might be complicated by variations in the times of feeding and egg-laying.

An analysis of blood from the anterior mesenteric artery of the laying fowl showed that it contained 15·3 mg % calcium, while the corresponding vein leaving the intestine contained blood with 21·8 mg % calcium [11]. This difference in calcium content was not found in non-laying birds and it corresponds with the increased calcium retention which occurs in reproducing females [13]. Any attempt to correlate the calcium level of the blood with the process of shell calcification must therefore take into consideration the absorption of calcium from the intestine and the feeding habits of birds. When this is done, it can be shown that a fall in the total calcium level of the blood occurs at the time of shell formation (table 12.19). The fall is greatest when the birds are kept on calcium-deficient diets and occurs

Table 12.19 *Total calcium content of the blood of domestic fowl at various times of the day, showing that a fall is due to eggshell formation rather than a decline in intestinal absorption* [32]

Calcium level of blood when	10.00–15.00 hr (1–6 hr after preceding oviposition) (i.e. no shell formation) (mg %)	21.30–24.00 hr (12½–15 hr after preceding oviposition) (i.e. shell being formed) (mg %)	9.00–10.00 hr (24–25 hr after preceding oviposition) (i.e. end of shell formation) (mg %)
(a) egg present	27·5	25·2	23·5
(b) egg absent	—	29·1	28·0

in both diffusible and non-diffusible fractions of the blood (table 12.20). The exact relationship of the calcium between these fractions is complicated by the fact that the blood from the oviduct mixes with blood from other organs before being sampled in the peripheral circulation. A number of analyses have, however, been made on arterial blood and blood leaving

Table 12.20 *Changes in diffusible and non-diffusible calcium in the peripheral blood of domestic fowl on normal and low calcium diets, and in various reproductive states* [61]

Reproductive state	Diet	Total calcium (mg %)	Diffusible calcium (mg %)	Non-diffusible calcium (mg %)
Egg present	2% Ca	22·8	8·45	14·35
No egg	2% Ca	23·9	9·45	14·45
Egg present	0·1% Ca	17·9	7·1	10·8
No egg	0·1% Ca	21·5	8·1 mg	13·4

the shell-forming region of the oviduct (table 12.21). The results vary, depending upon the method of preparation of the samples, but they show three points. First, about 20% of the calcium is removed from the blood as it passes through the region of the oviduct which is forming the eggshell. Secondly, both diffusible and non-diffusible fractions of the blood calcium are diminished in this process. Thirdly, it appears that the two fractions of plasma calcium are in equilibrium, as they are present in roughly the same proportions before and after they pass through the oviduct. The most likely explanation of these phenomena is that the oviduct takes up calcium ions from the diffusible fraction of the blood and this then rapidly equilibrates with the other calcium fractions. It is not known whether the oviduct actively absorbs calcium ions or whether they simply diffuse out of the

Table 12.21 *The effect of shell formation upon the diffusible and non-diffusible level of plasma calcium in the arterial system and oviducal vein* [34, 78]

Reproductive state	Diffusible Ca (mg %)		Non-diff. Ca (mg %)		Diff./non-diff.	
	Artery	Vein	Artery	Vein	Artery	Vein
Hard shell	10·4	9·4	14·3	10·4	0·73	0·90
Slight calcif.	8·8	7·2	20·6	18·4	0·43	0·39
Shell forming (1)	5·6	4·6	21·0	17·0	0·27	0·27
Shell forming (2)	6·4	5·4	17·5	12·8	0·37	0·42
No egg (1)	5·9	5·0	19·8	18·5	0·30	0·27
No egg (2)	6·1	6·1	14·0	13·8	0·44	0·44

(1) = artery sampled before vein. (2) = vein sampled before artery.

blood. The former would seem the more probable but, if such a system does exist, it is relatively indiscriminate, since experiments with mixtures of the radio-isotopes Sr^{89} and Ca^{45} showed that the barrier between the blood and the forming eggshell has a Sr/Ca discrimination ratio of only 0·927 [25].

The avian oviduct contains considerable quantities of the enzyme carbonic anhydrase. The amount is greatest in the epithelium of the shell-forming region and increases in the laying bird (table 12.22). This enzyme catalyses the hydration of carbon dioxide and it appears that it is involved in the secretion of the calcareous eggshell since inhibition of the enzyme by a number of drugs, such as sulphanilamide, results in poorly calcified eggshells [31]. It has been suggested that the enzyme is involved in the formation of carbonate ions from bicarbonate,

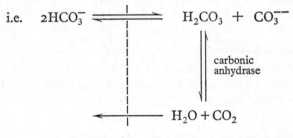

i.e. $2HCO_3^- \rightleftharpoons H_2CO_3 + CO_3^{--}$

carbonic anhydrase

$H_2O + CO_2$

(blood) (oviduct wall)   (eggshell)

The bicarbonate ions are derived from the plasma and the carbonic anhydrase results in a return of carbon dioxide to the blood-stream.

The theory receives some support from analyses of the blood of laying fowl. It is argued that the formation of the eggshell involves a loss of carbonate ions and hence an acidose metabolism, which is compensated by hyperventilation, i.e. an alkalose respiration. Thus the partial pressure of

Table 12.22   *Carbonic anhydrase content of the oviduct of the domestic fowl* [19]. *Units of enzyme activity/mg fresh tissue*

| | Blood | Region of oviduct | | Scrapings of shell-secreting | Vagina |
		Magnum	Shell-secreting		
Laying bird	1·14	0·043	0·040	0·076	Nil
Non-laying	1·15	0·042	0·026	0·046	Nil

the carbon dioxide in the blood falls in an attempt to stop the pH of the blood from falling. The results given in table 12.23 show that the pCO_2,

Table 12.23   *Analyses of the blood of the domestic fowl during shell formation showing changes in the level of carbon dioxide and its hydration products* [44]

Hours after oviposition	pH	HCO_3 (meq/1)	pCO_2 (mm Hg)
0	7·522	29·6	37·7
3·5	7·530	31·2	38·1
5	7·533	31·5	38·2
10	7·523	27·5	34·7
15	7·478	24·6	34·4
20	7·454	22·4	33·4
22	7·411	20·7	32·1
25	7·435	23·7	35·5
30	7·483	29·1	38·7

HCO_3, and pH all tend to fall as shell formation progresses. The blood of the male bird shows none of these changes.

The values obtained in these analyses are probably not absolute as they are based upon the application of methods devised for mammalian blood. The results are important, however, for they could explain the production of thin-shelled eggs in hot weather on the basis that, under these conditions, birds hyperventilate in order to regulate their temperature and thus probably disturb the bicarbonate system in the blood. Feeding ammonium chloride to birds also produces thin-shelled eggs and probably for the same reason, i.e. it induces an acidose metabolism and a loss of blood bicarbonate [35].

During the formation of the eggshell, calcium and carbonate ions are extracted from the blood-stream at a rate of about 5 g/15 hr. This corresponds to 100–150 mg Ca/hr, and since the domestic fowl only possesses about 100 ml plasma containing 25 mg % calcium, it would deplete its circulation of calcium within 10–15 min were this not being continually replaced [32]. A healthy fowl will probably absorb up to 1·5 g Ca/day. If absorbed evenly over the day, this would amount to about 60 mg Ca/hr, so that dietary sources of calcium are both too small and too slow to replenish the blood. If the absorption of calcium by the bird does not occupy 24 hours, it is possible that for a time the bird may approach a state where dietary calcium can replenish the drain on the blood during eggshell formation, but in this case there will be a stage in the calcification of the shell when the intestine is depleted of available calcium. It would seem inevitable, therefore, that skeletal reserves of calcium must be used to supply calcium to the blood even when the bird is on a good calcium diet. This conclusion is confirmed by some experiments in which domestic fowl were fed between 9.30 and 11.00 a.m. with a meal containing Ca^{45}. The laying

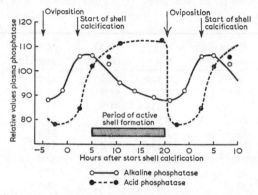

FIG. 12.13. Variations in the levels of acid and alkaline phosphatase in the blood of the laying fowl in relation to the formation of the eggshell (after [67]).

of eggs was timed, and the eggshells were sectioned tangentially and autoradiographed. The results showed that eggs laid almost 24 hours after feeding had a layer of calcium on the outer part of the shell which was not radioactive. Apparently, therefore, during the night the dietary supply of calcium diminished and was replaced by non-radioactive calcium from the skeleton. A number of estimates have been made as to the amount of calcium in the eggshell which is derived from skeletal sources as opposed to the diet. The lowest values indicate 25–40% [24] while the highest suggest that up to 65% of the shell calcium is derived from the bones [41]. The compartmental analysis of the avian skeleton (p. 179) indicates that 36% of the calcium entering the blood-stream of a laying fowl is derived from skeletal sources.

These changes in the calcium metabolism of laying birds all appear to be related to the formation of a large egg with a well-calcified eggshell. The outstanding peculiarity of the avian reproductive system would, thus, be the extreme rate of calcium mobilization necessary for the formation of the eggshell. The demand for calcium is so great during this period that it can only be met by a specialized type of tissue, the medullary bone. Analyses of the blood of laying birds for alkaline and acid phosphatase show that the alkaline phosphatase declines after the start of shell formation and then increases again after oviposition. The acid phosphatase increases at the time of shell deposition and decreases after oviposition (fig. 12.13). These changes can be correlated with changes in the skeletal system, for it seems possible that the alkaline phosphatase of the blood is at least partly derived from the osteoblasts, whereas acid phosphatase could be derived from the osteoclasts (table 2.1). If this interpretation is correct, the changes in blood phosphatase demonstrate changes from bone formation to bone destruction similar to those which can be seen in medullary bone during eggshell formation. This would, therefore, be additional evidence for the resorption of medullary bone to provide calcium for eggshell formation but it is also possible that these changes in enzyme levels originate from other organs such as the ovary, kidney or intestine which are also influenced by egg-laying and similarly contain large amounts of phosphates.

REFERENCES

[1] ASCENZI, A., FRANOICS, C., and BOCCIARELLI, S. (1963), 'On the bone induced by oestrogens in birds', *J. Ultrastruct. Res.*, 8, 491–505.

[2] BAKER, J. R. and BALCH, D. A. (1962), 'A study of the organic material of hens' eggshell', *Biochem. J.*, 82, 352–61.

[3] BEADLE, B. W., CONRAD, R. M., and SCOTT, H. M. (1938), 'The composition of the uterine secretion of the domestic fowl', *Poult. Sci.*, 17, 498–504.

[4] BELL, D. J. and SILLER, W. G. (1962), 'Cage-layer fatigue in Brown Leghorns', *Res. vet. Sci.*, 3, 219–30.

[5] BENOIT, J., CABANES, R., MESSERSCHMITT, J., and CLAVERT, J. (1942), 'Contribution à l'etude histologique de l'ostéogenèse provoquée par la folliculine chez le Canard', *C.R. Soc. Biol., Paris*, 136, 755–6.

[6] BENOIT, J. and CLAVERT, J. (1945), 'Action ostéogénétique directe et locale de la folliculine démonstrée chez le Canard et le Pigeon, par son introduction localisée dans un os long', *C.R. Soc. Biol., Paris*, 139, 728–30.

[7] BENOIT, J., CLAVERT, J., and GRANGAUD, R. (1942), 'Action de la folliculine sur le métabolisme du calcium chez les oiseaux. I. Ossification folliculine. Variations quantitatives des principaux constituants chimiques de l'os provoqúees chez le Canard et le Pigeon par l'hormone sexuelle femelle', *Trav. Soc. Chim. biol.*, 24, 1311–322.

[8] BLOOM, M. A., BLOOM, W., DOMM, L. V., and MCLEAN, F. C. (1940), 'Changes in avian bone due to injected estrogen and during the reproductive cycle', *Anat. Rec.*, 78, 143.

[9] BLOOM, M. A., MCLEAN, F. C., and BLOOM, W. (1942), 'Calcification and ossification. The formation of medullary bone in male and castrate pigeons under the influence of sex hormones', *Anat. Rec.*, **83**, 99–120.

[10] BLOOM, W., BLOOM, M. A., and MCLEAN, F. C. (1941), 'Calcification and ossification. Medullary bone changes in the reproductive cycle of female pigeons', *Anat. Rec.*, **81**, 443–75.

[11] BUCKNER, G. D., MARTIN, J. H., and HULL, F. E. (1930), 'The distribution of blood calcium in the circulation of laying hens', *Amer. J. Physiol.*, **93**, 86–9.

[12] CLAVERT, J. (1942), 'Disparition par l'arrêt des injections de folliculine de l'os medullaire formé sous l'action de cette hormone', *C.R. Soc. Biol., Paris*, **136**, 756–7.

[13] CLAVERT, J. and BENOIT, J. (1942a), 'Enrichissement du squelette en calcium chez le Pigeon sous l'action du proprionate d'oestradiol', *C.R. Soc. Biol., Paris*, **136**, 509–11.

[14] CLAVERT, J. and BENOIT, J. (1942b), 'Action de la folloculine sur le metabolisme du calcium chez les oiseaux. 4. Retention du calcium alimentaire determinée chez le pigeon par le diproprionate d'oestradiol', *Trav. Soc. Chim. biol.*, **24**, 1469–74.

[15] COMMON, R. H. (1933), 'Observations on the mineral metabolism of pullets. 1', *J. agric. Sci.*, **23**, 555–70.

[16] COMMON, R. H. (1936), 'Observations on the mineral metabolism of pullets. 2', *J. agric. Sci.*, **26**, 85–100.

[17] COMMON, R. H. (1938), 'Observations on the mineral metabolism of pullets. 3', *J. agric. Sci.*, **28**, 347–66.

[18] COMMON, R. H. (1941), 'Observations on the mineral metabolism of pullets. 5. Acid base equilibria and reproductive activity', *J. agric. Sci.*, **31**, 281–94.

[19] COMMON, R. H. (1941), 'The carbonic anhydrase activity of the hen's oviduct', *J. agric. Sci.*, **31**, 412–14.

[20] COMMON, R. H., AINSWORTH, L., HERTELENDY, F., and MATHUR, R. S. (1965), 'The estrone content of hens' urine', *Can. J. Physiol.*, **43**, 539–47.

[21] COMMON, R. H., RUTLEDGE, N. A., and HALE, R. W. (1948), 'Observations on the mineral metabolism of pullets. 8. The influence of gonadal hormones on the retention of calcium and phosphorus', *J. agric. Sci.*, **38**, 64–80.

[22] CONKIE, D. (1963), 'P.A.S. positive component of the medullary bone of the laying domestic fowl', *Nature, Lond.*, **197**, 808–9.

[23] DALLEMAGNE, M. J. (1948), 'The theory of primary calcification in bone', *Nature, Lond.*, **161**, 115–17.

[24] DRIGGERS, J. C. and COMAR, C. L. (1949), 'The secretion of radioactive calcium (Ca[45]) in the hen's egg', *Poult. Sci.*, **28**, 420–4.

[25] DRORI, D., VOLCANI, R., FEIGE, Y., SHALMON, E., and PASSY, N. (1964), 'Factors affecting the Ca[45] and Sr[89] transfer in the laying hen', *Poult. Sci.*, **43**, 486–91.

[26] FOOTE, J. S. (1916), 'A contribution to the comparative histology of the femur', *Smithson. Contr. Knowl.*, **35**, 1–242.

[27] FRIEDMANN, H. (1935), 'Notes on the differential threshold of reaction to vitamin-D deficiency in the house sparrow and the chick', *Biol. Bull. Wood's Hole*, **69**, 71–4.

[28] FUSSELL, M. H. (1960). Unpublished results quoted by Taylor, T. G. (1962), *q.v.*

[29] GOVAERTS, J. and DALLEMAGNE, M. J. (1948), 'Influence of folliculin on bone metabolism studied by means of radiophosphorus $^{32}_{15}P$', *Nature, Lond.*, **161**, 977.

[30] GOVAERTS, J., DALLEMAGNE, M. J., and MELON, J. (1951), 'Radio-calcium as an indicator in the study of the action of estradiol on calcium metabolism', *Endocrinology*, **48**, 443–52.

[31] GUTOWSKA, MARIE S. and MITCHELL, C. A. (1945), 'Carbonic anhydrase in the calcification of the eggshell', *Poult. Sci.*, **24**, 159–67.

[32] HERTELENDY, F. and TAYLOR, T. G. (1961), 'Changes in blood calcium associated with eggshell calcification in the domestic fowl', *Poult. Sci.*, **40**, 108–14.

[33] HOU, H. C. (1930), 'Further observations on the relation of the preen gland of birds to rickets', *Chin. J. Physiol.*, **4**, 79–92.

[34] HUNSAKER, W. G. and STURKIE, P. D. (1961), 'Removal of calcium from uterine blood during shell formation in the chicken', *Poult. Sci.*, **40**, 1348–52.

[35] HUNT, J. R. and AITKEN, J. R. (1962), 'The effect of ammonium and chloride ions in the diet of hens and eggshell quality', *Poult. Sci.*, **41**, 434–8.

[36] HURWITZ, S. (1964a), 'Calcium metabolism of pullets at the onset of egg production as influenced by dietary calcium level', *Poult. Sci.*, **43**, 1462–72.

[37] HURWITZ, S. (1964b), 'Bone composition and Ca^{45} retention in fowl as influenced by egg formation', *Amer. J. Physiol.*, **206**, 198–204.

[38] HURWITZ, S. (1965), 'Calcium turnover in different bone segments of laying fowl', *Amer. J. Physiol.*, **208**, 203–7.

[39] HURWITZ, S. and GRIMINGER, P. (1961), 'Partition of calcium and phosphorus excretion in laying hen', *Nature, Lond.*, **189**, 759–60.

[40] HUTT, F. B. and BOYD, W. L. (1935), 'Idiopathic hypoparathyroidism and tetany in the fowl', *Endocrinology*, **19**, 398–402.

[40a] JOHNSTON, H. S., AITKEN, R. N. C., and WYBURN, G. M. (1963), 'The fine structure of the uterus of the domestic fowl', *J. Anat. Lond.*, **97**, 333–44.

[41] JOWSEY, J. R., BERLIE, M. R., SPINKS, J. W. T., and O'NEIL, J. B. (1956), 'Uptake of calcium by the laying hen and subsequent transfer from egg to chick', *Poult. Sci.*, **35**, 1234–8.

[42] KYES, P. and POTTER, T. S. (1934), 'Physiological marrow ossification in female pigeons', *Anat. Rec.*, **60**, 377–9.

[43] MCDONALD, MARGARET R. and RIDDLE, O. (1945), 'The effect of reproduction and estrogen administration on the partition of calcium, phosphorus, and nitrogen in pigeon plasma', *J. biol. Chem.*, **159**, 455–64.

[44] MONGIN, P. and LACASSAGNE, L. (1964), 'Physiologie de la formation

de la coquille de l'œuf de Poule et équilibre acido-basique du sang', *C.R. Acad. Sci., Paris*, **258**, 3093–4.

[45] MORGAN, C. L. and MITCHELL, J. H. (1938), 'The calcium and phosphorus balance of laying hens', *Poult. Sci.*, **17**, 99–104.

[46] MUELLER, W. J., SCHRAER, ROSEMARY, and SCHRAER, H. (1964), 'Calcium metabolism and skeletal dynamics of laying pullets', *J. Nutr.*, **84**, 20–6.

[47] POLIN, P., STURKIE, P. D., and HUNSAKER, W. (1957), 'The blood calcium response of the chicken to parathyroid extracts', *Endocrinology*, **60**, 1–5.

[48] RIDDLE, O., RAUCHE, V. M., and SMITH, G. C. (1944), 'Changes in medullary bone during the reproductive cycle of female pigeons', *Anat. Rec.*, **90**, 295–305.

[49] RIDDLE, O. and REINHART, W. H. (1926), 'Studies on the physiology of reproduction in birds. 21. Blood calcium changes in the reproductive cycle', *Amer. J. Physiol.*, **76**, 660–76.

[50] SCHMIDT, W. J. (1962), 'Liegt der Eischalenkalk der Vogel als submikroskopische Kristallite', *Z. Zellforsch.*, **57**, 848–80.

[50a] SCHRAER, R. and SCHRAER, H. (1965), 'Changes in metal distribution of the avian oviduct during the ovulation cycle', *Proc. Soc. exp. Biol.*, **119**, 937–42.

[51] SIMKISS, K. (1961), 'Calcium metabolism and avian reproduction', *Biol. Rev.*, **36**, 321–67.

[52] SIMKISS, K. (1962), 'Viviparity and avian reproduction', *Ibis.*, **104**, 216–19.

[53] SIMKISS, K. (1963), *Bird Flight*, Hutchinson, 96 pp.

[54] SIMKISS, K. and TYLER, C. (1959), 'The possible calcification mechanisms in some reptilian eggshells', *Quart. J. micr. Sci.*, **100**, 529–38.

[55] SIMONS, P. C. M. and WIERTZ, G. (1963), 'Notes on the structure of membranes and shell in the hen's egg. An electron microscopical study', *Z. Zellforsch.*, **59**, 555–67.

[56] SOLOMON, A. K. (1960), 'Compartmental methods of kinetic analysis', in *Mineral Metabolism*, 1A, eds. Comar, C. L. and Bronner, F., Academic Press, 119–67.

[57] STRINGER, D. A. and TAYLOR, T. G. (1961), 'The calcification mechanism as exemplified by a histochemical study of avian medullary bone', *Biochem. J.*, **78**, 19P.

[58] TAYLOR, T. G. (1962), 'Calcium absorption and metabolism in the laying hen', in *Nutrition of Pigs and Poultry*, eds. Morgan, J. T. and Lewis, D., Butterworth, 148–57.

[59] TAYLOR, T. G. (1965a), 'Calcium–endocrine relationships in the laying hen', *Proc. Nutr. Soc.*, **24**, 49–54.

[60] TAYLOR, T. G. (1965b), 'The availability of the calcium and phosphorus of plant minerals for animals', *Proc. Nutr. Soc.*, **24**, 105–12.

[61] TAYLOR, T. G. and HERTELENDY, F. (1961), 'Changes in the blood calcium associated with eggshell calcification in the domestic fowl. 2. Changes in the diffusible calcium', *Poult. Sci.*, **40**, 115–23.

[62] TAYLOR, T. G. and MOORE, J. H. (1954), 'Skeletal depletion in hens laying on a low calcium diet', *Brit. J. Nutrit.*, **8**, 112–24.

[63] TAYLOR, T. G. and MOORE, J. H. (1956), 'The effect of calcium depletion on the chemical composition of bone minerals in laying hens', *Brit. J. Nutrit.*, **10**, 250–63.

[64] TAYLOR, T. G. and MOORE, J. H. (1958), 'The effect of high and low levels of dietary inorganic phosphate on the pre-laying storage of calcium and phosphorus and on the composition of the medullary and cortical bone in pullets', *Brit. J. Nutrit.*, **12**, 35–42.

[65] TAYLOR, T. G., MOORE, J. H., and LOOSMORE, R. M. (1958), 'Some effects of bone fracture in hens', *Zbl. Veterinarmedizin.*, **5**, 579–88.

[66] TAYLOR, T. G., MORRIS, T. R., and HERTELENDY, F. (1962), 'The effect of pituitary hormones on ovulation in calcium deficient pullets', *Vet. Rec.*, **74**, 123–5.

[67] TAYLOR, T. G., WILLIAMS, ANN, and KIRKLEY, JEAN (1965), 'Cyclic changes in the activities of plasma acid and alkaline phosphatases during eggshell calcification in the domestic fowl', *Can. J. Physiol.*, **43**, 451–7.

[68] TEREPKA, A. R. (1963a), 'Structure and calcification in avian eggshell', *Exp. Cell. Res.*, **30**, 171–82.

[69] TEREPKA, A. R. (1963b), 'Organic–inorganic interrelationships in avian eggshell', *Exp. Cell. Res.*, **30**, 183–92.

[70] TYLER, C. (1940), 'Studies of calcium and phosphorus metabolism in relation to chemical structure of bone. I. Experiments with laying birds', *Biochem. J.*, **34**, 202–12.

[71] TYLER, C. (1946), 'Studies in the absorption and excretion of certain minerals by poultry', *J. agric. Sci.*, **36**, 263–74.

[72] TYLER, C. (1948–49), 'The mineral requirements and metabolism of poultry. Calcium and Phosphorus. Part 1', *Nutr. Abst. and Rev.*, **18**, 261–74; 'Part 2', *Nutr. Abst. and Rev.*, **18**, 473–83.

[73] TYLER, C. (1964), 'Einige chemische, physikalische und strukturelle Eigenschaften der Eischalen', *J. Orn. Lpz.*, **105**, 57–63.

[74] URIST, M. R. (1959), 'The effects of calcium deprivation upon the blood, adrenal cortex, ovary and skeleton in the domestic fowl', *Rec. Prog. Hormone Res.*, **15**, 455–77.

[75] URIST, M. R. and DEUTSCH, NANCY M. (1960), 'Effects of cortisone upon blood, adrenal cortex, gonads and the development of osteoporosis in birds', *Endocrinology*, **66**, 805–818.

[76] URIST, M. R., DEUTSCH, N. M., POMERANTZ, G., and MCLEAN, F. C. (1960), 'Interrelations between actions of parathyroid hormone and estrogens on bone and blood in avian species', *Amer. J. Physiol.*, **199**, 851–55.

[77] WEISS, H. S., FISHER, H., and GRIMINGER, P. (1960), 'Chemical control of onset of egg production', *Poult. Sci.*, **39**, 1221–3.

[78] WINGET, C. M., SMITH, A. H., and HOOVER, G. N. (1958), 'Arteriovenous differences in plasma concentration in the shell gland of the laying hen during shell formation', *Poult. Sci.*, **37**, 1325–8.

[79] WOODWARD, A. E. and MATHER, F. B. (1964), 'The timing of ovulation, movement of the ovum through the oviduct, pigmentation, and shell deposition in Japanese Quail (*Coturnix coturnix japonica*)', *Poult. Sci.*, **43**, 1427–32.

CHAPTER 13

The Utilization of Calcium by the Avian Embryo

Calcium has been the subject of one of the keenest controversies which has ever taken place in the study of chemical embryology. The history of this debate dates back to 1822, when William Prout published *Some experiments on the changes which take place in the fixed principles of the egg during incubation,* and the results which caused so much discussion are shown in table 13.1. The work was intended to investigate the origin of the chick's skele-

Table 13.1 *Results of Prout's experiment on changes in composition of the egg contents during incubation. Analyses expressed in parts per thousand wet weight (from [17])*

Day	Phosphoric acid	'Alkaline matters' (potash, soda, and their carbonates)	'Earthy carbonate' (lime, magnesia, and their carbonates)
0	4·15	3·28	0·94
10	4·14	3·11	1·05
15	3·97	2·87	1·15
21	4·13	2·50	3·90

ton, and exception was taken to the finding that there was a four-fold increase in the 'earthy carbonates' in the egg contents during the development of the embryo. Prout himself was not too sure what his results meant, but commented that the increase in the lime in the egg contents was derived from some unknown source during the process of incubation. The obvious source of calcium is, of course, the eggshell, but Prout doubted this for two reasons. First, he said, there are no blood vessels in the shell membranes and therefore it is difficult to see how anything could pass through them into the interior of the egg. Secondly, the yolk apparently contained more calcium at the end of incubation than it did at the beginning, and thus it seemed unlikely that the embryo would use the shell as a source of calcium while ignoring the yolk:

'I by no means wish to assert that the earth is not derived from the shell, because in this case the only alternative left to me is to assert that it is formed by transmutation from other matter; an assertion which I confess myself not bold enough to make in the present state of our knowledge however strongly I may be inclined to believe that within certain limits this power is to be ranked among the capabilities of the vital energies.'

The argument as to whether the chick used the eggshell as a source of skeletal calcium continued for almost a century and is well reviewed by Needham [17]. The matter was only settled when analytical techniques improved sufficiently to enable successive investigators to obtain similar results. Table 13.2 is based upon work published in the last fifty years, and

Table 13.2   *The quantity of calcium in the yolk (or egg contents) before incubation and in the hatchling, showing the amount of calcium considered to be derived from the eggshell. The most recent work is in the bottom of the table* [2, 4, 11, 16, 19]

Species	Before incubation (a)		mg Ca in hatchling (b)	Calcium derived from eggshell (i.e. b–a)	
	mg Ca in yolk	mg Ca in egg contents		(mg)	(% in chick)
Duck	58	—	221	163	74
Pea fowl	75	—	351	276	79
Domestic fowl	25	—	142	117	82
Domestic fowl	38	—	171	133	78
Domestic fowl	26–27	—	114–175	88–148	77–84
Domestic fowl	20	23	118	95	80
Domestic fowl	18·9	21·9	125	103·1	82

it is apparent that it confirms Prout's original results, for the hatchling does indeed contain about four times more calcium than was present in the original egg contents. The ultimate source of the extra calcium is undoubtedly the eggshell, and the amount absorbed is about 100 mg or 5% of the eggshell of the domestic fowl.

In order to understand the absorption of the shell and its utilization by the embryo it is necessary to note the composition of the calcium stores of the embryo and their changes during incubation. The composition of the albumen, the yolk, and the eggshell of the domestic fowl are given in table 13.3. Besides acting as stores of calcium, both the albumen and the yolk contain appreciable quantities of magnesium. The origin of the albuminous magnesium is not known, but it seems likely that the magnesium in the oocyte may simply become incorporated with the calcium during the

Table 13.3 *Quantities of various ions in the blood of a reproducing fowl and in the fully formed egg* [14, 28]

	Ca (mg)	Mg (mg)	P (mg)	Na (mg)	K (mg)
Diffusible level in plasma	8·1%	2·2%			
Non-diffusible in plasma	13·4%	1·3%			
Albumen (33 g)	2·0	3·6	11	64	49
Yolk (20 g)	26·0	3·0	100	10	15
Shell	2210	20	20		
(5% of shell)	110	1	1		

transport of the yolk precursors through the blood. The Ca/Mg ratio of the non-diffusible fraction of the blood of a laying bird is approximately the same as the Ca/Mg ratio of the yolk (table 13.3). In discussions of the distribution of ions in the developing embryo, we may accept that the embryonic skeleton has to be derived from the yolk and about 5% of the eggshell.

The embryo of the domestic fowl has been analysed for calcium at all stages of its development, and when the calcium content is plotted semi-

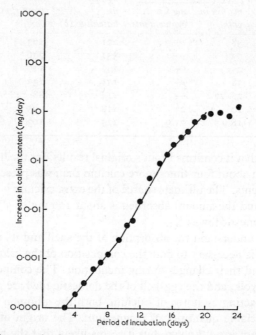

FIG. 13.1. The increase in the calcium content of the embryo of the domestic fowl during incubation (after [11]).

logarithmically against age a sigmoid curve similar to a growth curve is obtained (fig. 13.1). The incorporation of calcium into the embryo does not occur at a constant rate, but at roughly three rates covering days 1–9, 9–15, and 15–hatching. The first period corresponds with growth prior to the formation of skeletal tissue.

The calcium content of the yolk falls during the first 10–11 days of incubation and then begins to rise so that towards the end of development it contains about 75% more calcium than it did originally. The phosphoprotein content of the yolk is constant up until about 9 days of incubation. It then decreases exponentially at a rate of about 20% per day (fig. 13.2). After about 14 days of incubation, the protein content of the yolk

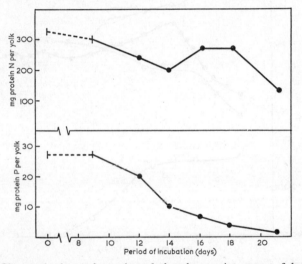

FIG. 13.2. Changes in the total protein and phosphoprotein content of the yolk of an incubated fowl's egg (after [15]).

increases for a few days, apparently because about 30% of the egg albumen enters the yolk sac at this time (figs. 13.2, 13.4).

In an attempt to find how the calcium metabolism of the embryo is correlated with these changes, Johnson and Comar [11] injected 25 μc Ca[45] into the albumen of fertile eggs of the domestic fowl. They then incubated the eggs and analysed the embryo and egg contents at daily intervals for labelled and total calcium. The results are shown in fig. 13.3 and table 13.4. It was found that the Ca[45] was evenly distributed throughout the albumen within a few days of the injection. The inner layers of the eggshell then became rapidly labelled by the exchange of Ca[40] from the shell with Ca[45] from the albumen. The level of radioactivity in the shell is fairly constant until about 9 days, after which it shows a rapid decline. The specific activity of the yolk was characterized by a rapid increase up to the 7th day and a plateau from then to the 12th day. This was interpreted as showing a relatively free movement of Ca^{45} from the albumen across the vitelline membrane, but with a restricted exchange when the cellular layers of the yolk sac started to form. The increase in specific activity after day 12 was therefore interpreted as showing an absorption of Ca^{45} from the blood. The

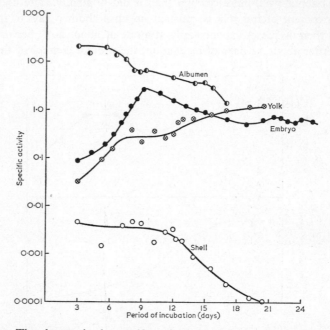

FIG. 13.3. The changes in the specific activity of calcium in the components of a fowl's egg which had been injected with Ca^{45} into the albumen prior to incubation (after [11]).

effect could also be explained by the fact that the yolk sac appears to absorb some of the albumen protein (and presumably Ca^{45}) from day 14 onwards. This might be a factor in explaining the observation that there is an increase in the specific activity of the yolk, although its calcium content is fairly stable from the 15th to 16th day until hatching (table 13.4).

The most interesting interpretations of this experiment can be derived from calculations which determine the specific activity of the calcium which the embryo accumulates each day. This can be obtained by measuring the daily accumulation of both Ca^{45} and total calcium. If it is then assumed that this is a one-way process, the specific activity of the daily increment can be calculated and compared with the specific activity of the albumen and yolk (table 13.4). It is apparent from these calculations that the albumen has such a high specific activity that only small amounts of calcium from that source could possibly be entering the embryo at any one time throughout most of the incubation period and, in fact, the specific activity of the daily increment can only be explained on the basis that 85–95% of the calcium accumulated by the embryo in the first 10 days is derived from the yolk. On the 11th day, the specific activity of the daily increments

Table 13.4 *Eggs of the domestic fowl were injected with 25 μc Ca*[45] *into the albumen prior to incubation. The eggs were analysed daily and the specific activity values determined in order to indicate possible sources of embryonic calcium (after* [11])

Days of incubation	Calcium content (mg)			Specific activity			Specific activity of embryonic calcium accumulated each day
	Albumen	Yolk	Embryo	Albumen	Yolk	Embryo	
4	3·14	—	0·016	14·5	—	0·099	0·16
6	3·55	16·8	0·046	16·5	0·099	0·22	0·62
8	3·7	14·0	0·14	10·5	0·31	0·66	0·92
10	3·3	13·9	0·61	6·2	0·28	1·4	1·7
11	2·6	14·0	0·76	6·4	0·23	2·2	5·3
12	2·7	15·1	2·3	—	0·27	1·9	1·7
14	1·6	20·6	9·8	—	0·49	1·1	0·55
16	3·5	33·1	29·0	3·5	0·75	0·78	0·66
18	—	26·2	58·0	1·3	0·76	0·54	0·28
20	—	30·9	117·0	—	0·95	0·60	1·3
21	—	—	125·0	—	—	0·64	—

reaches a very high level and thereafter starts to fall. This is interpreted as showing that the shell is starting to be absorbed on that day, and since the layers nearest the albumen are the most highly radioactive part of this store, this calcium has a very high specific activity. The calcium which is later removed from the shell will have a progressively lower specific activity. From day 12 onwards, there is a rapid rise in the quantity of calcium in the egg contents which is in keeping with the observation that the shell is now being absorbed. This agrees with the observed increase in the calcium content of the yolk which occurs at this time.

A somewhat similar experiment has been performed by Nozaki, Horri, and Takei, although their analysis is less detailed. A fowl was fed on Ca[45] during reproduction and the eggs collected. The radio-isotope was only administered to the bird just before egg formation started, so that the yolk and albumen were not labelled and 99% of the isotope in the egg was in the shell. The eggs were incubated and the distribution of the Ca^{45} was determined on the 5th, 12th, and 18th days, and in the hatchling. The results are expressed as percentage of radioactivity in the various parts of the egg (table 13.5). It is apparent that during the first half of incubation the egg-

Table 13.5 *Changes in the distribution of* Ca^{45} *during the incubation of an egg with a labelled eggshell. Results expressed as % of total radioactivity* [18]

Region of egg	Extent of incubation				
	Laying	5 days	12 days	18 days	Hatching
Shell	98·28	98·14	98·36	90·43	87·8
Albumen	0·91 ⎫	1·86	0·25	—	—
Yolk	0·81 ⎭		0·55	2·51	4·26
Embryo	—	—	0·66	6·96	7·93

shell was not utilized as a calcium source and the embryo presumably used the non-labelled yolk. During the latter half of incubation, more than half the calcium absorbed by the embryo came from the shell, which showed a marked decline in radioactivity after the 12th day. It was suggested that towards the end of incubation the yolk was again the main source of calcium for the embryo, but that the yolk itself was receiving a considerable amount of calcium from the shell. Thus it was concluded that the yolk acts as an intermediate during the transfer of calcium from the shell to the embryo [18].

The physiological processes involved in the absorption of the eggshell are incompletely understood, although there is little doubt that the extra embryonic membranes provide the anatomical basis for the resorption. There are three sets of membranes that may be involved in this process (fig. 13.4). The first to form consists of a sheet of ectoderm and mesoderm which becomes raised up and folded over the embryo. The inner part of this fold is the amnion, and it encloses the embryo in a fluid-filled amniotic space. The outer part of the fold is the chorion. The second membrane system arises shortly after that of the amnion and chorion on about the fifth day of incubation of the fowl's egg. It develops as a sac-like diverticulum from the cloaca representing a precociously formed urinary bladder. This is the allantois, within which nitrogenous wastes are deposited until the time when the chick hatches and leaves behind much of this structure within the eggshell. The allantois consists of an inner layer of endoderm covered with mesoderm, and as it increases in size, it comes to lie against the outer chorionic fold enclosing the embryo. It fuses with this layer to form the chorio-allantois, which becomes enormously enlarged as incubation progresses. The chorio-allantois is a well-vascularized structure which, in the latter half of incubation, lies immediately beneath the shell membranes of the eggshell. Its most obvious function is to act as a respiratory surface, allowing the embryonic blood to give up carbon dioxide and

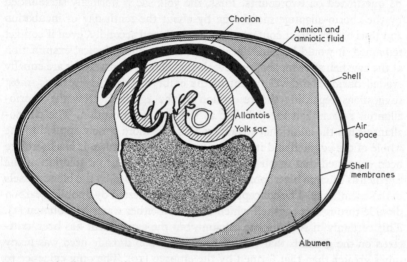

FIG. 13.4. A diagrammatic representation of the extra embryonic membranes in relation to the avian embryo and the eggshell.

absorb oxygen through the pores in the eggshell. The third extra embryonic membrane consists of the yolk sac; a layer of mesoderm and endoderm cells which slowly surround the yolk. The endoderm cells are in continuity with the cells lining the intestine, and the yolk sac is, in fact, withdrawn into the alimentary canal when the chick hatches. The yolk sac is well supplied with vitelline blood vessels which are involved in carrying nutrients from the yolk into the embryo.

Both the yolk sac and the chorio-allantois have been considered as being responsible for the removal of calcium from the eggshell by the embryo. The yolk has been implicated mainly because of the fact that during development its calcium content at first falls but then rises again and remains high until the time of hatching. The calcium content of the yolk sac starts to rise after about twelve days of incubation (table 13.4), which is also a time when the shell is actively being dissolved and, according to Plimmer and Lowndes, the time when 'phosphoric acid' starts to appear in the yolk sac circulation [19]. These events form the basis of their hypothesis, which postulates that the carbon dioxide which is produced by the embryo during incubation, attacks the eggshell forming a solution of calcium bicarbonate. This diffuses in towards the embryo and is trapped by the phosphoric acid in the yolk sac, eventually being incorporated into the yolk and the embryo. According to this theory, the yolk sac is considered to be in close contact with the eggshell throughout incubation, but this may be questioned on two counts. First, the yolk sac is normally surrounded by the chorio-allantoic membrane by about the tenth day of incubation and thus has no direct contact with the shell, and secondly, even if contact remained, it would be fairly localized, whereas a histological examination of the eggshell after incubation reveals that almost all parts of it are equally eroded during the development of the embryo. For these reasons, most suggestions regarding the resorption of the eggshell stress the chorio-allantois rather than the yolk sac as the site of absorption. The chorio-allantois has the additional advantage that it is more closely applied to the whole of the eggshell and it is also a respiratory structure. It has therefore been suggested that respiratory carbon dioxide leads to a solution of the eggshell as calcium bicarbonate which is then absorbed by the blood vessels in this membrane. The concept has been crudely tested by bubbling carbon dioxide through an eggshell which contained either water or albumen [1]. This certainly dissolves some calcium, but the experiment has been criticized on the grounds that the quantity of carbon dioxide used was many times greater than that formed by the embryo [16]. The only evidence to substantiate this theory comes from analyses of the shell membranes where there was no bicarbonate in the fresh egg but increasing amounts after 7, 14, and 19 days of incubation [8]. The theory implies that there must be a considerable concentration of carbon dioxide within the egg and possibly some way of hydrating it.

The air space between the shell membranes provides a convenient source of gas for estimating the concentration of carbon dioxide within the egg. During the first ten days of incubation, it contains little carbon dioxide and about 20% oxygen. The oxygen content falls rapidly to about 16% at the end of the second week of incubation and 12% as hatching approaches. The carbon dioxide content rises steadily after the second week and eventually reaches about 6% [22]. This level of carbon dioxide appears to be a true reflection of conditions within the egg, for if a part of the shell is covered, the carbon dioxide concentration within the air space rapidly increases [32]. There is little doubt, therefore, that a high concentration of carbon dioxide does exist within the egg during the latter part of incubation, and it has been suggested on a number of occasions that this is hydrated by means of the enzyme carbonic anhydrase and the carbonic acid which is then formed attacks the shell. The carbonic anhydrase content of the chick embryo certainly increases rapidly after four to five days of incubation but the allantois and yolk sac contain extremely small amounts of this enzyme, at least in those early stages of development which have been investigated [23]. The blood contains considerable amounts of this enzyme which, by the tenth day of incubation have been considered to be 'sufficient to promote dissolution of the shell' [11], but this is probably wishful thinking, for in this part of the circulation, the enzyme is more likely to be dehydrating carbonic acid and releasing carbon dioxide. What the theory requires is a region of enzyme activity closely applied to the eggshell, so that respiratory carbon dioxide can be rehydrated in the neighbourhood of the calcite deposits. This situation has, in fact, been described, for it has been claimed on histochemical evidence that the mammillary knobs contain carbonic anhydrase [21]. Unfortunately, this has since been denied [5] and in view of the fact that it cannot be detected biochemically [3], it seems unlikely that the enzyme does occur at this site. It will be apparent, therefore, that although the erosion of the eggshell by means of carbonic acid is still the simplest and most attractive theory, it is virtually unproven, and an alternative theory has been suggested which advocates citric acid in place of the undetected carbonic acid.

The citric acid content of the embryo rises progressively throughout incubation, and on about the twelfth day of incubation there is one molecule of citric acid for every twenty calcium ions in the embryo [6]. Citric acid is well known for its ability to form complexes with calcium ions, and it would thus be an ideal acid for dissolving the eggshell. The citric acid content of the blood continues to rise throughout incubation and hatching up until puberty in the domestic fowl. During early life it is always at a higher concentration in the blood of the female than in the male [10] and this may be a complicating factor in this theory, for it has been demonstrated that during the later stages of incubation the male embryo removes more calcium from the eggshell than the female [12]. There is therefore not a simple relationship between the concentration of citric acid in the blood of the embryo and the removal of calcium from the eggshell. There is no other evidence either for or against this theory.

From what has been said, it will be apparent that none of the proposed theories of shell resorption have been sufficiently well investigated to be particularly convincing. It seems, however, that the chorio-allantois is in some way involved in the process, for if one examines the shell from which a chick has hatched, it is readily apparent that the shell membranes have become separated from the rest of the shell throughout the egg except in the region of the air space (fig. 13.4). The air space is the only region of the egg where the chorio-allantois is prevented from coming close to the egg-shell. If one examines the isolated shell membrane in more detail, it is apparent that it has become detached in the region of the mammillary cores which always separate with the membrane and carry with them some calcareous portions of the eggshell [30]. Electron micrographs of decalcified eggshells show a membrane like condensation of the matrix in these regions, and it has been suggested that these may be preformed fracture lines for the detachment of the shell membranes [24] (plate 3, p. 226). There is also some evidence that the calcium carbonate above this region is more readily soluble than the rest of the eggshell [29]. These changes in the eggshell can best be explained on the basis of some interaction with the chorio-allantois. Electron micrographs of this extra-embryonic membrane taken at various stages of development show that as incubation progresses there is a reduction in the size of the cellular barrier between the embryonic blood and the eggshell. At the same time, there develop numerous microvilli in the chorion cells where they make contact with the shell membranes [13]. This strongly suggests the active uptake of material by these cells, but there are indications that if the eggshell is previously labelled with a mixture of the radio-isotopes Ca^{45}, Sr^{89}, and Ba^{133}, then the embryo withdraws all three cations in the same proportions that they exist in the eggshell [7]. The indiscriminate nature of this resorption possibly suggests that the shell is dissolved by some relatively simple interaction rather than one involving many cellular processes.

If one accepts the postulate that the chorio-allantois resorbs the shell by some relatively simple process, one still has to explain the changes which occur in the calcium content of the yolk. In this respect there are some interesting observations on the calcium and magnesium content of embryonic blood and bones (fig. 13.5). The 14-day embryo of the domestic fowl has blood which contains 5·1 mg % calcium and 5·5 mg % magnesium. This Ca/Mg ratio of 0·9 is extraordinarily low and would induce anaesthesia in most mammals. The source of the magnesium ions is probably the albumen and yolk (table 13.3), and it seems at least a possibility that the increase in the calcium content of the yolk which occurs during the second week of incubation might be correlated with the high magnesium content of the blood. The extra calcium which is brought into the circulation of the embryo by the resorption of the eggshell may displace the magnesium from the yolk proteins and thus account for the unusual composition of the blood and the increase in the calcium content of the yolk. This is certainly not the whole explanation, however, for as the magnesium content of the blood falls towards the end of incubation, the bones become increasingly rich with values of 0·52% of the skeletal ash on the 14th day up to 1·09% on the 20th day. An even more unusual phenomenon is that the changes in blood calcium and magnesium are briefly reversed at the time of hatching [27] (fig. 13.5).

The steady rise in the calcium content of embryonic blood may indicate that it is dependent upon the rates of eggshell and yolk mobilization rather than upon any internal regulating system. The adult level of about 10 mg % is not reached until the chick hatches, and Taylor therefore considers that the parathyroids are probably not active in regulating the level of blood

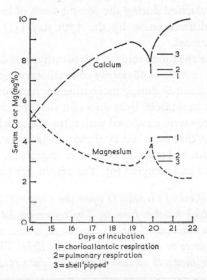

FIG. 13.5. The concentration of calcium and magnesium in the serum of embryonic chicks at various stages of incubation. Note in particular the effect of hatching (data from [27]).

calcium until this time [27]. In contrast to this, it has been found that 13-day-old embryos have parathyroid glands which respond to variations in calcium concentration when they are maintained in tissue culture for two days. It is, of course, not possible to say whether the glands have been modified by this *in vitro* treatment in any way other than by the calcium [20]. When normal embryos were examined histologically, Sun [26] found that in the last two to three days of incubation the parathyroid gland became very similar in appearance to the adult gland. He was, however, of the opinion that the gland was not functional in the embryo. In another article, the same author discussed the endocrine organs in relation to two abnormal conditions in the chicken embryo. These monsters were recognized by having deformed heads, feeble limbs, and bones which were soft and small when compared with normal specimens. The skeletons of the diseased embryos had a low calcium content, and the whole condition of these animals appeared to be related to an inadequate calcium metabolism. The parathyroid glands of all these deformed embryos were enlarged. This could be interpreted as indicating that the glands were active in the embryo and attempting to readjust the imbalance of the calcium metabolism, although this was not the conclusion drawn by Sun [25]. More recent work on the histology of the parathyroid glands of the avian embryo shows that they become vascularized during the second week of incubation and have completed their differentiation by the 17th day [31]. They were then thought to be functional.

The evidence for the functioning of the parathyroids during the development of the avian embryo is obviously contradictory, but the experiments on the need for vitamin D during incubation are more conclusive. Domestic fowl were kept in artificial light on a diet that was deficient in vitamin D. Some of the birds were irradiated with ultra-violet light while the others were not. The eggs that were laid by these two groups of birds were either analysed for calcium and vitamin D or were incubated. The chicks which hatched were killed and analysed [9]. The results are shown in table 13.6.

Table 13.6 *The effect of vitamin D upon the composition of the egg and of the embryo which hatches from it. The eggs were laid by domestic fowl which had been maintained for at least 100 days on a vitamin-D-deficient diet in the presence or absence of ultra-violet light. The eggs from irradiated birds were shown to contain vitamin D (data recalculated from [9])*

Treatment	Weight of eggshell (mg)	Calcium in yolk (mg)	Calcium in embryo (mg)	Calcium removed from shell (mg)	% of calcium in embryo derived from shell
Eggs laid with vitamin D	5,820	30·3	152	122	80
Eggs laid without vitamin D	4,110	23·7	75	51	68

The birds which were irradiated laid eggs with thicker shells and with more calcium and vitamin D in their yolks. The chicks which hatched from the eggs rich in vitamin D contained about twice as much calcium as the vitamin-poor chicks. This was partly to be expected, because the vitamin-deficient embryos developed on yolk with a poor calcium content, but this handicap accounted for only a fraction of the calcium that was absent from their skeletons. In fact, far from making good the deficiency in the calcium content of their yolks, these chicks removed less than half as much calcium from their shells as did the vitamin enriched chicks. Thus, even in comparative terms, these embryos obtained only 68% of their total calcium from the eggshell, whereas the chicks from the irradiated birds obtained 80% of theirs from this source.

This example demonstrates a general principle of reproduction which is sometimes overlooked when comparing the avian and mammalian systems. There is a continuity of metabolism from the adult to the offspring in the bird as much as in the mammal. In terms of calcium metabolism, this is clearly seen when the hen bird stores calcium in its bones, which it then resorbs to form the eggshell, which is itself resorbed to form the skeleton of the embryo. To what extent the calcium metabolism of the embryo is regulated by its own endocrine system is unknown, but again the embryo is dependent upon the parent for a supply of vitamin D, and in the absence of this material it is unable to develop satisfactorily, with consequent inadequacies in its own calcium metabolism.

REFERENCES

[1] BUCKNER, G. D., MARTIN, J. H., and PETER, A. M. (1925), 'Concerning the mode of transference of calcium from the shell of the hen's egg to the embryo during incubation', *Amer. J. Physiol.*, **71**, 253–5.

[2] BUCKNER, G. D., MARTIN, J. H., and PETER, A. M. (1926), 'Calcium and phosphorus content of strong and weak chicks from hens with and without calcium carbonate in their diet', *Amer. J. Physiol.*, **76**, 28–34.

[3] COMMON, R. H. (1941), 'The carbonic anhydrase activity of the hen's oviduct', *J. agric. Sci.*, **31**, 412–14.

[4] DELEZENNE, C. and FOURNEAU, E. (1918), 'Sur la part que prend la chaux de la coquille de l'oeuf de Poule à la formation du squellette du poussin pendant l'incubation', *Ann. Inst. Pasteur.*, **32**, 413–29.

[5] DIAMANTSTEIN, T., BRONSCH, K., and SCHLIMS, J. (1964), 'Carbonic anhydrase in the mammillae of the hen's egg shell', *Nature, Lond.*, **203**, 88–9.

[6] DICKEN, F. (1941), 'The citric acid content of animal tissues with reference to its occurrence in bone and tumour', *Biochem. J.*, **35**, 1011–23.

[7] EDWARDS, H. M. and MRAZ, F. R. (1961), 'Transference to egg and chick of the radionuclides Sr^{89}, Ca^{45} and Ba^{133} when administered to laying hens', *Poult. Sci.*, **40**, 493–503.

[8] GLASER, O. and PIEHLER, E. (1934), 'The mobilization of calcium during development', *Biol. Bull. Wood's Hole.*, **66**, 351–6.

[9] HART, E. B., STEENBOCK, H., LEPKOVSKY, S., KLETZIEN, S. W. F., HALPIN, J. G., and JOHNSON, O. N. (1925), 'The nutritional requirement of the chicken. 5. The influence of ultraviolet light on the production, hatchability and fertility of the egg', *J. biol. Chem.*, **65**, 579–95.

[10] HERTELENDY, F. and TAYLOR, T. G. (1964), 'The citric acid content of blood plasma and tissues of the domestic fowl', *Comp. Biochem. Physiol.*, **11**, 173–82.

[11] JOHNSTON, P. M. and COMAR, C. L. (1955), 'Distribution and contribution of calcium from the albumen, yolk and shell to the developing chick embryo', *Amer. J. Physiol.*, **183**, 365–70.

[12] KOSIN, J. L. and MUNRO, S. S. (1940), 'Evidence of sex differential in the utilization of shell calcium by the chick embryo', *Sci. Agric.*, **21**, 315–19.

[13] LEESON, T., S. and LEESON, C. R. (1963), 'The chorio-allantois of the chick. Light and electron microscopic observations at various times of incubation', *J. Anat., Lond.*, **97**, 585–95.

[14] MCCANCE, R. A. and WIDDOWSON, E. M. (1960), *The Composition of Foods*. M.R.C. Special Report 297, 3rd edn., H.M. Stationery Office, London.

[15] MCINDOE, W. M. (1960), 'Changes in the protein content of yolk during chick embryogenesis', *J. Embryol. exp. Morph.*, **8**, 47–53.

[16] MANKIN, W. R. (1929), 'Concerning the source of calcium required by the developing chick embryo', *Med. J. Aust.*, **2**, 916–19.

[17] NEEDHAM, J. (1931), *Chemical Embryology*, 3 vols., Cambridge Univ. Press, 2021 pp.

[18] NOZAKI, H., HORII, S., and TAKEI, Y. (1954), 'Utilization of shell calcium by chick embryo', *Bull. Nat. Inst. Agric. Sci.*, **G.9**, 89–95.

[19] PLIMMER, R. H. A. and LOWNDES, J. (1924), 'The changes in the lime content of the hen's egg during incubation', *Biochem. J.*, **18**, 1163–9.

[20] RAISZ, L. G. (1963), 'Regulation by calcium of parathyroid growth and secretion *in vitro*', *Nature, Lond.*, **197**, 1115–16.

[21] ROBINSON, D. S. and KING, N. R. (1963), 'Carbonic anhydrase and formation of the hen's egg shell', *Nature, Lond.*, **199**, 497–8.

[22] ROMIJN, C. and ROOS, J. (1938), 'The air space of the hen egg and its changes during the period of incubation', *J. Physiol.*, **94**, 365–79.

[23] SHEPARD, T. H. (1962), 'Carbonic anhydrase activity in early developing chick embryos', *J. Embryol. exp. Morph.*, **10**, 191–201.

[24] SIMONS, P. C. M. and WIERTZ, G. (1963), 'Notes on the structure of membranes and shell in the hen's egg. A electron microscopical study', *Z. Zellforsch.*, **59**, 555–67.

[25] SUN, T. P. (1932a), 'Histo-physiological study of the glands of internal secretion and their effect on ossification in the chondrodystrophic and "sticky" chicken embryo', *Physiol. Zool.*, **5**, 375–83.

[26] SUN, T. P. (1932b), 'Histo-physiogenesis of the glands of internal secretion – Thyroid, Adrenal, Parathyroid, and Thymus – of the chicken embryo', *Physiol. Zool.*, **5**, 384–96.

[27] TAYLOR, T. G. (1963), 'Calcium and magnesium in the blood and bones of chick embryos', *Biochem. J.*, **87**, 7P.

[28] TAYLOR, T. G. and HERTELENDY, F. (1961), 'Changes in the blood

calcium associated with eggshell calcification in the domestic fowl. 2. Changes in the diffusible level', *Poult. Sci.*, **40**, 115–23.

[29] TEREPKA, A. R. (1963), 'Organic–inorganic interrelationships in avian eggshell', *Exp. Cell. Res.*, **30**, 183–92.

[30] TYLER, C. and SIMKISS, K. (1959), 'Studies on eggshells. 12. Some changes in the shell during incubation', *J. Sci. Fd. Agric.*, **10**, 611–15.

[31] VENZKE, W. G. (1947), 'Morphogenesis of the parathyroid glands of chicken embryos', *Amer. J. vet. Res.*, **8**, 421–6.

[32] VISSCHEDIZK, A. H. K. (1962), *Praenatale gaswisseling by de kip*, Uitgeverÿ, G. van Dyk, N. V. Breukelen, 159 pp.

CHAPTER 14

Calcium Metabolism of the Reproducing Reptile

Introduction

The reptiles are of especial interest in most comparative studies of tetrapods. They represent the descendants of the first vertebrates which successfully and completely colonized the land. They also represent the ancestors of the birds and mammals, so that there is always the possibility of tracing the specialized physiology of these homeotherms back to some reptilian group that may have left a surviving form. Unfortunately, while the reptiles are of great interest to the zoologist, they are of relatively little commercial value, and have never been exploited as laboratory animals in the way that other vertebrates have. The consequence of this is that their physiology is relatively poorly understood. No calcium balance experiment has ever been performed upon a reptile, and while the embryology of the group is fairly well appreciated, the basic physiology of their reproductive processes is poorly understood. Because of this, it is necessary to give a general survey of reproduction in the reptiles so that the available information concerning their calcium metabolism can be put in its true perspective.

It has been known for over a hundred years that the ovary of reptiles contains oocytes of different sizes which fall into groups where the number of follicles in each group is approximately equal to the number of eggs found in a clutch. This has been frequently confirmed among the turtles [2], and it has been observed that up to 85 ova may be ovulated almost simultaneously in some snakes [4]. The development of the ovarian follicles takes place in two well-defined stages in the snake (*Thamnophis saurituous*). The first stage occurs in the female ribbon snake during March or April when about 12 follicles begin to show signs of activity. The immature follicle weighs only about 5 mg, and is white and translucent, but during the 'hydration stage' it swells and becomes a more opaque structure weighing about 40 mg. Most of this increase in weight is due to the absorption of water, and at this stage, each follicle contains only about 30 µg of calcium.

Shortly after the eggs have reached this stage of development, there is a sharp increase in the solid content of the follicle. This is the second or deutoplasmic stage of development and the follicle becomes yellow in colour as it accumulates protein, lipid, and calcium. The protein which enters the follicle contains much phosphate and it appears to be associated with the calcium. Thus the deutoplasmic follicle has a molar ratio of protein nitrogen/protein phosphorus/calcium which is approximately 10 : 1 : 1. The follicles grow during this period to a size of about 1 g, although there is considerable variation in ovum size, especially between individuals [3]. The ripe oocytes which are to form a clutch are all ovulated simultaneously in May or June and pass into the oviduct. Little is known about the formation of the tertiary membranes of the reptiles, although the structure of the eggshell has been described for a number of species [3, 14, 19].

Many different systems of reproduction have been evolved among the reptiles. They may be oviparous, in which case the egg may be contained within a parchment-like shel as in many snakes and lizards or, alternatively, the shell may be thick and greatly impregnated with calcium carbonate as in the crocodiles and some turtles, where the eggshell resembles that of the bird in constitution. Some snakes and lizards retain the fertilized egg within the oviduct until the young are ready to hatch (i.e. ovoviviparity), while in others there is a metabolic connexion between the embryos and the mother, resulting in a true form of viviparity. The transfer of metabolites may occur between the walls of the oviduct and both the yolk sac and the allantochorion of the embryo. Various degrees of complexity occur, ranging from a relatively simple apposition of these membranes in *Hoplodactylus maculatus* to the more complex interlocking of these structures in *Egernia entrecasteauxi* [1]. In these cases of true viviparity one would expect some calcium to pass from the mother to her offspring during their development. Unfortunately there is no information on this point, but there is no reason to consider that, if it did occur, it would put any strain on the calcium metabolism of the mother. On the contrary, as development is a fairly long process, the effect of viviparity would be to extend the time available for providing the egg and embryo with calcium. Most of the problems of calcium metabolism during reproduction are related to the rate at which this ion can be metabolized, so that viviparity generally reduces these difficulties. There are, however, other complications in assessing the rate of calcium metabolism, which make this study particularly difficult in reptiles.

Frequently, the only way to tell the reproductive state of a reptile is by a post-mortem examination, and if this approach is to be taken, it must involve an extensive study of a large number of animals and a pooling of data.

As an alternative, one might take the time between copulation and oviposition as being the time necessary to form the tertiary membranes. This approach can lead to errors, however, as it is known that sperm may survive for up to four years in the oviduct of the turtle and up to six years in some snakes [8]. Thus, unless it is known that an animal is a virgin female, there is no guarantee that the formation of the tertiary membranes of an egg was not proceeding prior to an observed copulation. Similarly, there is no guarantee that ovulation does not lag quite a long time behind copulation. Thus, even assuming that the chemical composition of a clutch of eggs is known, it is very difficult to assess the rate of metabolism necessary for its formation.

Most reptiles live on diets which one would expect to be adequate in their calcium content, so that in the absence of any experimental evidence it will be assumed that they have access to an ample source of calcium. Food passes through the alimentary canal of reptiles at somewhat uncertain rates, so that the time scale and significance of a balance experiment would be rather variable. The amount of information which could be deduced from the fact that, for example, 1 g of calcium was absorbed by a reptile during two to three weeks is much less than if the time scale was reduced.

In the face of these difficulties in determining the rates of absorption and metabolism of calcium, it is necessary to make some indirect assessments, first, for the metabolism of calcium necessary to form the yolk, and secondly, for the rate of shell secretion.

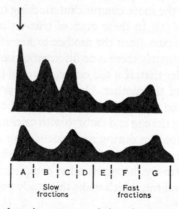

FIG. 14.1. The electrophoretic patterns of the plasma proteins of a reproducing (*top*) and an immature female (*bottom*) ribbon snake. The arrow indicates the application of the plasma. Note the extra component (*B*) in the plasma of the reproducing snake (after [3]).

Calcium Metabolism during Vitellogenesis

Just before the onset of the deutoplasmic stage of follicular development, a number of changes occur in the plasma of the female ribbon snake (*Thamnophis sauritus*). A study of the plasma proteins by means of electrophoresis shows that at this time a new component appears in the slow-moving anodal fraction (fig. 14.1). Chemical analyses demonstrate that there is a simultaneous increase in the calcium, magnesium, phosphorus, and protein portions of the blood (table 14.1). They reach a maximum

Table 14.1 *Changes in the concentration of various constituents of the plasma of female ribbon snakes during reproductive activity* [3]. *All figures are mean values*

| | Stage of reproductive cycle | | | | |
| | | Vitellogenesis | | | |
Constituent	Inactive stage	Hydration stage	Deuto-plasmic stage	Near ovulation	Early gravid
Calcium (mM/I)	2·74	3·35	7·32	43·5	3·61
Magnesium (mM/I)	1·96	1·54	4·06	8·98	2·23
Inorganic phosphorus (mM/I)	1·64	1·50	2·41	7·00	2·31
Lipid phosphorus (mM/I)	1·43	2·10	2·65	6·00	2·02
Protein phosphorus (mM/I)	0·36	0·86	3·65	40·1	1·15
Total protein g/100 ml.	4·06	4·22	4·95	6·67	3·91

shortly after ovulation and then return to their normal values. The changes coincide with an increase in the size of the liver and a decrease in the size of the fat bodies (fig. 14.2). These events are all in agreement with the concept that yolk proteins are synthesized by the liver and transported in association with calcium ions to the developing follicle [18]. The phenomena have been observed in a number of species of snakes [4] and can be reproduced artificially by injecting oestrogens into male snakes [3] or turtles [18].

When this reproductive cycle of the ribbon snake was followed in the laboratory, a number of important points emerged. First, the animals in the study were starved for one to two weeks prior to the experiments, so that it seems likely that any calcium moving into the ovary was derived, in this case, mainly from the bones rather than from the food. Secondly, the rise in total calcium in the snake's plasma may reach enormous proportions, and in one case was over thirty times the normal level [3]. This increase occurs around the time of ovulation, apparently because of a reduction in the rate of incorporation of yolk proteins into the ovary at this time and the increase is probably so large because of the simultaneous development of many follicles. Shortly after ovulation, the calcium content of the plasma returns to normal (fig. 14.2). There are, unfortunately, no measurements of the level of ionic calcium in the plasma during these events. If, however, the calcium proteinate in the blood is acting as a weak electrolyte, it would be expected that a large increase in the level of non-diffusible calcium would produce at least a small increase in the ionic calcium. In experiments on birds, this has actually been demonstrated, although the total calcium level of the blood had to be artificially raised, by

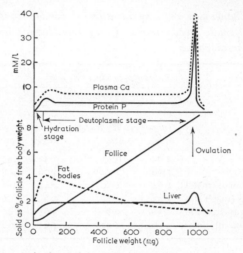

FIG. 14.2. The changes in dry weight of the various organs of the garter snake correlated with the changes in the level of plasma calcium. Note the enormous increase in the concentration of blood calcium at the time of ovulation (after [3]).

injecting oestrogens, until it reached about 100 mg % before the diffusible calcium rose by 1–2 mg % [16]. In the snake, the total calcium in the blood may reach the remarkable level of 200–400 mg % shortly after ovulation. It might be reasonable to assume, therefore, that the diffusible calcium in the blood also rises at this time. Unfortunately, not only is there no experimental evidence for this, but there is also no evidence as to whether or not it influences the parathyroid gland. One might, by *a priori* reasoning, expect the gland to suppress the secretion of the parathyroid hormone during this period of hypercalcaemia, in which case the animal might be in a very odd situation if it tried to secrete the calcium carbonate of its eggshell at a faster rate than the parathyroid-bone resorption system could be reactivated. Actually most reptiles secrete the tertiary membranes very slowly, and the ova may remain in the oviduct for several weeks before they are laid. There would, therefore, be plenty of time for the physiology of the animal to readjust to the fall in the total level of blood calcium. Thus if there is a possibility of vitellogenesis leading to an inactivation of the parathyroid gland, then it has been avoided by retaining the eggs and delaying the formation of their shells until the effect of transporting the yolk proteins in the blood-stream has subsided.

The other possible effect which vitellogenesis may have upon the reptile is that the secretion of the yolk may itself be a large drain upon the calcium reserves of the mother. Certainly reptilian yolk is very rich in calcium and many eggs are produced simultaneously. Frequently yolk formation is a slow process, but taking the figures of Dessauer and Fox [3] for the ribbon snake one can appreciate that it may be a problem. The adult female of this species weighs between 20 and 100 g (say 60 g). It produces about twelve eggs in a clutch, each of which weighs about 1 g and contains about 14 mg calcium. The yolk is mainly secreted between April and May (say thirty days). This gives a rate of calcium metabolism of

$$\frac{12}{24} \times \frac{14}{30} \times \frac{1,000}{60} = 4 \text{ mg/kg/hr}$$

This is a surprisingly high rate of calcium metabolism, although it is probably not outside the rate of normal metabolism, especially if the animal is well fed. It might be expected to be near the maximal rate, however, and exceeds in these terms most pregnant mammals and is equivalent to the strain imposed upon the calcium metabolism of a champion cow during lactation. The example of the ribbon snake may not be typical of most reptiles, for it produces a considerable number of eggs which are extremely rich in calcium and very large for the size of the parent. The eggs amount, in fact, to 20% of the mother's body weight.

An Estimate of Calcium Metabolism during Eggshell Formation

The green sea turtle (*Chelonia mydas*) is particularly suitable for estimating the calcium requirements of a reproducing reptile because it has been well studied during its breeding season and has a number of very useful peculiarities. During the breeding season, the female turtle comes ashore at night, lays a clutch containing an average of 105 eggs, and returns to the sea within a few hours. The same turtle will lay another clutch of eggs about ten days later and may repeat this six to seven times in a season [9]. The eggs are quite large, weighing about 70 g or slightly more than that of the domestic fowl. The shell is pliable but contains a distinct layer of calcium carbonate.

If we assume first of all that all the eggs which are to be laid in a season by a turtle are ovulated and fully formed before any are laid, then the eggs in the last clutch will be laid about sixty days after the eggs in the first clutch. This, however, is about the time it takes for the eggs to hatch, and yet there is no evidence for any variations of this sort in the incubation times of first and last clutches. Therefore the original assumption would appear to be false, and a better conclusion would be that each clutch of eggs is formed in the ten days between successive sets of eggs. There is some evidence that this is so, for the oviduct appears to be able to hold about 100 eggs at a time and the females have been observed to copulate between laying one clutch of eggs and the next [11].

Samples of the eggshells of green sea turtles indicate that they weigh between 2·0 and 2·5 g and contain about 80% calcium carbonate. If one assumes that, as in birds, oviposition is the stimulus for ovulation and that the formation of the albumen occupies only 20% of the time necessary to produce all the tertiary membranes, then the quantity of calcium mobilized by the turtle for each clutch can be calculated as follows:

$$2 \cdot 5 \times \frac{80}{100} \times \frac{40}{100} \times 105 = 84 \text{ g calcium}$$

The rate at which this calcium is metabolized can also be calculated,

$$\text{i.e. } \frac{84}{24} \times \frac{1}{10} \times \frac{100}{80} = 438 \text{ mg calcium/hr}$$

The turtle weighs about 120 kg, of which about 60 kg are carapace. Thus comparative figures for the rate of metabolism are:

$$\frac{438}{120} = 3 \cdot 6 \text{ mg Ca/kg body wt/hr or } \frac{438}{60} = 7 \cdot 3 \text{ mg Ca/kg flesh/hr}$$

During reproduction, the domestic fowl metabolizes calcium at a rate of about 50 mg/kg body wt/hr, i.e. about fourteen times faster than the turtle on a body-weight basis, or about seven times faster if one ignores the carapace of the reptile. The turtle metabolizes calcium at about the rate of a lactating sow. On the basis of these calculations, the turtle is not comparable to the fowl, with its store of calcium as medullary bone, but rather to the lactating mammal which appears to be able to manage without this physiological adaptation.

It is readily admitted that these calculations represent an oversimplification of the problem. They are, however, the only estimates available for the calcium metabolism of a reptile. The reptile chosen is one which appears to have a fairly intense reproductive season, laying 600–700 eggs within two months. The calculations suggest that this may be possible without any special physiological adaptations such as medullary bone, and the experimental evidence is in agreement with these conclusions.

Bone Metabolism in the Chelonia

There are four possible ways in which changes in the calcium metabolism of turtles could be detected during reproductive activity. The first method involves a study of the macroscopic changes which occur in the skeletons of male and female turtles. The second method involves a histological examination of the bones to determine any changes in their cellular activity, while the third method tries to induce these changes by injecting sex hormones in an attempt to simulate the onset of reproductive activity. Finally, changes in metabolism could be detected by suitable balance experiments. In the last few years the first three of these techniques have been used upon various turtles.

It has been shown that a good indication of the density of a bone can be obtained by using the following relationships:

$$\rho_x = \frac{\rho_1}{1 - W_1/W_a}$$

where ρ_x is the density of the bone; ρ_1 is the density of distilled water at the temperature at which the weighings are made, and W_1 and W_a are the weight of the bone in water and air respectively [7]. Using this method, Edgren has studied the density of the bones of musk turtles (*Sternothaerus odoratus*) collected from a wild population during their breeding season. The sex, body weight, size, weight of gonad and state of reproduction were all recorded, while the density of the major bones in the left hind-leg were determined using the equation given above [6].

Seasonal changes in the density of the bones of female turtles were quite marked, and are shown in figure 14.3 with pooled data obtained from the bones of male turtles for comparison. During the early part of the breeding season there were no differences between the densities of the bones of the two sexes. Of eight females autopsied on 3 May, four contained eggs in the oviduct, but only one of these showed any sign of calcification of the shell, and that was only slight. The average weight of the ovaries of these four turtles was 4·5 g, whereas the average weight of the other four which had not ovulated was 8·0 g [5]. The data indicate that at this date half of the sample had ovulated, whereas the other half were almost ready to ovulate. The initiation of calcification in one turtle tends to support the assumption that the formation of the eggshell occurs fairly soon after ovulation. During June, the densities of the bones of the females fell. This period corresponded with a time when completely calcified eggshells had been formed, although the eggs remained in the oviduct. A field study showed that turtle nests were found on 29 June, and females caught in August contained no eggs in their oviducts. The densities of the bones of the females rose after June and were almost back to normal by late August. According to this work, therefore, the eggs remain within the oviduct for from five to eight weeks, during which time there is a progressive loss of calcium from the skeleton as shown by the fall in the densities of the bones of female turtles.

The two important points that are demonstrated by this work are first, that there is no indication of an increase in the densities of the bones prior to ovulation. Thus the turtle appears to make no special provision of calcium such as that of medullary bone in birds. Secondly, the turtle appears to

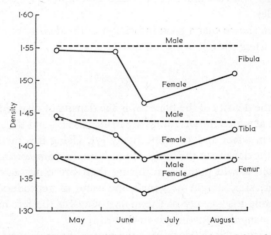

FIG. 14.3. The changes in density of the long bones of male and female musk turtles during reproductive activity. Note the fall in the density of the bones of the females at the time of eggshell calcification (after [6]).

pass through a period of calcium stress in so far as the diet obviously does not provide all the calcium necessary for the metabolism of the female during reproduction. The skeleton is mobilized during this period and the bones are partially resorbed to provide the calcium that is required for the formation of the eggshell. There is no reason to consider that this requires any special physiological adaptations, and the bones are quickly replenished after the eggs have been laid.

Similar conclusions have been reached by Suzuki following an extensive histological study of the slider turtle (*Pseudemys scripta elegans*) [15]. During this study, 17 turtles were examined which contained shelled eggs within the oviduct. In these reproducing turtles the cortical bone of the femur appeared to be thinner than in mature turtles of comparable size but without eggs. The femurs of turtles containing eggs were described as having an 'osteoporotic appearance of the cancellous bone', while this condition was never observed in mature males, immature males, or immature females. Again, therefore, there is evidence for bone resorption from the skeleton of reproductively active females. There was no evidence for any medullary bone formation or any other specialized type of bone formation which might act as a store of calcium prior to ovulation. The bone which was resorbed by the female for use in the secretion of the eggshell came primarily from a thinning of the trabeculae and secondarily from the cortex. No concomitant changes were observed in the carapaces of the turtles. This study confirms the work of Edgren on the densities of reptilian bones and also indicates that in calculations of the calcium metabolism of turtles, the carapace should be ignored, as it does not appear to enter into the process.

Finally, a number of attempts have been made to stimulate any possible systems of calcium storage in the turtle by injecting massive doses of oestrogens [12, 15, 17]. Both male and female turtles have been injected with doses of 0·25 mg estradiol valerate every 10 days for 4 weeks [15] or 0·5 mg estrone every day for 12 days [12]. Four different species have been studied, but in no case has any endosteal or medullary bone formation been initiated.

Evidence from a variety of sources is therefore available to suggest that extra stores of calcium are not needed and are not found in the Chelonia where normal bone resorption appears to be sufficient to meet the needs of reproduction.

The Calcium Metabolism of Other Reptiles

The Chelonia are only one of the three main groups of modern reptiles. They are, however, the only group where much work of any sort has been done on calcium metabolism. This is no doubt because it is easier to capture, keep, and study a turtle than a member of the Crocodilia or one of the other main group of reptiles, the Squamata. It is, however, among this latter group of snakes and lizards that one of the most remarkable adaptations of calcium metabolism is found.

There are a few species of lizards, mainly geckos together with a few iguanids, where a large swelling occurs behind the ear opening during the reproductive season. This swelling consists of a white mass of calcareous material which is often half as large as the skull. The early discoverers of this structure considered it to be a pathological condition or, more popularly, to be the fully formed eggs which the females were supposed to carry about in some type of pouch prior to depositing them in a safe place. This suggestion, while being anatomically highly unlikely, did at least fit the circumstantial facts, which were that the white masses occurred mainly in the females during the breeding season. It is now known that these masses are actually part of the endolymphatic sacs of the inner ear. They were investigated by Ruth in 1918 in a most interesting paper, but have since attracted little attention.

There are, on the island of Manila in the Philippines where Ruth was working, four common species of house lizard. They are *Cosmybotus platyurus*, *Peropus mutilatus*, *Hemidactylus frenatus*, and *Hemidactylus luzonenis*. All four species were described as ovoviviparous, although this only implies that the embryos had reached a size of about 1 mm by the time that the egg was laid. The endolymphatic sacs were only large and conspicuous in the first two species [10].

The endolymphatic sacs of *Cosmybotus* occur on both sides of the neck immediately posterior to the tympanic membrane (plate 4, p. 226). They lie superficially beneath the skin and are semi-circular in shape, about 8 mm long anterio-posteriorly and 6 mm dorso-ventrally. In *Peropus*, they are slightly smaller and lie beneath the superficial fascia.

Those specimens of *Cosmybotus* which were female and contained eggs, had endolymphatic sacs which were described as being 'engorged with calcium milk'. The calcium milk consisted of a suspension of calcium carbonate which was considered to be amorphous but which crystallized on drying. In this engorged state, the calcium sacs could be seen to communicate with an 'occipito–parietal sinus' which was also filled with the calcareous material. In those females in which the eggs had been formed and their calcified shell secreted prior to oviposition, the calcium sacs were practically devoid of their contents. In this they resembled the males or immature females where the gland measured only 4 mm by 3 mm. *Peropus* showed a similar phenomenon, and in a large number of geckos (*Gecko gecko*) which were studied, 80% of the males showed a complete absence of calcium, while the other 20% had only small deposits. In all the females a calcium deposit was present in the sacs.

The histological structure of the endolymphatic sacs of *Cosmybotus* and *Peropus* is not unusual. The sac is lobulated and composed of a single layer of epithelial cells. The organ has a rich capillary supply that no doubt carries the calcium away from the sacs when it is required. Cells are described as wandering into the lumen of the sacs and being involved in the formation and dissolution of the calcium deposits, but this observation needs confirming.

There appears to be no doubt that the endolymphatic sacs of these species contain stores of calcium which may be mobilized to provide calcium for the shells of the eggs. Whether the sacs act simply as a depository of extra calcium, or whether they are an adaptation which enables the lizards to metabolize calcium at a faster rate than they could otherwise, is unfortunately not known. The suggestion that the sacs always collapse might indicate a need for a high rate of calcium metabolism. This, however, is not compatible with the fact that these reptiles retain their eggs for some time in the oviduct after they are formed, nor with the fact that related species do not possess the sacs in such an enlarged state. Many species of *Hemidactylus* do, in fact, have endolymphatic sacs which contain more calcareous matter in the female than in the male, but these sacs are restricted to the skull and therefore not as conspicuous. It is not known whether the quantity of calcareous material in the sacs of these species varies during reproduction (plate 5, p. 226).

Nothing is known about the mechanism whereby the calcium is laid down or withdrawn from these sacs. Three facts suggest, however, that the process may be activated by a sex hormone, as first, the sacs are only well developed in the female; secondly, this occurs in reproductively mature specimens; and thirdly, the activity of the sacs is directly related to variations in the reproductive cycle. To this extent the sacs behave in an analogous way to medullary bone in birds, and it would seem a reasonable speculation that perhaps their activity is controlled by an oestrogen secreted by the ovaries of the reptile.

REFERENCES

[1] AMOROSO, E. C. (1952), 'Placentation', in *Marshall's Physiology of Reproduction*, ed. Parkes, A. S., 3rd edn., Longmans, 127–311.

[2] CAGLE, F. R. (1944), 'Sexual maturity in the female of the turtle *Pseudemys scripta elegans*', *Copeia*, 149–52.

[3] DESSAUER, H. C. and FOX, W. (1959), 'Changes in ovarian follicle composition with plasma levels of snakes during estrus', *Amer. J. Physiol.*, **197**, 360–6.

[4] DESSAUER, H. C., FOX, W., and GILBERT, N. L. (1956), 'Plasma calcium magnesium and protein of viviparous colubrid snakes during estrous cycle', *Proc. Soc. exp. Biol. N.Y.*, **92**, 299–301.

[5] EDGREN, R. A. (1960), 'Ovulation time in the musk turtle *Sternothaerus odoratus*', *Copeia*, 60–1.

[6] EDGREN, R. A. (1960), 'A seasonal change in the bone density in female musk turtles, *Sternothaerus odoratus* (Latreille)', *Comp. Biochem. Physiol.*, **1**, 213–17.

[7] EDGREN, R. A. and CALHOUN, D. W. (1956), 'Density as an index of the effects of oestrogens on bone', *Endocrinology*, **59**, 631–6.

[8] FOX, W. (1956), 'Seminal receptacles of snakes', *Anat. Rec.*, **124**, 519–33.

[9] HENDRICKSON, J. R. (1958), 'The green sea turtle, *Chelonia mydas*, in Malaya and Sarawak', *Proc. zool. Soc. Lond.*, **130**, 455–535.

[10] RUTH, E. S. (1918), 'A study of the calcium glands in the Philippine house lizard', *Philipp. J. Sci.*, **13**, 311–18.

[11] SIMKISS, K. (1961), 'Calcium metabolism and avian reproduction', *Biol. Rev.*, **36**, 321–67.

[12] SIMKISS, K. (1961), 'The influence of large doses of oestrogens upon the structure of the bones of some reptiles', *Nature, Lond.*, **190**, 1217–18.

[13] SIMKISS, K. (1962), 'The sources of calcium for the ossification of the embryos of the giant leathery turtle', *Comp. Biochem. Physiol.*, **7**, 71–9.

[14] SIMKISS, K. and TYLER, C. (1959), 'The possible calcification mechanisms in some reptilian eggshells', *Quart. J. micr. Sci.*, **100**, 529–38.

[15] SUZUKI, N. K. (1963), 'Studies on the osseous system of the Slider turtle', *Ann. N.Y. Acad. Sci.*, **109**, 351–410.

[16] URIST, M. R. (1959), 'The effects of calcium deprivation upon the blood, adrenal cortex, ovary and skeleton in the domestic fowl', *Recent Progr. Hormone Res.*, **15**, 455–77.

[17] URIST, M. R. (1965), personal communication.

[18] URIST, M. R. and SCHJEIDE, A. O. (1961), 'The partition of calcium and protein in the blood of oviparous vertebrates during estrous', *J. gen. Physiol.*, **44**, 743–56.

[19] YOUNG, J. D. (1950), 'The structure and some physical properties of the testudian eggshell', *Proc. zool. Soc. Lond.*, **120**, 455–69.

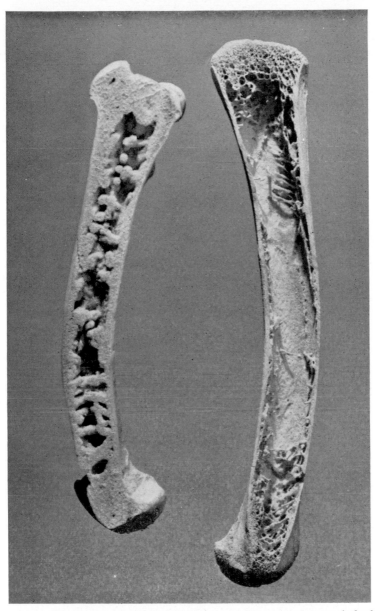

PLATE I. The femurs of a laying (left) and non-laying (right) domestic fowl split open and extracted with ethylene diamine to remove organic material. Note how the endosteal surface of the bone from the laying bird is covered with spicules of medullary bone which almost fill the medullary cavity.

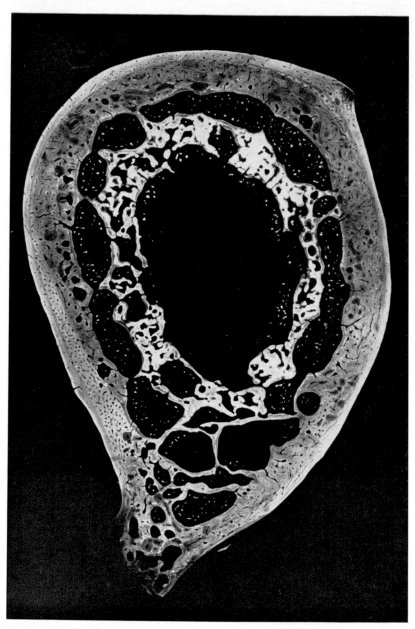

PLATE 2. An X-radiograph of a transverse section of a limb-bone of a laying fowl previously injected with 750 I.U. of parathyroid hormone. Note how the medullary bone is well mineralized as shown by its radiodensity. The parathyroid hormone induces a resorption of mineral from the endosteal surface of the cortical bone resulting in the detachment of the medullary bone from the rest of the osseous material ([76] Chapter 12).

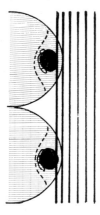

PLATE 3. The effect of incubation upon the structure of the eggshell. In the fresh egg the shell membranes are firmly attached to the mammillary knobs of the eggshell (*top*). During incubation the shell becomes separated from the membranes along a region immediately outside the mammillary cores (*bottom*). The region of detachment appears to correspond with a membrane-like condensation (Me) of the matrix as seen in electron micrographs of fresh eggshells (*left*). Fibres (F) of the shell membranes can also be seen penetrating the mammillary matrix (M) (Electron micrograph from [24] Chapter 13.)

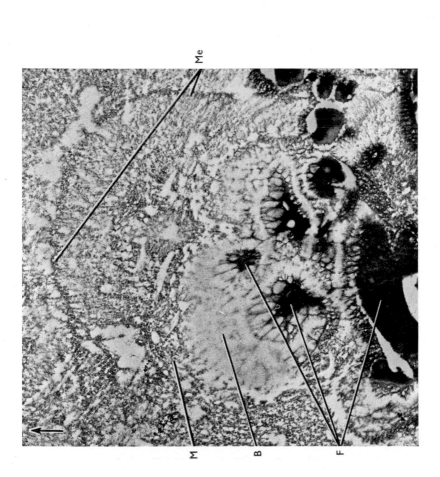

PLATE 4. The endo-lymphatic sacs of the female Philippine house lizard, *Cosmybotus platurus*, (right) are enormously enlarged structures filled with calcareous material and lying in the neck region. An X-radiograph of a male house lizard is shown for comparison (left).

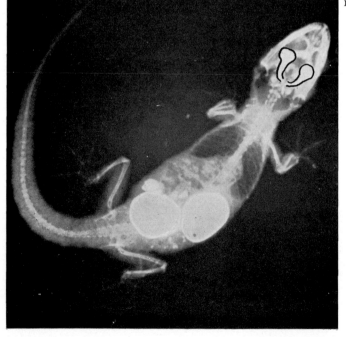

PLATE 5. An X-radiograph of a reproducing gecko (*Hemidactylus turcicus*) showing the calcification of two eggshells in the oviduct. The endolymphatic sacs lie within the skull and have been outlined to make their position more obvious.

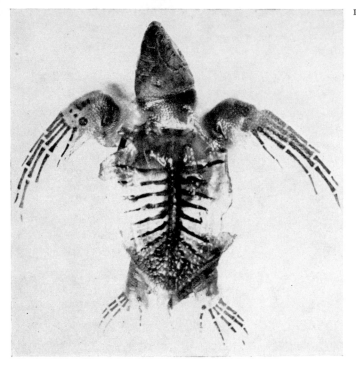

PLATE 6. The skeleton of a giant leathery turtle (*Dermochelys coriacea*) killed immediately on hatching and stained with alizarin red to show regions of calcification ([7] Chapter 15).

PLATE 7. An egg of the giant leathery turtle (*Dermochelys coriacea*) opened shortly before hatching to show the position of the chorioallantois immediately within the shell. The extraembryonic membrane is well vascularized ([7] Chapter 15).

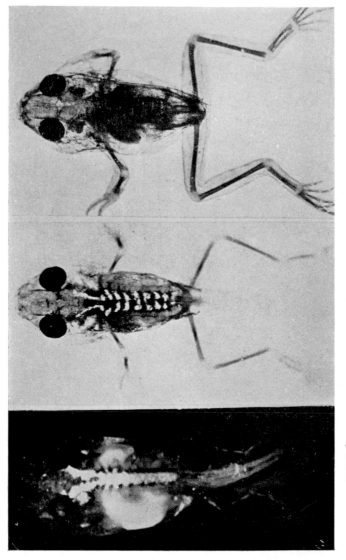

PLATE 8.

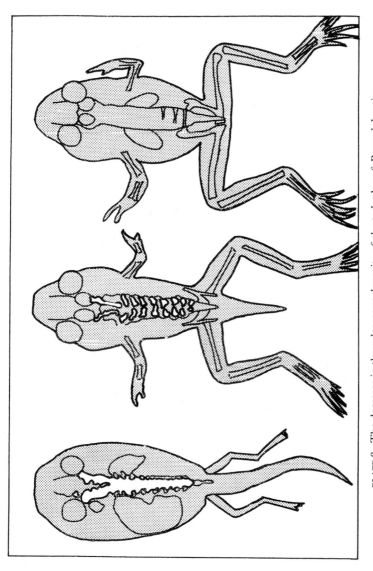

PLATE 8. The decrease in the calcareous deposits of the tadpoles of *Rana dalmatina* during metamorphosis. The animals are in the form of alizarin preparations with the skeleton darkly stained, while the endolymphatic sacs appear white (after [10] Chapter 16).

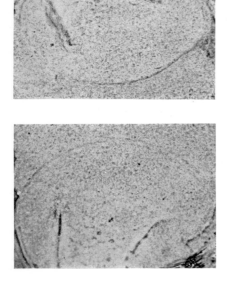

(c)

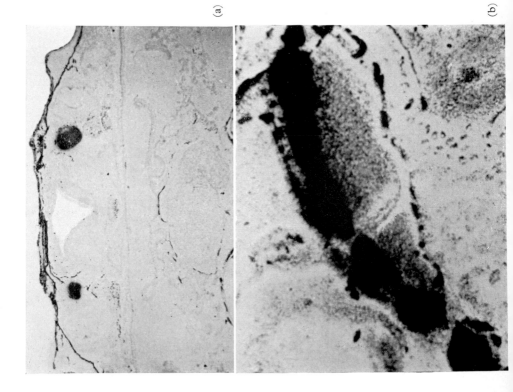

(a)

(b)

PLATE 9. Autoradiographs of tadpoles of the toad (*Bufo bufo*), fed Ca^{45} prior to metamorphosis. A transverse section of the tadpole shows an enormous accumulation of the radio-isotopes in the endolymphatic sacs which appear as two black masses in these pictures (a). As the animals metamorphose this Ca^{45} is resorbed from the sacs so that the radioactivity is no longer uniformly distributed throughout these structures and is concentrated in the epithelium lining the deposits (b). The radioactivity can then be detected in the periosteum of the ossifying bones (c) ([10] Chapter 16).

CHAPTER 15

The Reptilian Embryo

Reptiles are typically oviparous although a few are viviparous and develop either yolk sac or chorio-allantoic placentae. The histology of these placentae has been described sufficiently well to whet the appetite for more information, but unfortunately little has been done to correlate the morphological descriptions with investigations into their physiology. At this stage of our knowledge we have to consider, therefore, not so much the variety of the adaptations found, but the basic problems involved in reptilian reproduction. Thus, as far as their calcium metabolism is concerned we need to know the requirements of the embryo and the provisions made for the mother to supply these.

One would expect that the bones of hatchlings were moderately well ossified. Many reptiles such as the turtles and crocodiles have to dig themselves out of their nests and race for cover as soon as they hatch, and it would be reasonable to expect this vigorous muscular activity to be correlated with an ossified skeleton. The evidence which is available tends to support this. An investigation into the embryology of the ring-necked snake (*Diadophis punctatus punctatus*) concluded that the centres of ossification appeared in the bones of the embryo at similar stages of incubation to those of the chick, and the bones of the hatchling were well mineralized [4]. The snake is, of course, specialized in this respect because of the loss of the limbs and girdles, but my own examination of hatchling turtles confirms the fact that they have well-ossified skeletons (plate 6, p. 227). Only two sets of analyses of hatchling reptiles have been made, and unfortunately they are both upon turtles. The results are shown in table 15.1, and it is apparent that turtles contain approximately the same quantity of calcium as the young of a similarly sized bird or mammal.

The next question to be considered is the origin of this calcium, and table 15.1 also shows the available data for the calcium content of the yolk and albumen of reptile eggs. Three points are of interest. First, the yolk contains nearly all the calcium that is present in the egg contents, for there are only minor quantities in the albumen. Secondly, the concentration of

Table 15.1   *The weight and calcium content of reptilian eggs and hatchlings as compared with other tetrapods* [3, 5, 6, 7, 8, 9]

Animal	Yolk Wet weight (g)	Ca content (mg)	Ca (mg %)	Albumen Wet weight (g)	Ca content (mg)	Ca (mg %)	Hatchling Wet weight (g)	Ca content (mg)	Ca (mg %)
Mammals									
Rabbit	—	—	—	—	—	—	60	288	480
Rat	—	—	—	—	—	—	5·5	15·4	280
Bird									
Domestic fowl	18·7	19·0	104	33	3	9	35	120	350
Turtles									
'Turtle egg'	—	—	94	—	—	—	—	—	—
Dermochelys coriacea	32·8	30·9	94	35	3·4	10	40	138	345
Thalassochelys corticata	18·9	13·6	72	13·5	0·44	3·4	21	71	340
Pseudemys scripta	—	—	212	—	—	—	—	—	—
Snakes									
Vipera berus berus	2·94	28·2	959	—	—	—	—	—	—
Thamnophis sauritus	1·0	14	1400	—	—	—	—	—	—

calcium in the yolk is virtually the same in the marine turtles as in the domestic fowl. The fresh-water turtle *Pseudemys scripta troostii* has, however, yolk which is almost twice as concentrated with calcium [8], and the viviparous snake *Thamnophis sauritus* has yolk from seven to twenty times as rich in calcium as some turtles [3]. Thirdly, the amount of calcium available to the embryo depends not only upon the concentration of calcium within the yolk but also upon the quantity of yolk within the egg. Thus the giant leathery turtle (*Dermochelys coriacea*) has a yolk almost twice the size of that of the domestic fowl, although the hatchlings are of comparable size. Because of this, the turtle has a greater supply of calcium in its yolk than the bird, although this is still completely inadequate for the embryo which contains four to five times this amount on hatching. There is no information available as to the calcium content of the hatchlings of the ribbon snake (*Thamnophis sauritus*), but the yolk is so very rich in calcium that it would seem unnecessary to postulate any additional supplies during development. There is a little evidence, in fact, which shows that some viviparous snakes retain sufficient yolk to be able to use it as a store of food for several months after hatching [1]. It may be tentatively concluded, therefore, that some snakes provide sufficient calcium to meet all the needs of the embryo, but turtles require additional supplies from outside the egg contents.

There are only two sets of analysis available which throw any light upon the origin of this extra calcium. The first and more complete data are those of Karashima, who used the turtle *Thallassochelys corticata*. Unfortunately, these analyses date back to 1929 and have not been repeated since. The author's own work was an attempt to check some of Karashima's conclusions, but was restricted, to some extent, by the combined difficulties of having turtle eggs flown to London from Malaysia and of hatching these animals in the laboratory.

The results of Karashima's work were originally published as mg of oxide/100 g of egg contents. This makes it very difficult to follow the changes which occur during incubation, as, for example, the yolk decreases in size while changing its calcium content. Similarly, 100 g represents about three fresh turtle eggs but about five hatchlings because of the decrease in weight during incubation. For these reasons, all his results have been recalculated on a mg Ca/egg basis (table 15.2). It is apparent that the

Table 15.2 *Calcium and magnesium content of embryos and eggs of the turtle* Thalassochelys corticata (*recalculated from* [6])

Stage of incubation days	Albumen			Yolk			Embryo			Total egg contents		
	Wt (g)	Ca (mg)	Mg (mg)	Wt (g)	Ca (mg)	Mg (mg)	Wt (g)	Ca (mg)	Mg (mg)	Wt (g)	Ca (mg)	Mg (mg)
Fresh egg	13·5	0·44	0·46	18·9	13·6	5·05	—	—	—	32·4	14·0	5·5
15 days	7·1	0·96	0·7	26·6	14·7	7·0	0·04	trace	0·02	33·7	15·6	7·7
30 days	5·4	0·59	0·6	22·5	14·5	6·0	1·41	0·27	0·25	33·7	15·8	7·1
45 days	—	—	—	5·0	3·3	0·7	15·2	31·1	25·2	44·0	37·6	28·5
Hatchling	—	—	—	—	—	—	21·2	70·7	36·7	21·2	70·7	36·7

calcium in the egg contents increases rapidly in the latter part of incubation and is five times greater at the time of hatching than in the fresh egg. The yolk increases in weight during the first month of incubation, apparently at the expense of the albumen, which decreases in size. During this period, the calcium content of the yolk remains fairly constant. It then decreases to almost a quarter of its size by the 45th day of incubation, so that the fall in calcium content is mainly due to a decrease in size. This decrease in the absolute amount of calcium in the yolk corresponds with a much larger increase in the calcium content of the embryo, which is obviously obtaining calcium from other sources besides the yolk. It would be reasonable to suggest that this extra material is supplied by the eggshell, but Karashima's analyses for magnesium throw some doubt upon this. His results show that magnesium follows an almost identical series of changes to those shown by calcium, with the final result that there is about six times as much magnesium in the hatchling as was present in the original egg contents. This implies that if the eggshell is the source of these extra ions, it must either be composed of almost equimolecular parts of calcium and magnesium salts or, alternatively, the embryo for no apparent reason preferentially absorbs magnesium ions. There is no evidence to support either of these postulates, which therefore tends to reduce the evidence in favour of the eggshell being a source of these extra ions.

The analyses of the eggs and embryos of the giant leathery turtle *Dermochelys coriacea* confirmed the finding that there is approximately a fourfold increase of calcium within the egg during incubation (table 15.3). It

Table 15.3 *Calcium content of eggs, embryos, and hatchlings of the giant leathery turtle* (Dermochelys coriacea) [8]

Stage of incubation	Yolk (mg)		Albumen (mg)	Embryo (mg)
Not incubated	30·9		3·4	—
20 mm embryo (½ incubation time)		—— 37·2* ——		2·1
80 mm embryo (23 g)		—— 46* ——		96·3
'Dead in shell'	54		—	117
Hatchling (40 g)	—		—	138·6

   * Yolk and albumen.

was not possible to remove embryos at various stages of development because of the limited material available, but analyses of embryos which died during incubation confirmed what was to be expected, namely, that the increase of calcium in the embryo occurred mainly towards the end of development. The calcium content of the yolk did not fall in these experiments and a 'dead in shell' hatchling, which had not withdrawn the yolk sac into the body, contained more calcium in this structure than did the original yolk.

The extra embryonic membranes of the turtle develop in a similar way to those of the bird. The chorio-allantois lies immediately beneath the eggshell and is probably responsible for absorbing calcium ions and passing them via the abundant blood supply to the embryo (plate 7, p. 227). The eggshell does not show any structural changes during incubation and the shell membranes do not become detached from the calcified layers. There are, in fact, no well-defined mammillary structures in these eggshells, which appear to be composed simply of shell membranes with an external layer of calcified matrix. It is not clear, therefore, whether the turtle embryo absorbs calcium ions from the shell or whether the additional salts come from outside this structure. The turtle eggshell is only poorly calcified and is permeable to water. There is, therefore, the possibility that the embryos absorb ions from the sea-water, and this would provide a rather better explanation of the large quantities of magnesium which Karashima found. Unfortunately, this hypothesis also produces some difficulties. The giant leathery turtle lays its eggs in quantities of up to a hundred at a time in a hole in the sand above high tide. Thus, even if the sand was wet with sea-water, it seems unlikely that those eggs in the centre of a pile would have access to this source of ions.

The source of the magnesium is only one of the problems associated with this ion. If Karashima's results are accepted, there is a Ca/Mg ratio of almost 2 : 1 by weight in the hatchling turtles which he analysed, and this is almost unbelievable since most adult vertebrates have a ratio of about 40 : 1. Most of the magnesium in mammals is present in the skeleton, and the bones of a hatchling turtle (*Dermochelys coriacea*) were therefore cleared of flesh and analysed for calcium and magnesium [8]. The ions were found in a Ca/Mg ratio of about 16 : 1 by weight, and while this magnesium level is nowhere near as rich as that found in *Thalassochelys corticata*, it is several times richer than the bones of most vertebrates including adult turtles. It was, in fact, this discovery that these embryonic skeletons were excessively rich in magnesium that led to the analyses of magnesium in avian embryos to which we have already referred (p. 208).

Information on the calcium metabolism of reptile embryos is regrettably sparse. What is known about turtles shows that marine species resemble birds in that the embryo utilizes cations from outside the egg contents in order to form its skeleton. Whether these ions are derived from the eggshell or from sea-water is not clear, and possibly both sources are used in a relatively indiscriminate absorption of ions by a chorio-allantoic membrane lying immediately within a fairly permeable eggshell. Regardless of the source, however, there seem to be some oddities in the metabolism of magnesium by these embryos. Fresh-water turtles, and more especially some snakes, appear to have yolks so rich in calcium that, even though there are no data on the composition of the hatchlings, it would seem to be unnecessary to invoke any additional sources of calcium for the embryo. On the contrary, with such a rich yolk, the embryo may use the protein faster than

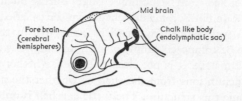

FIG. 15.1. The skull of an embryonic snake broken open to show the large endolymphatic sacs filled with calcium carbonate (after [2]).

the calcium which could thus be stored for later use. This would then explain Carus's observation of an accumulation of calcareous deposits in the endolymphatic sacs of embryonic snakes (*Coluber natrix*) and their later disappearance (fig. 15.1) [2]. Unfortunately, in the absence of any experimental evidence, these are simply speculations, but they perhaps indicate that the reptiles with their rich variety of reproductive adaptations should provide much new information for the chemical embryologist.

REFERENCES

[1] BELLAIRS, RUTH, GRIFFITHS, I., and BELLAIRS, A, D'A. (1955), 'Placentation in the adder *Viper berus*', *Nature, Lond.*, **176**, 657–8.
[2] CARUS, C. G. (1841), 'Merkwürdige Anhäufung mikroskopischer Krystalle am Hinterkopfe der Schlangenembryonen', *Arch. Anatomie Physiologie*, 216–20.
[3] DESSAUER, H. C. and FOX, W. (1959), 'Changes in ovarian follicle composition with plasma levels of snakes during estrus', *Amer. J. Physiol.*, **197**, 360–6.
[4] FRANKLIN, M. A. (1945), 'The embryonic appearance of centres of ossification in the bones of snakes', *Copeia*, 68–72.
[5] JENKINS, N. K. (1966), personal communication.
[6] KARASHIMA, J. (1929), 'Beitrage zur Embryochemie der Reptilien. V. Uber das Verhalten der anorganischer Bestand bei der Bebrüting des Meerschildkroteneies', *J. Biochem., Tokyo*, **10**, 369–74.
[7] PENYAPOL, A. (1958), 'A preliminary study of the sea turtles in the Gulf of Thailand', *Nat. Hist. Bull. Siam. Soc.*, **17**, 23–36.
[8] SIMKISS, K. (1962), 'The sources of calcium for the ossification of the embryos of the giant leathery turtle', *Comp. Biochem. Physiol.*, **7**, 71–9.
[9] URIST, M. R. and SCHJEIDE, ARNE O. (1961), 'The partition of calcium and protein in the blood of oviparous vertebrates during estrus', *J. gen. Physiol.*, **44**, 743–56.

CHAPTER 16

The Calcium Metabolism of Adult and Larval Amphibians

The Adult

The ability of the frog to osmoregulate has been one of the most intensively studied aspects of amphibian physiology, and the fact that the skin is able to absorb salts against a large concentration gradient is of particular importance in this process. By means of this system, the common Ranid frogs can actively absorb ions from the fresh waters in which they live and so replace some of the electrolytes which they lose in their urine. The system is obviously important for our present study if it enables the frog to absorb calcium ions through the skin.

In his early work on the frog (*Rana esculenta*) Krogh [24] was able to show that the absorption of salts by the skin was dependent upon a cation pump with a high specificity for sodium ions. Only a few experiments were performed with solutions containing calcium ions, but they indicated that the skin could not absorb this cation from a solution of calcium chloride. More recent work on the isolated skin has confirmed this result [18], but some confusion has arisen in the interpretation of *in vivo* experiments. It is generally accepted that the skin of the frog is permeable to water which is therefore continually entering a submerged frog along an osmotic gradient. There is, therefore, no need for frogs to drink, and they are only rarely observed to do so under normal circumstances. Despite this, it has been shown on a number of occasions that if frogs (*R. esculenta, R. temporaria*) are placed in a solution of calcium or strontium chloride there is, during the following weeks, a progressive accumulation of calcium or strontium carbonate in the endolymphatic sacs of these animals [21, 22]. From these experiments, it has been repeatedly argued that as the frog does not drink, the calcium ions must be absorbed by the skin. Unfortunately, this argument is not valid, for there are conditions under which frogs can be induced to drink, and the most common of these is when the animal is placed in hypertonic solutions [5]. An examination of the experimental conditions under which frogs have been reported to absorb calcium ion through the skin shows that solutions of from 0·04 to 0·08 M have been used. This range extends to a concentration similar to that of amphibian blood, and under these conditions, and with experiments which lasted for several weeks, it seems highly likely that the frogs would drink some of the water. Support for this suggestion comes from several sets of experiments. First, it has been shown by means of radiographs that if *Rana pipiens* is placed in solutions of radiopaque materials, such as thorium dioxide, and left there for several days, there is an accumulation of this material in the intestine, indicating that under these conditions the animals may swallow the waters in which they live. Secondly, it has been shown that if starved frogs are X-rayed before and after they have been placed in solutions of 0·07 M calcium chloride, it is sometimes possible to detect deposits of calcium carbonate and phosphate in the alimentary canal. If the animals were given injections of vitamin D and the experiments were repeated, these deposits were never seen, and it was suggested that the concretions represented calcium which had been swallowed in solution by the frog but incompletely absorbed in the absence of the vitamin [31].

It appears, therefore, that although frogs normally do not drink, they may do so under the abnormal conditions of some experiments, and it is unfortunate that these are the very conditions which have been used in attempts to demonstrate a cutaneous absorption of calcium ions. Thus it seems most reasonable to conclude that frogs can not absorb calcium ions through the skin. To this extent, therefore, the amphibian is like other tetrapods in that calcium must enter the body by absorption from material in the alimentary canal. We have already seen that vitamin D appears to be of importance in this process, and it is interesting to find that the cutaneous fat of *Rana temporaria* contains the precursors of this vitamin [25]. If the clawed toad *Xenopus laevis* is kept in captivity in the absence of sunlight the ovaries regress [37] probably because of the inability of the animal to transport yolk proteins to the ovary in cases of calcium deficiency. This animal appears to be very susceptible to vitamin D deficiencies, and may develop rickets even when living in hard water, a fact that is in keeping with our previous conclusions regarding the avenues of calcium absorption. When fed solely upon liver, *Xenopus* is obviously calcium deficient, and it requires both mineral and vitamin supplements to maintain and repair its skeletal system (table 16.1). The calcium level of the blood rises when vitamin D is injected into this animal and massive doses (50,000 units) result in a mobilization of skeletal calcium and eventually osteoporosis [31].

The suggestion has been made by a number of authors that the calcium metabolism of amphibia is mainly under the control of vitamin D. This concept is based upon the argument that as fish do not possess parathyroid glands, the amphibia are phylogenetically the first group of vertebrates to evolve this endocrine system of control. The implication is that the system is not perfected in the amphibia and there are certainly a number of unusual features in the results of work on amphibian parathyroids. Thus, Studitsky removed the parathyroid glands of 20 specimens of *Triton stellatus* and 100 *Rana ridibunda* in November 1940. He found that the frogs lived in captivity until May 1941, when they were liberated into a terrarium and lived there until the following winter. The operation appeared to

Table 16.1 *Nutritional requirements of* Xenopus laevis *for the repair and maintenance of its skeleton (after* [2])

Diet	% animals with normal skeleton	% with skeletal deficiencies, but showing healing	% with skeletal deficiencies, but without healing
Liver alone	0	0	100
Liver and minerals	14	38	48
Liver and cod-liver oil	38	50	12
Liver, minerals, and cod-liver oil	29	67	4

have no effect upon the ability of the frogs to reproduce normally in May 1941 [32]. As we have already seen (Chapter 5), some amphibians appear to be more dependent upon their parathyroids than others, but Studitsky is the only person to report both normal reproduction and the absence of side-effects after removing these glands. In view of the surgical difficulties in achieving complete parathyroidectomy, it would be valuable to have these experiments confirmed, although other workers have also obtained unusual results when studying the amphibian parathyroids and their relationship to bone physiology. Thus Irving and Solms found that injections of parathyroid hormone into *Xenopus laevis* produced no elevation in the level of serum calcium and only a weak osteoclastic effect upon the bones [19]. In *Rana pipiens* it has been shown by means of injections of radioisotopes that there is a constant remodelling of the amphibian bone, but when parathyroid hormone was also injected into these animals there was an increased deposition of Ca^{45} into the skeleton instead of the resorption which might have been expected [3]. These results are difficult to understand, and before accepting that they demonstrate an unusual aspect of amphibian physiology, one must question the techniques used, the use of preparations of mammalian hormones which may be specific in their action and the levels of the doses which have been administered. Other results indicate a more typical function of the parathyroid glands in amphibia. In particular, there are Waggener's detailed experiments on *Rana catesbiana* where the removal of these glands produced a fall in the level of serum calcium, together with attacks of tetany which, in this case, could be relieved by injections of mammalian parathyroid hormone [36]. The results of other experiments on the amphibian parathyroid gland have been summarized in table 5.7 (p. 54) which again indicates some unusual features.

One aspect of the physiology of the amphibian parathyroid upon which there is general agreement is that the gland undergoes a seasonal cycle of cytolysis and regeneration. In *R. catesbiana* the vacuolation and breakdown of the cells started in February and regeneration was completed by May to June. Frequently one or two of the glands degenerated while the others remained normal, and Waggener [35] pointed out that the amount of healthy tissue present at any one time probably did not represent less than a half of the total amount of tissue normally present in the gland. Furthermore, if the parathyroids were removed during this period of cytolysis, the frogs went into tetany and died. It appears, therefore, that these frogs are continually dependent upon their parathyroid glands, despite the seasonal variation in their activity. These observations have been confirmed by Studitsky [32], who added the information that his colleague Kovalsky had found a seasonal variation in the calcium content of the blood which corresponded with these changes. During the spring, when the cytolysis of the glands occurred, the serum calcium was 8·4 mg %. In the summer it fell to 5·4 mg %, during which time the parathyroids were recovering, and during the winter the serum calcium was 7·4 mg % and the glands were normal. These remarkable results have never been confirmed in their entirety, but there are two sets of observations which indicate that they may represent an important phenomenon. In *Bufo arenarum* there is a seasonal variation in the level of serum calcium of female, but not male, toads. The level in the male is fairly constant throughout the year at 12 mg %, but that of the female rises to a level of about 16 mg % from July to December and falls to 12 mg % in January [8]. The same phenomenon occurs in *Xenopus laevis*, where it has been related to the activity of the ovary (fig. 16.1). Apparently the rise in the level of serum calcium in the female is related to the transport of yolk precursors to the ovary. Thus, if the animals become vitamin-D-deficient, not only does the ovary regress but also the level of calcium in the blood of the female falls to that of the male [37]. Given this evidence, it is very tempting to speculate that the cytolysis of the amphibian parathyroid gland is related to a hypercalcaemia (as suggested by Koval-sky), which is in turn an indication of the transport of yolk precursors to the ovary in the form of calcium compounds (as implied by Zwarenstein and Shapiro). Unfortunately, there is no evidence available concerning the level of ionic calcium in the serum during these events and the activity of the parathyroids may be related to other seasonal variations such as temperature.

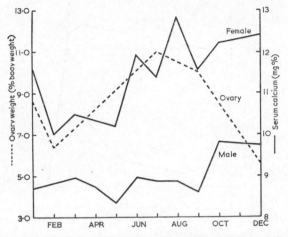

FIG. 16.1. The concentration of calcium in the serum of male and female clawed toads. Note the elevated blood calcium of the female at the time of ovary enlargement (after [37]).

It has been shown that there are both sexual and seasonal differences in the ratios of the weights of bones of *Rana temporaria*, but none of these facts indicate that there is any resorption of bone to meet the needs of re-production [4]. *Rana temporaria* appears to be typical of amphibians living in a temperate climate, and in this species ovulation occurs in February to March, soon after the end of hibernation. During April to June there is a resorption of any unshed oocytes and spermatogenesis and vitellogenesis begins to occur shortly afterwards. Thus most of the yolk is formed during the summer months when there is a plentiful supply of food. The yolk has a low calcium content (27·2 mg/100 g protein in *R. catesbiana* [34]), and as it is formed slowly at a time of good nutrition, there is no reason to consider that reproduction makes any demands upon the mineral reserves of the adult. Injections of from 2 to 5 mg oestrogens/week did not induce any medullary bone formation in *Xenopus laevis*, nor did this produce any indi-cation of any other calcium storage system [20]; this is in agreement with the above conclusions.

The Tadpole

Most amphibians lay their eggs in ponds or slow-moving streams. As a generalization it may be stated that the tadpole which hatches from the egg does not possess any bones but normally lives and grows in water which contains an adequate source of food and calcium. Many tadpoles are filter feeders, and their food, and presumably a large quantity of water,

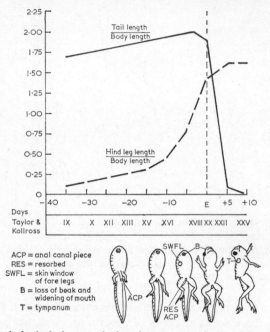

FIG. 16.2. Morphological changes during the metamorphosis of *Rana pipiens* tadpoles. Metamorphic climax is taken as the time when the forelimbs emerge (*E*) and other changes are timed in relation to this event (after [6, 7]).

passes through their alimentary tracts very quickly [30]. The amphibian yolk contains precursors of vitamin D [25] and the vitamins may also be obtained from the food, for it is reported that *Xenopus laevis* can be successfully reared in complete darkness [26]. The young animals have, therefore, an adequate supply of calcium ions and no obvious restrictions upon their absorption of this material. One might consider that under these circumstances the tadpole would slowly ossify its skeleton, using the available environmental calcium, and so mature without any crisis in its mineral metabolism. The fact that this does not happen is due to the unusual morphological and biochemical changes which occur during the metamorphosis of the tadpole into a frog.

The severity of the metamorphic changes varies between different groups of amphibians. In the urodeles the transformation is nowhere near as extensive or complex as in the anurans. In particular, the urodeles retain their tail throughout development and their limbs do not undergo any marked changes, for they appear to complete their differentiation at a very early stage of their larval life. Little is known about the calcium metabolism of urodeles so that the following discussion will be restricted to a consideration of the anurans.

The metamorphosis of an anuran larva is a gradual process and it is rather difficult to obtain a definite basis and standard for comparing the various changes which occur. Two main approaches have been used. First there are the detailed descriptions of the normal stages of development of both *Rana pipiens* [33] and *Xenopus laevis* [26] which provide a purely morphological assessment of the extent of metamorphosis. Alternatively it is possible to measure the tail, hindlimb, and body lengths of the tadpoles and by plotting various ratios of these parameters to obtain a measure of the extent of metamorphosis.

The two methods have been correlated by Etkin in his accounts of the metamorphosis of *Rana pipiens* [6, 7]. The process begins with the differential acceleration of hindlimb growth (fig. 16.2). The anal canal piece (ACP) begins to be resorbed when the hindlimbs are half grown and it is completely resorbed in about three days when the skin window over the forelimbs (SWFL) begins to disintegrate. The emergence of the forelimbs (E) marks the end of what has been termed prometamorphosis and the animal now goes into metamorphic climax when rapid morphological changes take place. Because of variations in the rate of growth and development it is often convenient to take the end of prometamorphosis as a standard stage in the life cycle of the frog.

During the metamorphic climax the tadpole stops feeding, the horny teeth and beaks (B) are lost and the mouth widens to that characteristic of the frog. In a series of rapid changes the tongue enlarges, the intestine becomes shorter, the tail is resorbed, and the legs grow, while the eye and tympanic apparatus (T) assume their adult form. The gills and remains of the operculum are resorbed and the skin begins to take on its adult structure. These changes may all occur in about one week and the details of the transition are fairly general for most Ranid frogs.

At the time of metamorphic climax the tadpole is to some extent an isolated system. This would certainly seem to be the case as regards its calcium metabolism. Little is known about the ability of tadpoles to osmoregulate, although there is some evidence that their skin does not possess the power of active ion absorption found in the adult [24]. Similarly, the gills are lost early in metamorphosis so that they could not be involved in ion regulation at the time when bone formation occurs. Food is not eaten during the metamorphic climax and presumably water does not pass through the alimentary tract during the period when these tissues are undergoing their reorganization. It may be concluded therefore that the metamorphosing tadpole has no outside source of calcium available to it once it enters the metamorphic climax. This places the animal in a most interesting situation. A small amount of bone is formed in the young tadpole, mainly in its skull, but ossification does not proceed to any great extent until the limbs and skeleton start to form prior to the animal becoming terrestrial. In fact, the mineralization of the skeleton only proceeds rapidly during the metamorphic climax when environmental and dietary sources of calcium appear to be relatively inaccessible.

There is evidence from two separate sources that the time of metamorphosis is one of particular importance in the calcium metabolism of the frog. In *R. temporaria* and *R. ridibunda* Studitsky found that there was a liquefaction of the protoplasm of the parathyroids during metamorphosis at a time when skeletal ossification was just beginning. He compared the situation with a similar cytolysis which occurs in the adult during the spring and the implication was made that it reflected a time of intense calcium metabolism [32]. A similar conclusion was reached by Bruce and Parkes in a study of rickets and osteoporosis in *Xenopus laevis*. They found that at metamorphosis the frog was extremely susceptible to a deficiency of vitamin D with the disease being particularly severe and affecting the whole of the skeleton at this time [2].

Most of the skeleton of the young frog only ossifies after the tadpole has ceased to feed, and a detailed investigation of the source of this mineral has been undertaken by Guardabassi [15]. It will be recalled that in the amphibians the endolymphatic sacs of the inner ear are very well developed. They form precociously in the tadpole and contain a considerable quantity of calcium carbonate in the form of fine crystals of aragonite. At the time of metamorphosis the endolymphatic system has penetrated the vertebral canal and runs the whole length of most Ranid tadpoles, dorsal to the spinal cord. It has a good vascular system, in the form of a dense network of capillaries.

If the tadpole is killed it is possible to render the flesh transparent with glycerine and stain the skeleton with alizarin red. Using this technique, Guardabassi was able to colour the bones red but leave the calcium carbonate in the endolymphatic sacs as a white mass. It was then possible to judge arbitrarily the distribution of calcium between the calcareous and osseous systems. It was found that in certain species (*Bufo bufo, Rana dalmatina*) the growth and mineralization of the skeleton which occurs during metamorphosis is accompanied by a decrease and sometimes a complete disappearance, of the calcareous deposits in the endolymphatic sacs (plate 8). The process was most conspicuous in those regions of the endolymphatic system which were located in the vertebral canal and it was suggested that the calcium carbonate had been resorbed from this region to provide the calcium ions necessary for the mineralization of the skeleton [10]. This evidence was certainly suggestive, but not conclusive, and in order to demonstrate that the calcium in the endolymphatic sacs was indeed transported to the bones during metamorphosis, further experiments were performed with radio-isotopes.

Tadpoles appear to be rather sensitive to radiation [13] so it was necessary to build up the concentration of Ca^{45} over a period of five days until the final dosage was 0·12 mc in 15 litres of water. This procedure gave 100% survival of Bufo bufo tadpoles when they were treated with radioactive calcium lactate for seven to eight days. The experiment was timed so that the larvae were treated with the Ca^{45} before they metamorphosed and before the mineralization of the skeleton had commenced. A longer treatment with the radio-isotope was avoided in case the tadpoles should start to mineralize their skeletons while they still had access to the radioactive solution. Some of the tadpoles were killed immediately after removing them from the labelled solution, while others were placed in fast-running tap-water so that any Ca^{45} excreted by the animals could not be reabsorbed. They were left in the running water for 20 to 30 days until they had completed their metamorphosis. Specimens were then killed and fixed in alcohol, and sections were cut for autoradiographs [15].

The results demonstrated two events. First, the Ca^{45} had been concentrated in the endolymphatic sacs by the time that the tadpoles were removed from the labelled solution (plate 9 (a)). Secondly, it was shown that after metamorphosis the radio-isotope was unevenly distributed in the sacs although the epithelial cells were strongly radioactive (plate 9 (b)). Sections of the hindlimbs cut across the femoro-iliac joint showed a slight concentration of Ca^{45} in the diaphyses (plate 9 (c)). It was concluded from these observations that calcium was first stored in the endolymphatic sacs and then mobilized at the time of metamorphosis to provide minerals for the ossification of the skeleton. The presence of Ca^{45} in the epithelium of the endolymphatic sacs was interpreted as demonstrating the movement of this ion from within the endolymph to the blood-stream. The skeleton contained only a low concentration of Ca^{45} and this was interpreted by Guardabassi as showing that 'the amount of calcium supplied by the endolymphatic sacs is obviously small as compared with that taken up from the food and running water' [15].

This elegant work certainly provides confirmatory evidence in favour of Guardabassi's hypothesis that the endolymphatic sacs contain a store of calcium which is used to mineralize the bones during metamorphosis. Unfortunately, however, the experiments are not conclusive. On the basis of autoradiographs, one cannot be sure that the decrease in the content of Ca^{45} in the endolymphatic sacs is not an apparent effect due to the later deposition of non-labelled calcium carbonate outside the earlier formed mass. The amount of radioactivity later found in the skeleton is quite small, and there is no way of knowing that it has not arrived at that site simply by ion exchange between the calcium in the sacs and that in the bone. If such was the case the radioactivity found in the bones would be no indication of the resorption of calcium carbonate from the endolymphatic system.

Recently an attempt has been made to confirm Guardabassi's hypothesis by obtaining quantitative data on the distribution of calcium carbonate and calcium phosphate in the tadpole of *Rana temporaria* during metamorphosis. A technique has been devised by Pilkington for analysing the various calcium deposits in individual tadpoles. The method consists of macerating the eviscerated animal in warm ethylene diamine and isolating the inorganic matter by centrifugation. These minerals can then be analysed for carbonate by a microdiffusion method performed within the centrifuge tube. The dissolved material remaining in the tube can then be analysed for calcium and phosphate ions [29].

The tadpoles used in this work were all reared from a single batch of spawn and they were all fed a uniform diet of canned spinach. When the animals were approaching metamorphosis they were split into four groups and reared in artificial pond waters with either a high pH (7·5–8·0) or a low pH (5·6–5·9) value and with either a high or low calcium content. The solutions with a high calcium content contained 1·5 m.eq./l and the low calcium water contained no calcium. It is referred to as 'low calcium', however, because although the solutions were changed every 24 hours there was inevitably some contamination of the solution with dietary and urinary calcium from the tadpoles. All the tadpoles used in this work continued to be fed the same food and only the environmental water was modified.

Specimens of various ages were removed from the four treatments and the stage of metamorphosis was determined by studying the morphological changes that occurred during development and by using the ratios of tail: body length and hindlimb length: body length (fig. 16.2). The important event in these experiments is when the tadpole enters metamorphic climax and this was taken as occurring when the forelimbs emerged. This was defined as day 0 and the results of the analyses were therefore plotted as days before or after this event (fig. 16.3 (a)). It is apparent that there is a progressively increasing difference in the calcium content of the tadpole's mineral deposits depending upon whether they were allowed to undergo metamorphosis in the water of high or low calcium content. The results also clearly show that shortly after metamorphic climax (i.e. day + 2) the animals cease to accumulate more calcium and in fact the minerals in the body decrease in calcium content by between 100 and 150 μg/6 days. It appears that much of the calcium absorbed by tadpoles comes from the water in which they live rather than from their food. They cease to absorb this calcium when they stop feeding, indicating that it probably enters via the alimentary tract. The animals continue to lose calcium from day + 2 onwards and as faecal strings are not produced during the metamorphic climax it appears that there is probably a renal loss of about 20 μg/day. This calcium is ultimately derived from the mineral stores of the tadpole.

An analysis of the details of the mineral metabolism of tadpoles reared in a water of high calcium content can be derived from fig. 16.3 (b). The experimental period divides itself into three clear phases. From day −8 to day −4 the tadpole contains almost no bone, but there is an enormous deposition of calcium carbonate in the endolymphatic sacs. In the second phase, from day −4 to day +2 there is a large increase in bone mineral, while the calcium content of the endolymphatic sacs remains constant. Finally, as the animals enter metamorphic climax the bones continue to grow and ossify, although there is no increase in total calcium during this phase (fig. 16.3 (a)). Instead, there is evidence of a redistribution of the calcium deposits in the animal. Thus the content of the endolymphatic sacs decreases by an amount slightly in excess of that necessary for the formation of the extra skeletal mineral. The extra calcium which is lost from the endolymphatic sacs is sufficient to account for the renal loss of 20 μg/day.

On the basis of these experiments it was concluded that the endolymphatic sacs acted as a storage system for calcium. The young tadpole deposits calcium carbonate in these sacs at a time when the material is freely available but when development has not progressed as far as the formation of the skeleton. When the bones start to ossify the calcium absorbed from the diet is diverted to this requirement and the sacs cease to store extra mineral. At metamorphic climax the dietary calcium is no longer available and the skeleton is then mineralized at the expense of the calcareous deposits in the sacs [29].

This interpretation obviously raises additional problems, for if calcium is stored before metamorphic climax as a carbonate and then used to lay down the calcium phosphate of the bones there must obviously also be a store of phosphate in the body of the tadpole. Phosphate, however, is

R

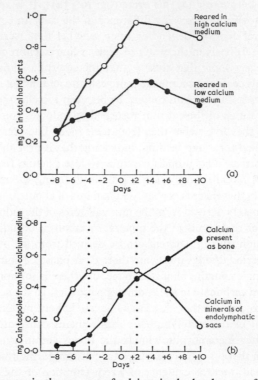

FIG. 16.3. Changes in the amount of calcium in the hard parts of tadpoles during metamorphosis. The emergence of the forelimbs is designated as day 0 with prometamorphosis being days before and climax as days after this event.

The amount of calcium in the mineral deposits increases continuously until the animals stop feeding shortly after they enter metamorphic climax. Most of the calcium is, however, apparently obtained from the water in which they live (a). The data on the distribution of calcium between the endolymphatic sacs and the bones is given for the high calcium treatment in (b). Metamorphosis is divided into the three periods referred to in the text by means of the vertical dotted lines. In the first period the calcium is stored in the sacs. In the second period the bones account for all the extra calcium being stored in the body. Finally, when the animals stop feeding during metamorphic climax, the bones grow at the expense of calcium derived from the endolymphatic sacs (data from [29]).

unlike calcium in that it is retained in large amounts in the soft tissues, and Pilkington has shown in some preliminary experiments that with the resorption of the tail and other organs during metamorphosis there is a liberation of phosphate from the soft parts that would assist in meeting the requirements for the ossification of the skeleton [28].

The demonstration that the endolymphatic sacs become depleted of calcium even when the tadpoles are allowed to undergo metamorphosis in water with a high calcium content indicates that this phenomenon must be a normal part of the developmental physiology of the tadpole and not just limited to frogs developing in water with a low calcium content. In fact, during the metamorphic climax of *Rana temporaria* about 350 μg of calcium was removed from the endolymphatic sacs of tadpoles reared in a high calcium medium, whereas only 190 μg was resorbed from the sacs of animals on the low calcium treatment. Similar experiments on the effects of environmental calcium were performed by Guardabassi who reared tadpoles of *Bufo vulgaris* in water containing 0·8 g/l of calcium glycerophosphate and reported on the basis of qualitative estimates, that the endolymphatic sacs were apparently more enlarged than those of tadpoles reared without the calcium supplement. When the tadpoles underwent metamorphosis the specimens from the calcium-enriched water showed a more advanced and an earlier ossification of the skeleton. It also appeared that less calcium had been removed from the sacs of these animals than from toads which had metamorphosed in distilled water [12]. This observation is probably deceptive since a similar appearance was seen in the specimens X-rayed by Pilkington and Simkiss, but in this case the chemical analyses demonstrated that more calcium was resorbed from the sacs of the calcium-enriched animals than from their controls reared in a low calcium medium [29]. This discrepancy in the interpretation of these results is important since Guardabassi has suggested on the basis of these observations that the tadpoles reared in calcium-enriched water can probably absorb calcium through the skin and thus do not need to resorb the calcium deposits of the inner ear [10].

The endolymphatic sacs do not appear to be indispensable to anurans and Guardabassi has surgically removed the otic vesicles from larvae of *Bufo vulgaris* and *Rana dalmatina* and maintained the surviving tadpoles through metamorphosis. Under these circumstances the animals never developed an endolymphatic system, but they still formed an ossified skeleton providing that they were kept in water which contained calcium ions [9, 10]. It was suggested that, under these circumstances, the tadpoles obtained their calcium directly from the water, or the food, or after the cessation of feeding at metamorphic climax, through the skin [10]. The evidence in favour of a cutaneous absorption of calcium does not seem convincing but it has been pointed out from comparative studies that calcium is mainly resorbed from the endolymphatic sacs of those species which leave the water during metamorphosis. The calcareous deposits are quite well developed in the permanently aquatic toad *Xenopus laevis*, but the calcium is normally resorbed to only a small extent in this species [23], and Guarda-bassi has interpreted evidence of this sort as indicating that the animal has a continual access to calcium in the water by absorption through the skin.

Little is known about the way in which the calcium is mobilized from the endolymphatic sacs. It has been shown that the epithelial cells contain an alkaline phosphatase and a mucoprotein which is orthochromatic with toluidine blue. The calcareous contents of the sacs appear to be deposited in a mucopolysaccharide matrix which is metachromatic with toluidine blue [17]. These characteristics are typical of calcified structures [16], but provide no clue as to the mechanism whereby the calcium carbonate is mobilized at the time of metamorphosis. One suggestion which has been made is that the deposits are dissolved by a lowering of the pH of the blood at metamorphosis. Such a change in the blood has been observed [1] and the hypothesis is an attractive one in view of the known acid-base regula-ting ability of the sacs of the adult. The increased acidity of the blood might itself be related to the thickening of the tadpole's skin at metamorphosis and the attendant difficulties in obtaining oxygen or excreting carbon dioxide. It should be pointed out, however, that in the experiments of Pilkington and Simkiss tadpoles were allowed to undergo metamorphosis in water of either a high or low pH, but these treatments had little effect upon the rate or extent of resorption of the endolymphatic minerals [29]. Under normal circumstances the calcareous deposits are removed from the more posterior parts of the sacs before they are lost from the cranial regions. The statoliths, which are situated in another part of the inner ear are ap-parently never resorbed and this probably accounts for the fact that there is always some calcium carbonate in the tadpole which is not depleted during metamorphic climax (fig. 16.3 (b)). This implies that either one region of the membranous labyrinth is adapted to resist resorption (i.e. the statoliths) or another region is specialized to facilitate it (i.e. the endo-lymphatic sacs).

A number of endocrine organs have been implicated in the regulation of the endolymphatic deposits. One of these was the thymus, but from our present knowledge of this organ in other vertebrates this now seems an unlikely suggestion and, in fact, more recent work has failed to show any effect after either removing the thymus or feeding this organ to tadpoles [10, 11]. Experiments on the thyroid have been more successful, but the results seem to be largely secondary to the effect of accelerating metamor-phosis. Thus thyroxine-treated tadpoles of *Rana dalmatina* show only a poor calcification of the skeleton, probably because development is so rapid that the calcium in the endolymphatic sacs cannot be mobilized fast enough to keep pace with the development of the skeleton [10]. Tadpoles treated with the antithyroid drug thiouracil, produced giant larvae with hypertrophied parathyroid glands and a reduction in the calcareous contents of the endolymphatic sacs [14].

It will be apparent from this discussion that the calcium metabolism of metamorphosing anurans presents a particularly interesting solution to the need to form a tetrapod skeleton in a relatively short period of time. Much remains to be discovered, however, regarding the regulation of the endolymphatic deposits and their integration into the total pattern of metamorphosis. It should also be realized that the amphibia show a remarkable range in their methods of reproduction. Most of the adaptations described in this chapter have been restricted to those of the more 'typical' anurans. There are, however, many examples of anurans where the tadpole is really almost an embryonic form, for it is never free-living and is only liberated from the parent after metamorphosis. Similarly, many urodeles are ovoviviparous and some, such as *Salamandra atra* appear to pass nutrients from the adult to the developing offspring [27]. Unfortunately, nothing is known about the calcium metabolism of either the adults or embryos of these species.

REFERENCES

[1] ALESCHIN, B. (1935), 'Metamorphose des amphibiens comme effet morphogénétique de la glande thyroide', *Bull. Histol. appl. Physiol. Path.*, **12**, 5-28.

[2] BRUCE, H. M. and PARKES, A. S. (1950), 'Rickets and osteoporosis in *Xenopus laevis*', *J. Endocrin.*, **7**, 64-81.

[3] CORTELYOU, J. R., HARGIS, G. K., and LEHRER, L. (1962), 'Influence of mammalian parathormone on bone composition in the frog *Rana pipiens*', *Amer. Zool.*, **2**, 400-1.

[4] DAUVART, ANNA (1930), 'Über die Zyklische Gewichtsvariation des Vorderbeinskelettes des Frosches', *Arch. Entw. Mech. Org.*, **122**, 140-51.

[5] DEYRUP, I. J. (1964), 'Water balance and kidney', in *Physiology of the Amphibia*, ed. Moore, J. A., Academic Press, 251-328.

[6] ETKIN, W. (1955), 'Metamorphosis', in *Analysis of Development*, eds. Willier, B. H., Weiss, P. A., and Hamburger, V., Saunders, 631-63.

[7] ETKIN, W. (1964), 'Metamorphosis', in *Physiology of the Amphibia*, ed. Moore, J. A., Academic Press, 427-68.

[8] GERSCHMAN, R. (1943), 'Variaciones estacionales o por hipofisectomia de los elementos minerales del plasma del salpo', *Revta. Soc. Argent. Biol.*, **19**, 170-81.

[9] GUARDABASSI, ANTONIETTA (1952), 'L'organo endolinfatico degli anfibi anuri', *Arch. ital. Anat. Embriol.*, **57**, 241-94.

[10] GUARDABASSI, ANTONIETTA (1953), 'Les sels de Ca du sac

endolymphatique et les processus de calcification des os pendant la metamorphose normale et expérimentale chez les têtards de *Bufo vulgaris*, *Rana dalmatina*, *Rana esculenta*', *Arch. Anat. microsc. Morph. exp.*, **42**, 143–67.

[11] GUARDABASSI, ANTONIETTA (1956), 'I sali di calcio del sacco endolinfatico e i processi di ossificazione in girini di *Xenopus laevis*', *Arch. ital. Anat. Embriol.*, **61**, 276–96.

[12] GUARDABASSI, ANTONIETTA (1957), 'I sali di calcio del sacco endolinfatico ed i processi di calcificazione in girini di *Bufo vulgaris* sottoposti a diverse condizioni sperimentali (acqua ricca di glicerofosfato di calcio e acqua distillata)', *Monit. zool. ital.*, **64**, 140–8.

[13] GUARDABASSI, ANTONIETTA (1959a), 'Osservazioni preliminari sur metabolismo del Ca^{45} in larve di *Bufo bufo bufo*', *Monit. zool. ital.*, **66**, 1–6.

[14] GUARDABASSI, ANTONIETTA (1959b), 'Tiroide, paratiroidi e sali di Ca del sacco endolinfatico in larve di *Bufo bufo bufo* trattate con tiouracile', *Arch. ital. Anat. Embriol.*, **66**, 105–27.

[15] GUARDABASSI, ANTONIETTA (1960), 'The utilization of the calcareous deposits of the endolymphatic sacs of *Bufo bufo bufo* in the mineralization of the skeleton. Investigations by means of Ca^{45}', *Z. Zellforsch.*, **51**, 278–82.

[16] GUARDABASSI, ANTONIETTA (1962), 'Le caratteristiche citologische ultrarastrutturali istochimiche e biochimiche di alcuni tessuti e organi che partecipano alla elaborazione di strutture calcificate', *Monit. zool. ital.*, **70**, 1–55.

[17] GUARDABASSI, ANTONIETTA and PIACENZA, M. L. (1956), 'L'epitelio secernenti del sacco endolinfatico di *Bufo vulgaris* e di *Xenopus laevis*', *Boll. Zool.*, **23**, 295–8.

[18] HUF, E. G. and WILLS, JOYCE (1951), 'Influence of some inorganic cations on active salt and water uptake by isolated frog skin', *Amer. J. Physiol.*, **167**, 255–60.

[19] IRVING, J. T. and SOLMS, C. M. (1955a), 'The influence of parathyroid hormone upon bone formation in *Xenopus laevis*', *S. Afr. J. med. Sci.*, **20**, 32.

[20] IRVING, J. T. and SOLMS, C. M. (1955b), 'The influence of oestrogen upon bone formation in *Xenopus laevis*', *S. Afr. J. med. Sci.*, **20**, 32–3.

[21] KIRCHBERG, H. (1940), 'Experimentelle Untersuchungen über die Auswirkung chemischer und hormonaler Einflüsse auf die Kalksackchen der Froschlurche', *Inaugural dissertation Physiologischen Institut Universitat, Liepzig*, 1–19.

[22] KRAUSE, K. (1935), 'Experimentelle untersuchungen über die funktion der Kalksackchen bei Froschlurchen', *Z. vergl. Physiol.*, **22**, 346–58.

[23] KREINER, J. (1954), 'Saccus endolymphaticus in *Xenopus laevis*', *Folia. biol. Krakow.*, **2**, 271–86.

[24] KROGH, A. (1938), 'The active absorption of ions in some freshwater animals', *Z. vergl. Physiol.*, **25**, 333–50.

[25] MORTON, R. A. and ROSEN, D. G. (1949), 'Carotenoids, vitamin A and 7-dehydrosteroid in the frog (*Rana temporaria*)', *Biochem. J.*, **45**, 612–27.

[26] NIEUWKOOP, P. D. and FABER, J. (1956), *Normal Table of Xenopus laevis* (*Daudin*), North Holland Publishing Co., 243 pp.

[27] NOBLE, G. K. (1954), *The Biology of the Amphibia*, Dover Publications, 577 pp.

[28] PILKINGTON, J. B. (1966). Personal communication.

[29] PILKINGTON, J. B. and SIMKISS, K. (1966), 'The mobilization of the calcium carbonate deposits in the endolymphatic sacs of metamorphosing frogs', *J. exp. Biol.* **45**, 329–341.

[30] SAVAGE, R. H. M. (1961), *The Ecology and Life History of the Common Frog* (Rana temporaria temporaria)', Pitman, 221 pp.

[31] SCHLUMBERGER, H. G. and BURK, D. H. (1953), 'Comparative study of the reactions to injury. 2. Hypervitaminosis D in the frog with special reference to the lime sacs', *Archs. Path.*, **56**, 103–24.

[32] STUDITSKY, A. N. (1945), 'Function of parathyroid glands in Amphibia', *C.R. Acad. Sci. U.R.S.S.*, **47**, 444–7.

[33] TAYLOR, A. C. and KOLLROS, J. J. (1946), 'Stages in the normal development of *Rana pipiens* larvae', *Anat. Rec.*, **94**, 7–23.

[34] URIST, M. R. and SCHJEIDE, A. O. (1961), 'The partition of calcium and protein in the blood of oviparous vertebrates during estrus', *J. gen. Physiol.*, **44**, 743–56.

[35] WAGGENER, R. A. (1929), 'A histological study of the parathyroids in the anura', *J. Morph.*, **48**, 1–44.

[36] WAGGENER, R. A. (1930), 'An experimental study of the parathyroids in the anura', *J. exp. Zool.*, **57**, 13–56.

[37] ZWARENSTEIN, H. and SHAPIRO, H. A. (1933), 'Metabolic changes associated with endocrine activity and the reproductive cycle in *Xenopus laevis*. 3. Changes in the calcium content of the serum associated with captivity and the normal reproductive cycle', *J. exp. Biol.*, **10**, 372–8.

CHAPTER 17

Conclusions and Speculations

The two problems in calcium metabolism during reproduction worth greatest attention are first, the need to provide stores of calcium which either the mother or the embryo can use when there is a deficiency, and secondly, the time factor which necessitates calcium being utilized at a rapid rate during certain phases of reproduction. The basic reasons for these two difficulties were discussed in the Introduction. It may be as well therefore to conclude by considering the ways in which these problems are overcome in various tetrapods.

The mode of reproduction of the eutherian mammals is probably one of the main reasons for the success of this group of vertebrates. All the indications are that pregnancy does not impose any strain upon the calcium metabolism of the mother unless the animal is fed a very deficient diet or breeding occurs continuously without any time for the body to recover from the effects of previous periods of reproduction. It is, in fact, often found that even when adverse conditions persist the mother is able to maintain a positive balance of calcium during her pregnancy. The reasons for this remarkable adaptation appear to be two-fold. First, mammalian development is a relatively slow process in comparison with the rate of formation of other embryos. This is probably because of the absence of many of the physiological restrictions imposed by, for example, the cleidoic egg within which the embryo can only live for a short time. The effect of a protracted period of development in the mammal is to decrease the rate at which the embryo utilizes substances such as calcium. Thus the rate of mineral metabolism is less critical during the reproduction of mammals than in other tetrapods. The second feature which reduces the strain on the calcium metabolism of the reproducing mammal is the placenta. This amazing organ performs a remarkable number of functions during pregnancy, but its effect on the calcium metabolism is relatively simple. Its main advantage stems from the fact that it puts the mother and her foetus into physiological communication so that there is little need for either animal to deposit calcium in any special storage system. Thus the two main problems of reproduction which are being discussed, i.e. the rate of calcium metabolism and the need for storage systems, are both to a large extent avoided in the mammalian system of viviparity. Despite this, important details remain to be added to our understanding of the mammalian placenta. In particular, we are remarkably ignorant of the way in which calcium passes across the placenta and there is some evidence which suggests that certain types of placentae may indeed be bottlenecks which severely restrict the passage of calcium from the mother to her foetus. Thus the epitheliochorial placenta of the pig may have this effect for the mineralization of the foetal bones does not seem to keep up with the growth of this embryo. It is therefore interesting to note that in this species there may be a store of calcium in the placenta which the foetus can use to augment its direct supply from the mother.

After parturition the female mammal continues to supply her offspring with many of the nutrients which they require by nursing them on her milk. During this period the young are growing rapidly and this imposes an increasing demand for calcium upon the mother. Under these conditions the mothers are normally in negative balance and rapidly lose the extra calcium they may have been able to store during their pregnancy. On rare occasions the adaptation to this change in the rate of calcium metabolism may not be immediately effective. Thus the mother may be more susceptible to tetany for a short time after parturition until her parathyroids have become adjusted to the new rate of calcium metabolism. This is probably the basis for the bovine disease of milk fever although there are still a number of puzzling characteristics to this condition. The composition of the milk secreted by various mammals differs greatly both in the amount of calcium it contains and in the ratio of this ion to other constituents. In some species the composition of the milk produced by the mother is not ideal for the optimum growth of the offspring's skeleton. It seems at least a possibility, however, that during evolution the composition of the milk of a particular species may have become a compromise between conflicting requirements. Thus, the ossification of the bones and the retention of calcium by the infant fed on human milk may be increased by supplementing it with phosphate or replacing it with cow's milk, but this may at the same time depress the level of serum calcium and so disturb the physiology of the offspring.

The rate of calcium metabolism found in the adult mammal during reproduction is reasonably similar to the rate of calcium resorption that can be measured in the normal skeleton (fig. 17.1). This, however, is certainly not the case in the birds where both the problems of a calcium store and an extremely rapid rate of calcium metabolism make this a particularly

s

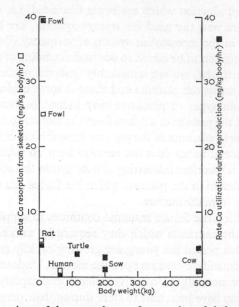

FIG. 17.1. A comparison of the normal rate of resorption of skeletal calcium (based upon radio-isotope studies) and the requirements of the animal for calcium during reproduction estimated in mg Ca/kg body wt/hr. Where two values are given for the calcium requirements of mammals the smaller one refers to pregnancy and the larger one to lactation. Note that for most animals the normal rates of skeletal resorption (white squares) appear to be sufficient to meet the needs for reproduction (black squares). The abnormally large values for the bird are due to the rapid formation of the eggshell and the metabolism of medullary bone. This representation of bone resorption and calcium requirements does not take into consideration the fact that calcium is also normally available to the animal from its diet.

interesting study. The formation of a thick eggshell which is secreted in the short time between two ovulations poses problems which have only been solved by the evolution of medullary bone. This store of calcium has three main peculiarities. It is formed under the influence of the sex hormones, it has an unusual composition both organically and inorganically, and it can be resorbed at a rate many times greater than any other form of bone. By means of this system the bird is able to form the eggshell at a time when it is also forming the yolk of a subsequent egg. These are, in fact, the two stores of calcium which the bird provides for her embryo and the fact that she forms them to some extent simultaneously raises some interesting speculations which will be considered later.

The eggshell and the yolk are stores of calcium of vastly different size. The whole of the yolk provides only about 20% of the calcium requirements of the offspring, while a fraction of the eggshell supplies the remaining 80%. The ways in which these two sources of calcium are made available to the avian embryo are not known with any certainty, although the extra embryonic membranes are obviously important in both processes. The two outstanding problems in considering these phenomena are the possible affects of the developing endocrine systems and the correlation between respiration and calcium metabolism. This latter possibility is particularly intriguing since carbon dioxide may be important in the resorption of the eggshell, while the cation content of the blood also appears to vary drastically during the change to pulmonary respiration at the time of hatching.

In the reptile there is good evidence that the reproducing female may resorb her skeleton to form the shells of the eggs. This process differs from that of the bird, however, for not only is there no store of medullary bone but all the eggs are apparently formed simultaneously. Thus all the yolk is deposited in the ovary before all the oocytes of a clutch are ovulated. The tertiary membranes are then formed on all the eggs, but without the speed which is necessary in avian reproduction. This has two important implications. First, vitellogenesis and shell formation occur successively and not simultaneously as in birds, and secondly, because a clutch is all formed at the same time, there is not the necessity for a rapid rate of calcium metabolism due to a succeeding ovulation. These two facts may explain the absence of medullary bone from reptiles, for not only are these animals able to resorb the calcium from their skeletons at a much slower rate but they probably also require a smaller quantity of this ion since the shells are not as heavily calcified as in the birds. There is always the intriguing possibility that some reptile may eventually be found which does produce medullary bone (one of the Crocodilia?) but a more fascinating aspect of this subject is the discovery of an analogous storage system in some geckos. In many of these animals there is an enormously enlarged endolymphatic sac which appears to provide an extra store of calcium which may be used during reproduction. Unfortunately almost nothing else is known about the calcium metabolism of these interesting animals.

The reduction in the extent to which many reptilian eggshells are calcified means that there is a reduction in the size of one of the stores of calcium available to many of the embryos. This may be reflected in the composition of the yolk. Thus at one extreme there are the ovoviviparous snakes which lack a calcified shell but produce a yolk fourteen times richer in calcium than that of the birds so that there is no need to consider any other source of calcium for these embryos. In fact, these animals are probably able to store some of the excess of this calcium in their endolymphatic sacs for use after hatching. At the other extreme are some of the turtles which have a yolk of about the same composition as that of the birds and like the birds the embryo has to obtain about 80% of its calcium from outside the egg contents. In the marine turtles this extra calcium is obtained from either the eggshell or the sea-water.

These variations in the size of the calcium stores available to the reptilian embryo raise some interesting speculations regarding the evolution of the birds. Reptiles such as the ribbon snakes produce yolk which may contain as much as 1400 mg % calcium. In transporting the yolk precursors to the ovary there is, therefore, a large increase in the total calcium content of the blood. This rise is greatest about the time of ovulation when it averages about 174 mg % and may reach a level of 360 mg %. In this latter case the eggs had been ovulated and had developed in the oviduct of the snake as far as the blastodisc stage by the time that the sample of blood was taken. Unfortunately nothing is known about either the affinity of these yolk proteins for calcium or the dissociation constants of their calcium complexes. It would seem at least a possibility, however, that with a rise in total calcium to 360 mg % there must be at least a small rise in ionic calcium. If this is the case, then, after ovulation there is an elevated level of ionic calcium which will presumably tend to repress the activity of the parathyroid. Again, almost nothing is known about how long it takes the parathyroid to stimulate a large amount of skeletal resorption once its hormone has been released, but one would suspect it to be a rather slow process. Thus it would seem that the snake probably cannot mobilize much skeletal calcium immediately after ovulation. This situation should not raise any problems, however, for the eggs are usually retained in the oviduct for several weeks after ovulation, so that if a shell is to be secreted it can be formed slowly after the blood and parathyroid glands have returned to normal. In the evolution of the birds, however, a problem may have arisen, for with the unusual system of ovulation found in these animals vitellogenesis occurs simultaneously with shell secretion and shell calcification also has to start shortly after ovulation. This could have led to two possible solutions. Either the yolk proteins have to be modified so as not to raise the level of ionic calcium significantly during their transport from the liver to the ovary, or there has to be a system for mobilizing skeletal calcium without the need for the parathyroid glands. Both or neither of these adaptations may have occurred, but it is interesting to note first that the avian yolk provides only 20% of the calcium required by the embryo whereas some reptiles apparently supply the whole of the embryo's needs in this material. Secondly, there is a skeletal store of calcium in the birds which many scientists believe is mobilized without the need for parathyroid hormone. This is, of course, the medullary bone which may be resorbed when the oestrogen level of the blood falls. If there is any truth in these speculations it probably lies in the suggestion that a system of ovoviviparity, such as is found in the ribbon snakes, requires physiological adaptations which are probably mutually exclusive to those required for the type of oviparity seen in birds.

The amphibia show an entirely separate solution to these problems of reproduction. The adult provides almost no store of calcium for the embryo which hatches as a larval form and during this tadpole stage manages to develop its own store of calcium. Since the limbs do not form and grow until metamorphosis most of the calcium is deposited in the endolymphatic sacs as calcium carbonate and then resorbed when required to form the skeleton. Little is known about the physiology of this process and since metamorphosis is a time when an enormous number of anatomical, physiological, and biochemical changes are occurring it is difficult to isolate any particular cause. An interesting possibility is that with the changes in the skin and respiratory system there may be a change in the acid-base regulating systems which could automatically lead to a solution of the calcareous deposits in the endolymphatic sacs at metamorphosis. The attraction of this suggestion is that it correlates with the acid-base regulating functions of the endolymphatic sacs of the adult frog. It may also form the basis for a much more general hypothesis involving acid-base regulation in both the secretion of avian and reptilian eggshells and in their resorption by the developing embryos. In this latter case the analogy is between a tadpole resorbing an internal deposit of calcium carbonate as the carbon dioxide tension of its body fluids rises at metamorphosis and an avian embryo resorbing an external deposit of calcium carbonate in the eggshell, as its carbon dioxide tension also rises towards the end of the incubation of the eggs.

These attempts at a synthesis will not conceal the fact that there have been large gaps in the treatment of the subject of this book. Some of these are no doubt due to the author's ignorance but others are undoubtedly real. Little or no mention has been made of the marsupials, monotremes, viviparous reptiles, the Crocodilia, or the viviparous amphibians, and it appears likely that when these animals are investigated they will provide an enormous increase in our knowledge of the metabolism of calcium during tetrapod reproduction.

Index